EXPERIMENTS IN MODERN PHYSICS

Hans Mark
N. Thomas Olson

EXPERIMENTS IN
MODERN PHYSICS

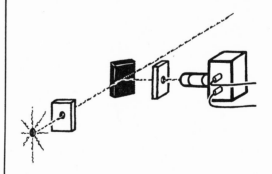

New York
San Francisco
St. Louis
Toronto
London
Sydney

McGRAW-HILL BOOK COMPANY

Preface

THIS BOOK is intended as a guide for a laboratory course in modern physics. Students taking the course are expected to be juniors or seniors in science and engineering who have taken (or are taking concurrently) a course in atomic physics and who are familiar with some elementary quantum theory. The experiments have been chosen to illustrate some of the important basic concepts of modern physics and to familiarize the students with modern laboratory techniques. An effort has also been made to deal with topics having important practical applications so that engineering students will find the material useful.

In any laboratory course, there is always a conflict between the educational content of an experiment and the desire to have it "work" properly. If a laboratory experiment is so designed that it works too well, there is a danger that the student will simply flip all the proper switches, read all the meters he is instructed to read, write an appropriate report, and learn no more than he would have learned from a properly designed lecture demonstration. On the other hand, if too much of the construction and design of the experiment is left to the student, the chances are that he will not be able to perform any significant measurements, and thus will be confused rather than enlightened. The secret in organizing an effective laboratory course lies in avoiding these two pitfalls.

A skillful choice must be made between the equipment supplied and that which the student must construct for himself. The items left for construction by the student should afford the widest possible scope for individual initiative and originality. They should not be trivial things, since the students must learn that experiments never "work" properly the first time. The frustrations encountered in making things work properly are difficult to face for many students. It is exceedingly important to impress upon prospective experimental scientists that patience, care, and thoroughness are absolutely essential if reliable results are to be obtained and that frustrations are an inevitable by-product of creative work.

Although wide latitude should be left to the individual instructor to deal with some of these problems, it might be useful to outline ways in which they have been handled in the past. In the nuclear magnetic resonance experiment, the magnet, its power supply, and a good laboratory oscilloscope are supplied. The student group working on this experiment might be asked to build the resonance head. This would include winding all the necessary coils, building the appropriate mount, and providing the proper leads to the measuring equipment. The student group would also perform all the preliminary calculations to make certain that the important parameters (dimensions, electrical properties of cables, etc.) are properly chosen. Another alternative would be to require the student group to construct the radio frequency oscillator circuit which drives the coil used to excite the sample. Here also, only the basic tools and materials (soldering guns, transistors and other electrical components, etc.) would be supplied. The actual design and construction would be performed by the students themselves. Both these approaches have been successfully employed in this experiment.

If the laboratory course is to be successful, some care must be taken in organizing the student groups. A high faculty-to-student ratio in such a course is clearly desirable. In the course given at the University of California, experienced teaching assistants and interested students who had taken the course previously have been used as section leaders. Laboratory sections are held twice a week for three-hour periods. The students taking the course are divided into groups of three or four in the beginning of the semester. Some care should be taken in organizing the groups. It is highly probable that four or five students in the class have had some experience in working with experimental equipment. These can be found by asking for people who have built model airplanes, hi-fi sets, or hot rods. One of the experienced students should be assigned to each of the experimental groups. He can then act as a guide and help the other students in the group to cope with practical problems that arise.

Eleven different experimental topics are offered in the course given at the University of California. If a reasonable fraction of the construction work is left to the students, it is not possible for them to perform all the available experiments in a sixteen-week semester, and it should not be attempted. In practice, three or four of the experiments are performed by each group. Approximately ten laboratory sessions should be allocated for each experiment.

The laboratory room in which the class is conducted should duplicate conditions usually encountered in research laboratories. Several sturdy benches should be available. All the loose equipment should be stored in cabinets, and a complete tool chest should be assigned to each group. A small stock of electronic equipment and parts should be provided, together with the necessary tools.

When organizing a laboratory course, sufficient equipment must be available for complete instrumentation of the experiments. The following list of equipment is a reasonable sample of what is desirable:

> Two vacuum systems
> One laboratory magnet
> Four DC power supplies
> Two pulse amplifiers
> Two oscilloscopes
> Two pulse counters
> Two volt-ohm-amp meters
> Optical pyrometer
> Ruby laser
> Double pulser
> Scintillation counter
> Polaroid scope camera and accessories
> Single or multi-channel pulse height analyzer
> Assorted electronic supplies
> Assorted tools

The cost of this equipment could be quite substantial if purchased new. However, the figure can be reduced considerably by picking up surplus and second-hand equipment which, although not suitable for the highest quality research, performs adequately for the experiments described in this book.

The authors have been working on this book and on the laboratory course for the past three years. A great many people have made important contributions to this venture. Professor Thomas H. Pigford of the University of California provided the initial stimulation, encouragement, and support for the organization of the laboratory course. He was also responsible for developing the experiment on thermionic emission. Much of the equipment required for the development of the course was purchased with funds granted by the Atomic Energy Commission on a special educational equipment grant. Professor Lawrence Ruby, Professor Selig N. Kaplan, and Dr. Robert V. Pyle of the Department of Nuclear Engineering at the University of California (Berkeley) all have participated in giving the course. Aside from spending many hours with the students in class, they also originated many new experiments and contributed important ideas to the book. The laboratory course could not have been organized successfully without the help of Mr. Lee Stollar, who saw to it that the equipment worked in spite of many shortages and difficulties. Professor Norman Rasmussen of the Department of Nuclear Engineering at the Massachusetts Institute of Technology spent much time discussing this project with one of the authors (Hans Mark) and carefully read the final manuscript. Many of the suggestions he made have been incorporated. The final draft of the manuscript was typed by Mrs. Betty J. Dial. She corrected many errors in spelling, punctuation, and grammar. In addition, we are also grateful for the excellent editing job she performed during the preparation of the manuscript. The lucid and instructive illustrations are the work of Robert David Wong. One of us (Hans Mark) owes thanks to his wife for her encouragement—and for countless pots of coffee she provided during the course of the work. Finally, the authors would like to express their thanks to the most important group of contributors to this effort—the students who have taken the course in the past three years.

HANS MARK
N. THOMAS OLSON

Berkeley, California

Contents

x Contents

EXPERIMENTS IN MODERN PHYSICS

| *Chapter 1* | **INTRODUCTION**
TO THE LABORATORY |

1.1 GENERAL REMARKS

The art of performing meaningful experiments is the heart of the scientific method. The word *art* is used deliberately because it is not always possible to specify precisely how a given experiment should be performed. Many important discoveries have been made by accident in the course of an experiment originally designed to learn something else. The discovery of penicillin by Sir Alexander Fleming,[1] the discovery of X rays by Wilhelm Roentgen,[2] and the discovery of radioactivity by Henri Becquerel[3] are examples of this. Other crucial results have come from a careful and deliberate attempt to choose between two theoretical alternatives or to verify a theoretical prediction. The Michelson-Morley[4] experiment is perhaps the classic example of the former, and the identification of vacuum polarization effects in the hydrogen spectrum by Willis Lamb[5] (the "Lamb" shift) is an excellent case of the latter type. In contrast, a great many experiments have as their object simply the collection of data and the cataloging of physical properties.

Although no hard and fast prescriptions to ensure success exist, certain very fundamental principles underly a fruitful experimental investigation. For instance, it is important to formulate in some detail the questions to be answered before the experiment is organized. Decisions must be reached about the important and the unimportant parameters. Only one experimental parameter must be varied at a time so that observed effects can be isolated and attributed to the proper cause. Judgments must be made regarding the statistical significance of the measurements, and background effects which could interfere with the measurements must be isolated. Above all, the experimenter must learn to be alert for the unexpected. Even a well-planned experiment may "fail" if the experimenter overlooks a small but unexpected deviation which could lead to an important new discovery.

The best way to become familiar with the principles outlined in the previous paragraph is through experience. The purpose of any laboratory course is to provide this experience. The extent to which the course succeeds depends on the freedom of choice and initiative left to the person performing the experiments. Obviously this freedom will be restricted by the equipment available and the time limits imposed by the academic schedule. Nevertheless, it has been possible to organize laboratory courses in which wide latitude of choice about what to do and how to proceed in a given situation is left to the experimenter. The experiments outlined in this book have been chosen with this approach in mind.

1.2 SUBJECT MATTER

The most important scientific development in the first half of the present century has been the process of understanding—for all practical purposes—the structure of matter. This process began in the latter half of the nineteenth century with the development of the atomic theory, statistical mechanics, and study of the interaction of radiation with matter, and reached a zenith with the advent of quantum mechanics in the first part of this century. It is possible to explain most phenomena dealing with matter in its various forms (atoms, nuclei, solids, liquids, gases, etc.) in terms of these theories. Several crucially important questions remain to be answered, of course, but these seem to border on other fields. Topics dealing with the nature of life processes and the principles of cosmology are in this category. It is probable that the next fifty years will see a large-scale application of our knowledge of the structure of matter to the solution of these problems.

Our understanding of the structure of matter has had far-reaching consequences in engineering and applied science. A great many devices have resulted from the research of the past fifty or sixty years in the field of the structure of matter. Among the best known are lasers, transistors, nuclear reactors, and synthetics such as plastics and fibers. There are, however, many other examples of equal importance but less well publicized.

The topics for the experiments described in the following chapters have been chosen to illustrate the important developments in the understanding of the structure of matter. An effort has also been made to deal in a more thorough manner with those principles likely to have important practical and engineering applications. These include topics in atomic structure, solid-state physics, nucleonics, and several others. In addition, the experiments illustrate new developments in instrumentation. A list of these instruments would include oscilloscopes (see Appendix I), power supplies, signal amplifiers, particle detectors, photomultipliers, magnetic field measuring devices, and others. Wherever possible, instruction manuals should be available and the equipment should be operated in accordance with them.

1.3 MEASUREMENT METHODS AND ERROR ANALYSIS

Certain general rules should be heeded in making measurements if they are to be reliable. The first step is to decide which quantity is to be measured as a function of the variable parameters of the experiment. The data taken should then be recorded in tabular form, preferably in a hard-cover notebook with pages that cannot be removed. *All* data and pertinent events that occur during the course of the experiment should be recorded. If anything subsequently appears to be incorrect, any recorded information may be useful in locating the trouble. It is also advisable to plot the data in graphical form while they are being taken. Often it is possible to spot malfunctions by observing trends in the graphs. In addition, if theoretical predictions are available, it is sometimes very useful to plot these on the same graph so that appropriate comparisons can be made as the data are being taken.

In every measurement, there are always background effects which must be subtracted from measured values. Background effects may come from many different sources. In most experiments involving electronic equipment, the noise level introduced by the various devices may be an important source of background. This "electronic noise" should be determined independently before the experiment is performed. Other background effects may be more difficult to isolate. For instance, in many experiments involving the counting of neutrons, the detector used may also be sensitive to gamma rays. Thus some method must be found to determine the counting rate which must be subtracted from the observed counting rate to obtain the true neutron signal rate. In this case, the objective might be accomplished by placing shields having different transmission characteristics for neutrons and for gamma rays in front of the counter. These examples illustrate the kind of steps which might be taken to isolate certain background effects. It is extremely important that this be done before the experiment is started. For every experiment, a "signal-to-noise ratio" should be calculated from the data available. If this ratio is of the order of 2:1 or larger, then the experiment can probably be performed. If it is less, special measures may be necessary to subtract the background.

No discussion of measurement methods would be complete without some mention of experimental errors. No measurement should ever be reported without also making some statements about the precision of the result. Experimental errors fall into two major categories: those which arise from statistical fluctuations in discrete samples being measured and those which are due to systematic changes in the equipment or errors inherent in reading metering devices. An example of the former might be the fluctuation in the number of counts observed from the decay of a radioactive sample. A typical systematic error might be caused in certain electronic instruments by periodic variation of the electric line voltage. In principle, all systematic errors may be traced and either eliminated or corrected, although this is rarely true in a practical case. Statistical errors, on the other hand, are always present and great care must be exercised to calculate them properly. For background material on this point, the student should consult several excellent texts on the subject (Cohen, Crowe, and DuMond,[6] and Worthing and Geffner[7]).

The practical issues which must usually be decided when experimental errors are assigned to a measurement are how to define the "error" and how errors propagate if the final result is a function of several measured quantities all having different experimental errors.

The definition of a measurement error is always somewhat arbitrary. If a series of measurements of a quantity $x_1, x_2, \ldots$ is distributed around a mean value $\bar{x}$ in a normal distribution, the standard deviation from the mean is usually defined as the "experimental error." A normal distribution results if the successive measurements are independent of each other. Since this is the most common circumstance, most of the mathematics of error analysis is based on normal (or Gaussian) distributions. Furthermore, many distributions which are not precisely normal distributions can be approximated with appropriate normal distribution functions so that the analysis may still be used. It is important, however, for the experimenter to recognize when these conditions are fulfilled and when they are not.

The "error" for a normal distribution is usually called the standard deviation, σ, and the experimental result for the measurement of $\bar{x}$ is usually quoted as $\bar{x} \pm \sigma$. The precise meaning of this statement is that the probability that a measurement of the quantity x yields the value x_1 is

$$p(x_1) = \frac{1}{\sqrt{2\pi}\,\sigma} e^{-(\bar{x}-x_1)^2/2\sigma^2} \tag{1.1}$$

It can easily be shown that if a set of n measurements are made, the quantity σ is

$$\sigma^2 = \frac{\sum\limits_{k=1}^{n} (\bar{x} - x_k)^2}{n} \tag{1.2}$$

and where

$$\bar{x} = \frac{\sum\limits_{k=1}^{n} x_k}{n} \tag{1.3}$$

The normal distribution function of Eq. (1.1) is illustrated in Fig. 1.1. Further, for a sufficiently large number of measurements, 68.3 percent of the values x_k will lie within $\pm\sigma$ of the mean value $\bar{x}$ and 95.4 percent will lie within $\pm 2\sigma$. It is thus perfectly possible that a repeated measurement x_k may lie outside the "experimental error." This point should be remembered when an experiment is repeated to determine whether the result is "correct."

If the result of an experiment is a function of two or more measured quantities, the experimental errors of all measured quantities must be included in the computation of the standard deviation of the final result. For example, assume that x is a function of two variables y and z so that the mean value $\bar{x}$ is expressed as follows in terms of the mean values $\bar{y}$ and $\bar{z}$:

$$\bar{x} = f(\bar{y}, \bar{z}) \tag{1.4}$$

This relation can be rewritten in terms of an individual set of measurements y_k and z_k

$$x_k + \Delta x_k = f(y_k + \Delta y_k, z_k + \Delta z_k) \tag{1.5}$$

when Δx_k, Δy_k and Δz_k are the differences between the measured values

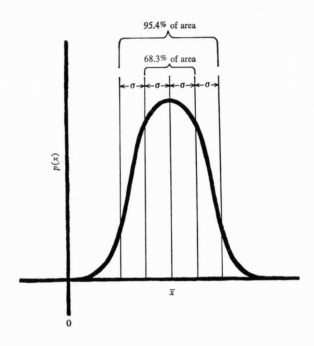

FIGURE 1.1

A normal distribution of the quantity x about a mean value $\bar{x}$.

and the respective mean values.   Expanding the right side of Eq. (1.5) yields

$$x_k + \Delta x_k = f(y_k, z_k) + \frac{\partial f}{\partial y_k}\Delta y_k + \frac{\partial f}{\partial z_k}\Delta z_k + \cdots \tag{1.6}$$

Since Eq. (1.4) also holds for individual measurements y_k and z_k, it follows that

$$\Delta x_k = \frac{\partial f}{\partial y_k}\Delta y_k + \frac{\partial f}{\partial z_k}\Delta z_k \tag{1.7}$$

According to Eq. (1.2), the standard deviation is proportional to the

6 *Introduction to the laboratory*

sum of the squares of the Δx_k's. Thus,

$$\Sigma(\Delta x_k)^2 = \left(\frac{\partial f}{\partial y_k}\right)^2 \Sigma(\Delta y_k)^2 + 2 \frac{\partial f}{\partial y_k} \frac{\partial f}{\partial z_k} \Sigma(\Delta y_k)(\Delta z_k) + \left(\frac{\partial f}{\partial z_k}\right)^2 \Sigma(\Delta z_k)^2 \tag{1.8}$$

The cross product term in Eq. (1.8) will vanish since the Δy_k's and Δz_k's are negative as often as positive. Hence

$$\sigma_x{}^2 = \left(\frac{\partial f}{\partial y}\right)^2 \sigma_y{}^2 + \left(\frac{\partial f}{\partial z}\right)^2 \sigma_z{}^2 \tag{1.9}$$

The most important examples of the foregoing development are the cases where the $\bar{x}$ is the sum (difference) or product (quotient) of two other quantities $\bar{y}$ and $\bar{z}$. It can easily be seen that for the sum (difference) case

$$\sigma_x{}^2 = \sigma_y{}^2 + \sigma_z{}^2 \tag{1.10}$$

and for the product (quotient) case

$$\frac{\sigma_x{}^2}{\bar{x}^2} = \frac{\sigma_y{}^2}{\bar{y}^2} + \frac{\sigma_z{}^2}{\bar{z}^2} \tag{1.11}$$

A common mistake is to spend too much time and effort reducing the error in one of the variables (say, Δy) without spending similar effort reducing Δz. The error in the final result is therefore determined almost entirely by Δz and the time taken to reduce Δy has been wasted. It is extremely important to develop sound judgment regarding the assignment of experimental errors; otherwise it is not possible to determine the reliability of the reported results. The scientific literature abounds with examples of results which later had to be withdrawn or modified because of insufficient attention paid to error analysis.

1.4 LABORATORY REPORTS

The preparation of reports is a perennial problem. In many laboratory courses the reports are standardized, and there is thus a great temptation not to spend much time or effort in their preparation. This is true in spite of the fact that the preparation of a comprehensive laboratory report is an excellent opportunity to gain experience in technical expository writing. In this matter also, wide differences will exist between various experiments, but there are certain common features which all reports should have. There should be a short abstract—not more than four or five sentences—describing the purpose of the experiment and outlining the methods employed. The body of the report should contain a brief description of the measurements and a summary of the calculations performed to obtain the final results. These should be tabulated and appropriate graphs should show the relationships between the important variables. The most essential portion of the report is an extensive but concise discussion of the results and the conclusions obtained. Whenever possible, drawings and diagrams should be used to illustrate what was done during the course of the experiment. Finally, one of the sections of the laboratory report should deal with the reliability of results and the analysis of errors as outlined in the previous section.

1.5 SAFETY AND LABORATORY PRACTICE

When working in the laboratory, certain rules should be observed to prevent personal injury and damage to equipment. The important areas in which care must be exercised in most of the experiments to be discussed in this text involve electrical equipment, the use of machine tools, and the safe handling of various radioactive materials.

In dealing with many of the electronic units to be used, it is well to remember that the lethal electrocution threshold is surprisingly low, if the proper circumstances exist. Only about 10 watts are necessary to kill a human being if the current passes through the region of the heart. If the proper contacts are made with ground, then the total resistance through a human limb is of the order of 10^4 ohms. Thus, a power supply operating at a few hundred volts could be lethal. Nor is this all. Even if the contacts with ground and the power supply are not perfect, a sufficiently strong shock may be delivered to cause serious injury. The best protection against injury from electrical shock is to make certain that the high-voltage terminals (>300 volts) are appropriately protected with grounded wire screens and that the screens themselves are appropriately interlocked. This means that if the screen is removed, the power supply high voltage cannot be turned on. A typical interlock circuit is shown in Fig. 1.2. The microswitch is set in such a way that the primary circuit of the high-voltage transformer is not closed unless the microswitch is closed. Reliable interlocks installed on all laboratory high-voltage supplies will eliminate much of the danger of shock or electrocution.

Another area where great care must be taken is in the handling of radioactive sources. There are two dangers which should be avoided. One is that long exposures to strong radiation fields must be prevented. This is best done by continuously using survey meters to check the radiation field carefully when an experiment is performed. In addition, students should use dosimeters and standard film badges to record the total exposure received during an experiment. The guidelines issued by the U.S. Atomic Energy Commission for radiation exposures should be employed to determine what exposures are permissible.[3] None of the experiments discussed in this book should result in a significant exposure. In addition to the over-all exposure received, it is also important to make certain that all the sources employed in experiments are packaged in such a way that they cannot be spilled. Spills may lead to ingestion of radioactive materials which may cause very high local internal doses. All sources should be sealed in an approved manner before they are used.

In the course of the laboratory work, there are some instances in which it will be necessary to use machine tools. There are many safety rules which should be observed in a machine shop. Most of these are usually posted in the shop in an appropriate place. The most important protective measures in a machine shop are designed to protect the eyes.

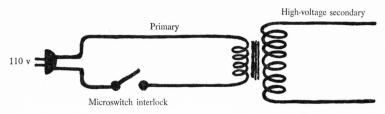

FIGURE 1.2

Typical location of a microswitch interlock in the power transformer primary.

Safety glasses or hoods should be provided and should be used by all students using machine tools in which chips or shavings are produced. Certain other precautions should also be taken when other tools are employed. For instance, soldering irons should always be unplugged immediately after they are used.

Finally, a few words should be said regarding the safe handling of bottled gas which is used in some of these experiments. Gases are usually stored in 60-liter metal pressure vessels at 1500 pounds per square inch. There is sufficient energy stored in the gas under these conditions so that the bottles constitute a hazard unless properly handled. The bottles should always be chained to tables or posts in the laboratory so that they cannot fall over and possibly burst. It is also important to see that the proper high-pressure pipe is used.

These are only a few of the safety rules which should be observed. If there is any doubt about whether a given procedure is safe, the student should immediately consult the instructor.

REFERENCES

1. Fleming, A.: *Journal of Experimental Pathology*, 1929.
2. Roentgen, W.: *Electrician*, **36,** 415, 850, 1896.
3. Becquerel's papers appear in *Compt. Rend.*, vol. 122, 1896.
4. Michelson, A., and E. Morley: *Silliman J.*, **34,** 427, 1887; A. Michelson and E. Morley, *Phil. Mag.*, **24,** 449, 1887.
5. Lamb, W. E., and R. C. Retherford: *Phys. Rev.*, **72,** 241, 1947.
6. Cohen, E. R., K. M. Crowe, and J. W. M. DuMond: "The Fundamental Constants of Physics," Interscience Publishers, Inc., New York, 1957.
7. Worthing, A. G., and J. Geffner: "The Treatment of Experimental Data," John Wiley & Sons, Inc., New York, 1943.
8. *Code of Federal Regulations*, Title 10, Part 20, U.S. Atomic Energy Commission, Washington, D.C.

Chapter 2

THE MEASUREMENT
OF ATOMIC MASSES

2.1 INTRODUCTION

It has been recognized for over two hundred years that matter consists of small, "indivisible," and identical objects called atoms. The atomic theory was first based on the quantitative study of chemical reactions. It was discovered that different elements, when they react to form various compounds, always do so in the same mass proportions.[1] No known chemical reaction violates this rule. From these facts it was inferred that all "elements" consist of small, identical particles (atoms) which form compounds by combining to form other small particles (molecules) which are characteristic of the compounds. Although this evidence for the existence of atoms from chemical reactions is very strong, it is indirect. The atoms themselves were not observed, nor were any of their properties apparent.

The next important discovery was that atoms apparently contain electric charges. This step was taken by the study of electric discharges in gases. The early experiments in this field were performed by Sir J. J. Thomson,[2] Wilhelm Roentgen,[3] and others in the last years of the nineteenth century. The fundamental experiment is shown in Fig. 2.1.

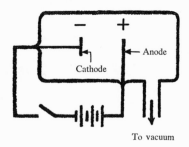

FIGURE 2.1

Discharge tube used to produce cathode rays (electrons) and canal rays (ions).

A glass tube with two metal electrodes inserted in the ends was evacuated to pressures of the order of a few microns (see Chapter 4). An electrical potential was then applied to the electrodes. It was discovered that certain radiations were emitted from the negative terminal (cathode). This was established by the fact that these so-called "cathode rays" impinged on the glass behind the positive terminal (anode), causing it to fluoresce. It was also discovered that cathode rays could be deflected by electric and magnetic fields. Therefore it was surmised that they were actually streams of small electrically charged particles. These particles were emitted by all cathode materials which were tried and are, therefore, not characteristic of the atoms of the cathode. Rather, the emitted particles seemed to be constituent parts of all atoms and were called "electrons" by J. J. Thomson.

If atoms contain electrons, then a charged fragment is left if an electron is pulled from the atom. These fragments are called ions. Ion beams can also be produced in the cathode ray tube shown in Fig. 2.1. Electrons move from the cathode to the anode and hence are negatively charged according to this convention. Ions (atoms from which one or more electrons have been removed) move in the opposite direction and strike the cathode and thus carry a positive charge. These ion beams can be observed by drilling small holes in the cathode through which some of the ions may pass. Positive ion rays were discovered and identified by Goldstein in 1886 and were called "Canal Rays."[4] Deflection experiments can then be performed to study ion beams behind the cathode. The ions in a cathode ray tube are characteristic of the residual gas in the tube. They are produced when cathode rays collide with residual gas atoms in the tube, stripping valence electrons away in the process. The resulting ions then move toward the cathode and pass through the holes to form the ion beams. The deflection experiments performed on the ion beams resulted in the first direct measurements of atomic masses. In order to understand how this can be done, the motion of charges in electric and magnetic fields must be investigated.

2.2 MOTION OF CHARGES IN ELECTRIC AND MAGNETIC FIELDS

The force $\mathbf{F}$ on a particle carrying an electric charge e in an electric field $\mathbf{E}$ is given by

$$\mathbf{F} = e\mathbf{E} \tag{2.1}$$

In a static situation, the electric field $\mathbf{E}$ can be computed using the appropriate Maxwell equations

$$\operatorname{div} \mathbf{E} = \frac{\rho}{\epsilon_0} \tag{2.2}$$

$$\operatorname{curl} \mathbf{E} = 0 \tag{2.3}$$

where ρ is the charge distribution. Equation (2.3) indicates that the static electric field is a conservative field, that is, the amount of work done to move a charge in the field from one point to another is independent of the path of the motion, but depends only on the end points of the motion. The field can thus be expressed in terms of a function V, called the electrostatic potential, in the following manner:

$$\mathbf{E} = -\operatorname{grad} V \tag{2.4}$$

This expression automatically satisfies Eq. (2.3), for the curl of the gradient of any scalar function always vanishes. The energy acquired (or lost) by an electrically charged particle in moving from point a to point b is

$$W = \int_a^b \mathbf{F} \cdot d\mathbf{r} = e \int_a^b \mathbf{E} \cdot d\mathbf{r}$$
$$= -e \int_a^b \operatorname{grad} V \cdot dr = -e[V(b) - V(a)] \tag{2.5}$$

The quantity $[V(b) - V(a)]$ is called the potential difference between the points a and b. If $V(b) < V(a)$ and if the particle starts at rest from point a, the kinetic energy of the particle at point b is given by

$$W = \tfrac{1}{2}mv^2 = e[V(a) - V(b)] \tag{2.6}$$

Thus a particle moving in an electric field may gain or lose energy depending on the relative magnitudes of V at the end points. Electric fields can be employed to accelerate charges to well-defined energies, a fact that will be most useful for the measurement of the masses of atomic particles.

Customarily, the energy of a charged subatomic particle is measured in electron volts. An electron volt is defined [according to Eq. (2.6)] as the kinetic energy an electron acquires when it passes through a potential difference of one volt. The conversion factor between electron volts and the usual mechanical energy units (joules or ergs) is

$$1 \text{ electron volt} = 1.6 \times 10^{-12} \text{ ergs} = 1.6 \times 10^{-19} \text{ joules}$$

An electron volt is thus a very small unit of energy when compared to the ordinary macroscopic units. The reason for this, of course, is that the charge carried by the electron is very small.

The interaction of charged particles with magnetic fields is quite different from their interaction with electric fields, since it is governed by the Maxwell equations relating electric currents with magnetic fields. For static magnetic fields,

$$\text{curl } \mathbf{B} = \mu_0 \mathbf{J} \tag{2.7}$$
$$\text{div } \mathbf{B} = 0 \tag{2.8}$$

Equation (2.7) is a general statement of Ampère's law. It determines the magnetic field $\mathbf{B}$ produced by a current density $\mathbf{J}$. Equation (2.8) states that all magnetic field lines must be closed, that is, the number of lines going into any region of space must equal the number of lines leaving the region. It reflects the fact that there are no "magnetic poles" which can act as sources for the magnetic field. The force on a charged particle due to a magnetic field $\mathbf{B}$ can be derived from Eqs. (2.7) and (2.8):

$$\mathbf{F} = e\mathbf{v} \times \mathbf{B} \tag{2.9}$$

where e is the charge of the particle, $\mathbf{v}$ is its velocity, and $\mathbf{B}$ is the magnetic field. The most important point about Eq. (2.9) is that the force vanishes if the charged particle is not moving. This fact is a consequence of the properties of Eq. (2.7). Magnetic fields are produced by currents (moving charges), and only moving charges are subject to forces from static magnetic fields. The second point is that the force defined in Eq. (2.9), which is called the Lorentz force after H. A. Lorentz, who first derived the law,[5] is always perpendicular to the direction of motion of the charged particle (see Fig. 2.2). Therefore a particle can never gain or lose energy when passing through a magnetic field because $\mathbf{F} \cdot d\mathbf{r}$ is always zero. A static magnetic field thus does not change the magnitude of the momentum vector of the particle, only its direction.

The orbits executed by moving charges in a magnetic field are particularly simple if the field $\mathbf{B}$ is constant and if the velocity of the moving charged particle is perpendicular to the field direction. The force perpendicular to the direction of motion of the particle is called

Field direction into plane of paper

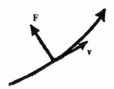

FIGURE 2.2

Lorentz force acting on a positively charged particle moving in a magnetic field.

the centripetal force and is given by

$$F = \frac{mv^2}{r} \tag{2.10}$$

where v is the instantaneous velocity of the particle and r is the instantaneous radius of curvature of the particle path. Equating expressions (2.9) and (2.10) results in the following relation between the orbit radius r, the particle velocity v, the particle mass m, and the particle charge e:

$$F = \frac{mv^2}{r} = evB \tag{2.11}$$

where it has been assumed that $\mathbf{v}$ and $\mathbf{B}$ are perpendicular. The orbit of the particle is

$$r = \frac{m}{eB} = \text{constant} \tag{2.12}$$

which is the equation of a circle in polar coordinates. If the velocity of the particle is directed parallel to the magnetic field, it will not be affected by the field and will keep moving in a straight line. However, if the velocity of the particle makes an angle θ with the magnetic field, its velocity can be expressed in terms of components parallel and perpendicular to the field, $v_\parallel$ and $v_\perp$. Equation (2.9) can be applied separately to each of the components. The parallel component is unaffected, while the perpendicular component behaves according to Eq. (2.12), except that the velocity v is now replaced by $v_\perp$. The path of the particle is therefore a helix as shown in Fig. 2.3. The motion is, of course, much more complicated if the magnetic field is not constant.

Several combinations of electric and magnetic fields are particularly important in mass spectroscopy. One is the so-called crossed-field

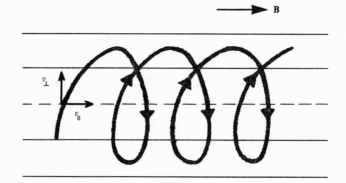

FIGURE 2.3

Helical path of charged particle which has velocity components both perpendicular and parallel to the magnetic field.

experiment. Suppose that a charged particle is passed through a region in which there is a constant electric field with a constant magnetic field perpendicular to the electric field. The velocity of the particle is perpendicular to both fields. If the fields are arranged as shown in Fig. 2.4, then the forces on the particle point in opposite directions. Moreover, if the fields are adjusted in such a way that the electrostatic and Lorentz forces are equal, the particle is not deflected in passing through the region. Therefore neither force does any work on the particle. The condition which the fields must obey is

$$F_E = F_B = eE = evB \qquad (2.13)$$

Thus the particle velocity is a constant of magnitude

$$v = \frac{E}{B} \qquad (2.14)$$

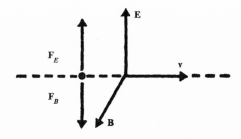

FIGURE 2.4

Method of velocity selection by balancing the Lorentz force F_B with the electrostatic force F_E.

It is clear from the preceding argument that a crossed-field device of the type described can be used as a velocity selector, that is, only particles with a velocity E/B will pass through the region.

From the foregoing paragraphs it is easy to see, in principle, how a mass spectrometer operates. The simplest device is the one illustrated in Fig. 2.5. A beam of particles with a constant uniform velocity is passed into a constant magnetic field. If the beam contains particles of differing masses, each of the species will be bent into a circular path with a different radius of curvature according to Eq. (2.12). Consequently, the different mass fractions of the beam will arrive at different places on the focal plane of the instrument. The larger mass particles are bent into orbits with larger radii of curvature. Almost all mass spectrometers operate on this principle. More detailed examples of these instruments will be given in a subsequent section.

A final, very important point must be made. According to Eq. (2.12),

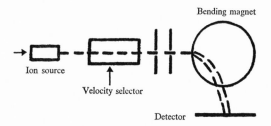

FIGURE 2.5

Simple mass spectrometer which deflects different masses through different radii of curvature.

the mass of the particles is

$$m = \frac{eB}{v} r \qquad (2.15)$$

It is therefore possible to determine the absolute value of the mass only if the charge e on the particle is also known. If this is not the case, then only the ratio of the charge to the mass, e/m, can be measured. The first accurate measurements of the electron charge were the famous oil-drop experiments performed by Millikan and his collaborators.[6] Accurate atomic mass determinations were not performed until after 1920, when more precise values of the electronic charge became available.

2.3 NUCLEAR AND ATOMIC MASSES

In order to understand the measurements to be performed, it is helpful to discuss the actual values of the masses to be measured. The first atoms to be investigated extensively were the atoms of residual gases in discharge tubes. Later, J. J. Thomson made careful measurements of e/m for many different ions and also established that the ratio of the proton to the electron mass is 1836.[7] When accurate measurements of the electronic charge became available, it was possible to compute accurately the absolute mass of the electron and the proton:

$$m_e = 9.107 \times 10^{-31} \text{ kilograms} \qquad (2.16)$$
$$m_p = 1.672 \times 10^{-27} \text{ kilograms} \qquad (2.17)$$

In addition to hydrogen, a large number of other mass measurements were performed. The first important result of this investigation was the discovery of isotopes. The chemical properties of an element are determined by the nuclear charge, that is, the number of protons in the nucleus. However, the mass of the atom is not fixed by the proton number but by the sum of the number of protons and neutrons. Many elements have several different isotopes. These are atoms having the same number of protons in the nucleus but differing numbers of neutrons. An important example of this case is the heavy isotope of hydrogen, deuterium, which has roughly twice the mass of hydrogen and occurs in nature with an abundance of 0.15 percent.

Another good example is oxygen, which has three stable isotopes, O^{16}, the most abundant, and two others, O^{17} and O^{18}, which occur with 0.04 percent and 0.20 percent abundance, respectively. The mass spectrum of this element is shown in Fig. 2.6. This experiment was performed using a high-resolution mass spectrometer built by Professor A. O. Nier[8] of the University of Minnesota. In this experiment, the particle beams which passed through the magnetic field consisted of singly ionized oxygen atoms.

Aside from establishing the existence of isotopes, mass spectroscopy has also been important in providing useful information about nuclear binding energies. The mass of a given isotope is not precisely equal to the sum of the masses of the protons and the neutrons in the nucleus.

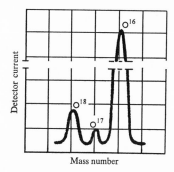

FIGURE 2.6

Abundance spectrum of O^{16}, O^{17}, and O^{18} as measured by A. O. Nier[8].

The neutrons and the protons are bound together by attractive forces, and therefore a certain separation energy is needed to break up the nucleus. This separation or binding energy is determined by the mass difference between the nucleus and the sum of its constituents, using the Einstein mass-energy relation. The mass difference, or mass defect, as it is usually called, is

$$\Delta M = ZM_p + NM_n - M(Z,N) \tag{2.18}$$

where M_p is the proton mass, M_n is the neutron mass, and $M(Z,N)$ is the mass of the nucleus. The total binding energy of the nucleus is thus given by

$$E_B = \Delta Mc^2 \tag{2.19}$$

where ΔM is the mass defect. The magnitude of the mass defect is of the order of 1 percent of the total mass of the nucleus, and this number indicates the accuracy with which nuclear mass measurements must be made if significant binding energy values are to be obtained. For example, if the binding energy of a nucleus is to be determined to an accuracy of 1 percent, then the mass of the nucleus must be measured to one part in 10^4.

Absolute measurements of atomic, and hence nuclear, masses with very high precision are possible. However, the atomic mass scale used

Nuclear and atomic masses **19**

in practice is not an absolute scale (in terms of kilograms) but a relative scale in which C^{12} has a mass of precisely 12 atomic mass units. The atomic mass scale relative to this standard is called the "Physical Mass Scale." (Until recently the Physical Mass Scale was defined relative to O^{16}, which was taken as 16. The new mass scale was introduced in 1964.) Relative masses can be determined with great precision using the "matched doublet" method. In these experiments, two ion beams whose charge-to-mass ratio are nearly the same are passed through the spectrograph. An example of such a "matched doublet" is $H_3{}^{2+}$ and C^{12++}. The first ion is a singly ionized molecule containing three deuterons, which is sufficiently stable for particle-beam experiments. The second ion is a doubly ionized atom of carbon 12. The masses of these ions are

$$
\begin{aligned}
M(H_3{}^{2+}) &= 3M_p + 3M_n - 3\,\Delta M_D + 2m_e \\
M(C^{12++}) &= 6M_p + 6M_n - \Delta M_C + 4m_e
\end{aligned}
\tag{2.20}
$$

where M_p, M_n, and M_e are the proton, neutron, and electron masses, respectively. The quantities ΔM_D and ΔM_C are the mass defect of the deuteron and C^{12}, respectively.

The difference between the line positions of the two ion species on the spectrograph focal plane will be proportional to the quantity $[M(H_3{}^{2+}) - \frac{1}{2}M(C^{12++})]$. The factor of $\frac{1}{2}$ in front of the carbon mass must be included to account for its double charge [see Eq. (2.12)]. The mass difference measured by the mass spectrograph is

$$
\delta M = \tfrac{1}{2}\,\Delta M_C - 3\,\Delta M_D
\tag{2.21}
$$

which depends only on the nuclear mass defects.

The value obtained in Eq. (2.21) can be employed in two ways. Since the mass defect of the deuteron (ΔM_D) is known precisely (one part in 10^3) from other data (Kazi, Rasmussen, and Mark[9]), the mass defect of C^{12} can be measured with a precision determined by the precision with which the distance between the two spectrograph lines can be measured. This is approximately 1 percent.

Alternately, the quantity δM can be used to calculate the deuteron mass relative to the mass of C^{12}, since

$$
\delta M = 3M(H^2) + 2m_e - \tfrac{1}{2}[M(C^{12}) + 4m_e]
\tag{2.22}
$$

Therefore the mass of the deuteron is

$$
M(H^2) = \tfrac{1}{6}M(C^{12}) + \tfrac{1}{3}\,\delta M
\tag{2.23}
$$

The measured mass difference δM has a magnitude of less than 1 percent of the deuteron mass. Thus, if it is known with a precision of 1 percent and the C^{12} mass is taken as a standard (12), the deuteron mass is determined relative to the standard to better than one part in 10^4.

Many other combinations of doublet ions are suitable for precise mass difference measurements. The only restriction is that the ions used to produce the beams must have very nearly the same charge-to-mass ratio so that the total deflections in the mass spectrograph are very nearly equal. A great many important nuclear measurements have been made using this technique.

Perhaps the most spectacular application of mass spectroscopy has been the large-scale separation of isotopes for industrial and military purposes. Large quantities of the rare isotope (0.71 percent abundant) of uranium, U^{235}, have been separated from natural uranium for use as a reactor fuel or for nuclear weapons. Other stable isotopes have also been produced in large quantities (several hundred grams or more) for medical and other research uses.

2.4 MASS SPECTROGRAPHS AND MASS SPECTROMETERS

Several types of mass spectrographs and mass spectrometers have been developed and will be described briefly. A mass spectrograph is an instrument in which the particle detector is an integrating device, usually a photographic plate. The mass spectrum is displayed on a focal plane, and all of the masses in a certain range are recorded at once. Mass spectrometers, on the other hand, are instruments having a continuous read-out detector, usually located at a fixed place on the focal plane. Particles of different masses may thus reach the detector only when the magnetic field and the accelerator potential are changed.

One of the first mass spectrographs was built by A. J. Dempster[10] in 1918. An important feature of the design of any mass spectrograph or spectrometer must be the collimating and focusing of the ion beam. It is this which defines the resolution of the instrument and hence its ability to separate ions having slightly different masses. In Dempster's instrument this result is achieved by magnetically bending the ion beam through 180 degrees. It can be seen from Fig. 2.7 that, even if the beam has an opening divergent angle δ, there will be an approximate focal point if the particles are bent through 180 degrees in a constant field. The focus is only approximate, since the diameters of the different orbits are not collinear. It can be seen that the central beam will be farthest away from the source and that beams making an angle δ with the center line will be closer to the source by approximately $2R\delta^2$ if δ is the maximum divergent angle of the ion beam at the source.

Figure 2.8 shows a sketch of a Dempster-type mass spectrometer, which consists of an ion source, a velocity selector, a deflection cham-

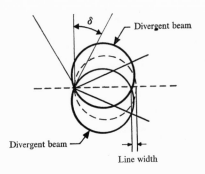

Approximate focusing of an initially divergent beam after 180° of deflection.

ber, and an ion detector. After the ions are produced, they are passed through a velocity selector of the crossed electric and magnetic field type described in Sec. 2.2.

Shortly after the 180-degree-type spectrograph was built, Aston[11] developed an instrument with more accurate beam focusing. In Aston's instrument the focusing properties of a combination of electric and magnetic fields are employed to bring the ion beam to a focus which produces an image of the collimators at the ion source exit slit. The ion detectors are accurately placed on the focal plane of the system. A schematic diagram of an Aston-type spectrometer is shown in Fig. 2.9. Initial collimation of the beam is accomplished by a pair of slits. In passing though the primary electrostatic deflectors, the beam diverges

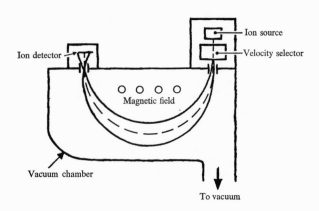

The Dempster 180° mass spectrometer.

22 *Measurement of atomic masses*

and the high-velocity particles follow path 1, while the slower particles follow path 2, as shown in Fig. 2.9. Focusing action results, for the magnet deflects the particles in the opposite direction from the electrostatic deflector plates. The fast particles coming through near the top end of the slit are deflected less strongly by the magnetic field than those with smaller velocities at the lower end of the slit. Qualitatively, this explains the focusing action of the Aston mass spectrometer.

Recently another method has been introduced to measure the masses of different ions. This instrument is called the mass synchrometer[12] and is based on the same principle as the cyclotron. An ion source is placed in the center of a constant magnetic field. The ions are accelerated by a radio-frequency field applied across the two electrodes as shown in

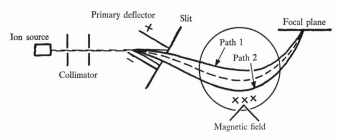

FIGURE 2.9

The Aston double-deflection mass spectrometer.

Fig. 2.10. The frequency of the applied radio-frequency field is determined by the charge-to-mass ratio of the ions. From Eq. (2.11) we have

$$\frac{mv^2}{r} = evB \tag{2.24}$$

or

$$\frac{v}{2\pi r} = \nu_c = \frac{eB}{m} \tag{2.25}$$

where ν_c is the so-called cyclotron frequency of the orbit. Notice that this frequency is independent of the velocity of the particle, so that it is not necessary to produce an ion beam with uniform velocity. Also, since frequencies are comparatively easy to measure accurately, this method promises to make it possible to obtain mass determinations which are more accurate than those possible using deflection methods. This instrument is called the mass synchrometer and is expected to be most useful for determining atomic masses with great precision. When the ions are in resonance, they will be accelerated until they strike the ion detector. The mass can then be computed from the resonant frequency given in Eq. (2.25).

The production and detection of ions are also important parts of the technique of mass spectroscopy. These techniques depend to a very great extent on the ions to be made and detected. It has already been mentioned that, in mass spectrographs, photographic plates are used as detectors if the ion energy is sufficiently high. In the case of metallic ions, the ions may be deposited directly on cooled glass plates. In mass spectrometers, the most commonly used method is to measure the ion current directly on a small wire or collector plate. The currents used in most mass spectrometers are quite small (of the order of a few microamperes) so that a sensitive amplifier is necessary to produce an easily detectable signal.

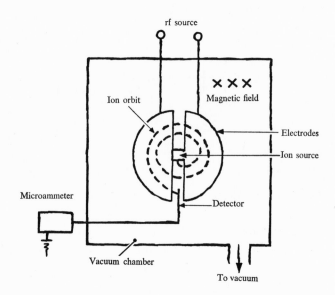

FIGURE 2.10

The mass synchrometer, a cyclotron principle mass spectrometer.

The production of the ion beam in a mass spectrometer is more difficult than the detection. Detection methods are more or less the same no matter what ions are being investigated, but the methods of ion production differ quite radically. The easiest ions to produce are those for which the parent atoms have very low electron binding energies. These atoms include the alkali metals (lithium, sodium, potassium, cesium) and some of the alkali earths such as calcium, strontium, and barium. For these materials it suffices to place a small sample on a metal with a work function larger than the binding energy of the valence electron in the sample atom. The metal thus has a stronger

24 *Measurement of atomic masses*

affinity for electrons than the sample atom, and if the metal is heated, ions of the sample are emitted rather than atoms, since the valence electrons will tend to remain attached to the metal. Another commonly used method with gases or with materials having relatively high-vapor pressures is the electron discharge-type ion source shown in Fig. 2.11. A gas discharge at a pressure of a few microns is started between two electrodes having a potential difference of roughly 300 volts. The gas to be ionized is introduced into the discharge. Ions of the gas are produced when the relatively high-energy electrons collide with the gas atoms, causing ionization. This type of source is sometimes difficult to

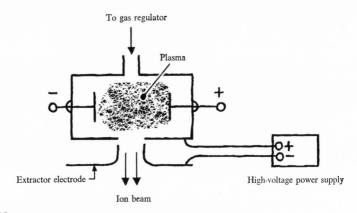

FIGURE 2.11

Electron bombardment ion source and extractor electrode.

regulate, for the equilibrium conditions in the plasma will vary depending on the kind of gas being ionized. The most difficult ions to produce are those of very refractory metals. In this case, electron or ion bombardment may be used to heat the metal surface, and the atoms driven off in this way can be ionized using the discharge method.

2.5 EXPERIMENTS

The instrument[13] used in the experiments to be described is not as elaborate as those described in the previous sections. In particular, no provision is made for focusing the ions other than by collimating slits. Also, the only ions which can be produced are the alkali metals and the alkali earths. Nevertheless, it is possible with this equipment to perform some experiments which will illustrate several of the points described in the previous section. The existence of isotopes of the same element can be established, and crude measurements of relative and absolute masses can be made.

A diagram of the apparatus is shown in Fig. 2.12. The mass spectrometer consists of a brass chamber which is evacuated to a pressure

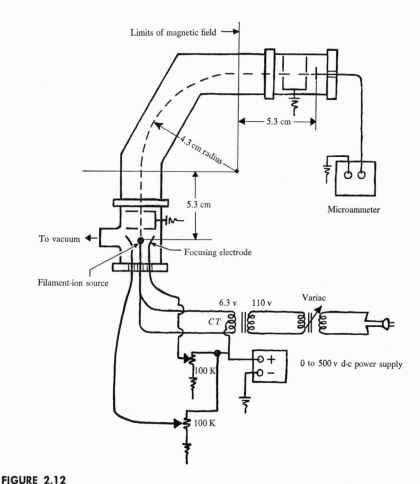

FIGURE 2.12

Schematic diagram of a student laboratory mass spectrometer.

of approximately 10^{-5} torr. (For a description of the vacuum system and the devices used to determine the pressure, see Chapter 4.) The vacuum required is determined by the condition that the mean free path for a collision between an ion in the beam and a residual gas atom must be much less than the distance between the ion source and the detector. Thus

$$\lambda = \frac{1}{\sigma n} \gg d \tag{2.26}$$

or
$$n \ll \frac{1}{d\sigma} \tag{2.27}$$

The collision cross section in this case is approximately 10^{-16} cm^2, and the distance between the source and the ion collector is about 7 cm (see Fig. 2.12). Thus

$$n \ll 1.4 \times 10^{15} \text{ atoms/cc} \tag{2.28}$$

At atmospheric pressure, the density n is about 10^{19} atoms/cc for a gas at room temperature ($\sim$300°K). Therefore the pressure must be at least 10^{-1} torr (atmospheric pressure $\sim$760 torr), and the experiment will be more successful if it is even lower in accord with the inequalities (2.26) and (2.27). The detailed geometry of the vacuum chamber is also shown in Fig. 2.12. It is necessary to know the radius of the ion trajectory if absolute atomic mass measurements are to be made. Finally, some means for measuring the magnetic field in the vacuum chamber must be available. This can be done either with a flip coil magnetometer, a Hall effect probe, or by using the proton NMR probe. In the flip coil magnetometer, the current induced by the field in a rotating coil is measured. The Hall probe works on the principle that the voltage developed perpendicular to the current direction across a flat, current-carrying strip depends on the magnetic field component normal to the surface of the strip. The NMR probe (see Chapter 9) uses the precessional frequency of the proton magnetic moment in a magnetic field as a measure of the field strength.

It is convenient to use the magnet current as a measure of the magnetic field rather than to use the flip coil or the Hall probe to determine the field for every measurement. The first thing that should be done, therefore, is to make a magnetization curve in which the field is plotted as a function of magnet current. When this method is used to determine the field, care must be taken that hysteresis effects are properly accounted for.

Verification of Equation ***(2.15).*** Equation (2.15) defines the mass of the particles in the ion beam in terms of the other parameters of the instrument such as radius, magnetic field, and accelerating potential. The radius is fixed by the instrument, but the magnetic field and the accelerating potential can be varied. For a given mass, it can be seen from Eq. (2.15) that the following relation must hold:

$$B \propto \sqrt{E} \tag{2.29}$$

The experiment is performed as follows: A magnetic field value is chosen and a beam of potassium ions is used. The potassium ions are produced by placing some potassium metal on the tungsten wire-ion source. This "ion source head" is mounted on the deflector chamber and the entire chamber is evacuated. Ions are then produced by passing a current (a few ma) through the tungsten filament and heating it until ions are driven off. An accelerating potential is applied so that the filament-ion source is positive and the collimator is grounded. The potential of the two focusing electrodes is variable to some value between that of the collimator and the filament-ion source. These focusing electrodes shape the electric field around the filament wire to ensure that as large a fraction of the ions as possible leave through the collimating slits.

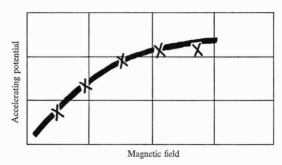

FIGURE 2.13

Graph for verifying Eq. (2.15) (i.e., $B \propto \sqrt{E}$).

The magnitude of the accelerating potential will have to be adjusted to give the maximum collector current. The ion potential required for the maximum collector current is measured for other settings of the magnetic field. The results when plotted as shown in Fig. 2.13 should be a parabola in accord with Eq. (2.29). For best results, magnetic fields of the order of 0.1 weber m⁻² should be used, which means accelerating potentials of the order of 100 volts are necessary. These accelerating potentials can be obtained using an ordinary bias power supply.

Measurement of masses of alkali metals. The masses of the alkali metals can now be determined using the methods outlined in the previous experiment. Ions of each of these elements are produced using the hot-wire method. For a given magnetic field, the accelerating potential necessary to produce a signal at the ion detector is determined. The procedure can then be reversed, and, holding the accelerating potential constant, the appropriate magnetic field values are determined.

The most difficult part of this experiment is to make certain that the ion source strength remains sufficiently stable while the measurements are being made. If the beam current is not constant as the accelerating potential is varied, it is not possible to determine, with sufficient accuracy to make meaningful measurements, the value of the accelerating potential producing the peak ion current. The best way to maintain constant beams is to use only small quantities of the material on the hot wire and to operate the wire at the lowest temperature consistent with sufficient ion emission. The accelerating potential should be provided by a regulated power supply. Finally, the pressure in the chamber should be sufficiently low so that there are no spurious discharges.

Demonstration of the existence of isotopes. Lithium has two stable isotopes which occur naturally, Li^6 and Li^7. The abundance of Li^6 is 7.5 percent and that of Li^7 is 92.5 percent. A beam of lithium ions is produced using the hot-wire method. The beam is then passed through the mass spectrograph, and two peaks, one corresponding to Li^6 and one for Li^7, should be observed. The mass spectrograph must have a sufficient resolving power if this is to be done successfully. In this case,

$$\frac{\Delta m}{m} \approx \frac{1}{7} \tag{2.30}$$

From Eq. (2.15), the corresponding change in the orbit radius is

$$\Delta m = \frac{eB}{v} \Delta r \tag{2.31}$$

or

$$\frac{\Delta m}{m} = \frac{\Delta r}{r} \tag{2.32}$$

Therefore the change in radius, Δr can be computed from the dimensions given in Fig. 2.12. The radius of the spectrometer is 4.3 cm; thus

$$\Delta r = \frac{4.3}{7} \approx 0.6 \text{ cm} \tag{2.33}$$

If the collimating slits of the instrument are set so that they define the beam to better than a millimeter, the peaks due to the different isotopes can be separated. It is important that the spectrometer be carefully cleaned and aligned for this experiment. The background current at the position of the Li^6 peak must be less than 5 percent of the current at the Li^7 peak position; otherwise, because of the relative abundances of the two isotopes, the Li^6 peak will not be observed. Figure 2.14 shows a good mass spectrum for lithium.

One more important point should be made. Equation (2.32) shows that it is much easier to separate isotopes with light masses than with heavy ones. For example, to separate U^{235} from U^{238}

$$\frac{\Delta m}{m} \approx \frac{3}{238} \approx \frac{1}{60} \tag{2.34}$$

so that the slits must be at least ten times as narrow as in the lithium case. It is for this reason that mass spectrometers with high resolution tend to have low transmissions and hence low efficiencies.

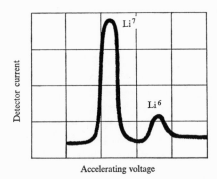

FIGURE 2.14

Mass abundance curve for Li^6 and Li^7 as measured on the student laboratory mass spectrometer.

REFERENCES

1. Hildebrand, J. H., and R. E. Powell: "Principles of Chemistry," 6th ed., The Macmillan Company, New York, 1952.

2. Thomson, J. J.: *Phil. Mag.*, **44**, 293, 1897.

3. Roentgen, W. K.: *Sitzber. Würzberger Physik.-Med. Ges.*, December, 1895.

4. Goldstein, E.: *Sitzber. Königlichen Akad. Wiss. Berlin*, p. 691, July 29, 1886.

5. Lorentz, A. H.: *Versuch Einer Theorie der Elektrischen und Optischen Erscheinunger* in *Bewegten Körpern*, Leiden, 1895.

6. Millikan, R. A.: *Phys. Rev.*, **2**, 136, 1913; *Phil. Mag.*, **34**, 1, 1917; The Electron, Chicago, 1917.

7. Thomson, J. J.: Papers on Positive Rays and Isotopes,

Phil. Mag., **13**, 561, 1907; **16**, 657, 1908; **18**, 821, 1909; **20**, 756, 1910; **21**, 225, 1911; **24**, 209, 669, 1912.

8. Nier, A. O.: *Phys. Rev.*, **50**, 1041, 1936; **52**, 933, 1937.

9. Kazi, A. H., N. C. Rasmussen, and Hans Mark, *Phys. Rev.*, **123**, 1310, 1961.

10. Dempster, A. J.: *Phys. Rev.*, **11**, 316, 1918.

11. Aston, F. W.: *Phil. Mag.*, **38**, 704, 1919.

12. Smith, L. G.: *Rev. Sci. Instr.*, **22**, 118, 1951.

13. Marcley, R.: *Am. J. Phys.*, **28**, 418, 1960.

GENERAL BIBLIOGRAPHY

1. Elliott, R. M.: "Advances in Mass Spectrometry," vols. I and II, The Macmillan Company, New York, 1963.

2. Robertson, A. J. B.: "Mass Spectrometry," Methuen & Co. Ltd., London, 1954.

3. Inghram, M. G.: "Modern Mass Spectroscopy, Advances in Electronics," vol. I, Academic Press, New York, 1948.

4. Inghram, M. G., and R. J. Hayden: "A Handbook of Mass Spectroscopy," National Research Council, Washington, D.C., 1954.

5. Barnard, G. P.: "Modern Mass Spectrometry," The Institute of Physics, London, 1953.

6. Bainbridge, K. T.: Charged Particle Dynamics and Optics, Relative Isotopic Abundances of the Elements, Atomic Masses, Part V of "Experimental Nuclear Physics," vol. I, edited by E. Segrè, John Wiley & Sons, Inc., New York, 1953.

7. McDowell, C. A.: "Mass Spectrometry," McGraw-Hill Book Company, New York, 1963.

	THE PASSAGE
Chapter 3	OF CHARGED PARTICLES
	THROUGH MATTER

3.1 INTRODUCTION

The discovery that certain heavy nuclei spontaneously emit high-energy helium nuclei[1] (alpha particles) provided an important means for the study of the properties of matter. Together with atomic spectroscopy, the work done with alpha particles revealed the most important features of the structure of the atom and the nucleus.

The interaction of charged particles with matter can be divided roughly into two categories—the interaction with the atomic electrons and the interaction with the atomic nuclei. Collisions between heavy charged particles and electrons give rise to a class of phenomena which is quite different from the nuclear collisions. Qualitatively the situation is this: When a heavy charged particle collides with an atom, the most likely event is that the atom is ionized. In the process the alpha particle (or other heavy charged particle) loses only a small amount of energy as a result of the large disparity between the alpha-particle mass and the electron mass. The conservation of momentum requires that the velocity of the light particle be roughly equal (at best) to the velocity

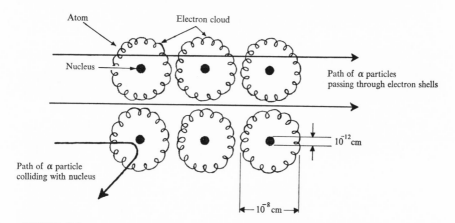

FIGURE 3.1

Possible trajectories of alpha particles passing through matter.

of the heavy particle. Because the alpha-particle mass is eight thousand times the electron mass, the kinetic energy of the electrons produced in collisions with 5-mev alpha particles is only a few hundred electron volts. It is also true that the alpha particle is not deflected very much during such a collision, again because the alpha particle cannot transfer much of its momentum to the electron.

Collisions between the alpha particles and the atomic nuclei are characterized by a large momentum transfer rather than a small one as in the case of collisions with electrons. The nucleus is heavier than the incident alpha particle and therefore behaves, in the first approximation, as if it were fixed. Thus the alpha particle may transfer up to twice its own momentum to the massive nucleus and be scattered back in the opposite direction. Figure 3.1 illustrates the situation.

A more quantitative treatment of the two interactions described in the foregoing paragraphs will now be given. The collision of energetic heavy charged particles with atomic electrons causes the incident particle to lose a relatively small fraction of its energy in each encounter. A more detailed description of this process will lead to a formula giving the rate at which the incident particles lose energy per unit distance traveled through matter. This is the so-called stopping power formula, which has a great many important practical applications. In the case of collisions with atomic nuclei, it is possible to calculate the number of scattered heavy particles observed as a function of scattering angle. The quantitative verification of this scattering law by Lord Rutherford[2] and his collaborators was the decisive experiment in establishing the existence of atomic nuclei, and was one of the most important turning points in modern physics.

3.2 ENERGY LOSS OF CHARGED PARTICLES PASSING THROUGH MATTER

In order to obtain the stopping power formula mentioned in Sec. 3.1, it will be necessary to make some assumptions about the structure of the atom and about how atoms are arranged in a solid. The atom consists of a very small, massive, and positively charged nucleus surrounded by a roughly spherical distribution of electrons. If the charge on the nucleus is Ze, then there are Z electrons surrounding the atom. These electrons are bound in their respective atoms and occupy well-defined energy levels. In order to absorb energy, an electron must be removed from one of the filled energy levels to an unoccupied one or it must be removed from the atom entirely. The average energy necessary to do this is called the mean excitation and ionization potential. This quantity will be denoted by $\bar{\epsilon}$. (For a more detailed discussion see Reference 3, p. 650.) In a solid, the atoms will be closely packed with as little "empty space" between neighboring atoms as possible. Thus in the close-packed situation the atomic electrons can be considered as uniformly distributed in the solid.

To compute the energy loss suffered by the incident particle per collision with an electron, it is necessary to refer to Fig. 3.2. The incident charged particle has a velocity v and a charge ze. The particle is not deflected in the collision because, as stated previously, it is much more massive than the electron. The force between the particle and the electron is determined by the electrostatic attraction law

$$\mathbf{F} = \frac{1}{4\pi\epsilon_0} \frac{ze^2}{r^2} \hat{r} = \frac{1}{4\pi\epsilon_0} \frac{ze^2}{x^2 + a^2} \hat{r} \tag{3.1}$$

where a is the distance of closest approach or the so-called "impact parameter." The momentum (and hence the energy) transferred to the electron in the collision is

$$\mathbf{p} = \int \mathbf{F}\, dt = \frac{1}{4\pi\epsilon_0} \int \frac{ze^2}{x^2 + a^2} \hat{r}\, dt \qquad (3.2)$$

The momentum transferred will always be perpendicular to the direction of motion of the charged particle because the components of the force not perpendicular to the direction of motion cancel as the particle moves past the electron. Hence the vector notation need not be employed, for only the transverse component of $\mathbf{p}$ must be considered. Since the velocity of the heavy particle is only slightly altered in the collision, the time integral in Eq. (3.2) can be changed to a line integral

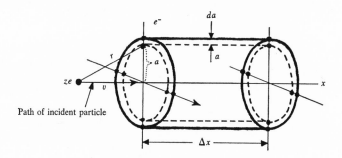

FIGURE 3.2

Cylindrical element of material which contributes to the slowing down of the alpha particle.

along the particle path using the variable transformation

$$dt = \frac{dx}{v} \qquad (3.3)$$

The total momentum transferred to the electron is thus

$$\Delta p = \frac{1}{4\pi\epsilon_0} \int_{-\infty}^{\infty} \frac{ze^2}{x^2 + a^2} \frac{dx}{v} = \frac{1}{4\pi\epsilon_0} \frac{ze^2\pi}{va} \qquad (3.4)$$

The energy transferred to the electron, and thus the energy lost by the incident particle in each collision, is

$$-\Delta\epsilon = \frac{\Delta p^2}{2m_e} = \left(\frac{1}{4\pi\epsilon_0}\right)^2 \frac{z^2e^4\pi^2}{2m_ev^2a^2} \qquad (3.5)$$

The number of electrons in a thickness element Δx of the material for which the impact parameter is between a and $a + da$ is given by the number of electrons in the annular volume shown in Fig. 3.2. If there are N atoms per cubic centimeter in the material, then there are ZN

electrons per cubic centimeter. Thus the number of electrons in the indicated volume is $NZ2\pi a \, da \, \Delta x$. The total energy lost by the incident particle $-\Delta E$ in passing through the distance Δx is obtained by multiplying $-\Delta \epsilon$, given in Eq. (3.5), by the number of electrons in the volume element and integrating over the impact parameters:

$$-\Delta E = NZ \, \Delta x \int_{a_{\min}}^{a_{\max}} \Delta \epsilon \, 2\pi a \, da \qquad (3.6)$$

It is customary to calculate $-\Delta E/\Delta x$, the energy lost per unit distance traversed. This quantity is given by

$$-\frac{\Delta E}{\Delta x} = \left(\frac{1}{4\pi\epsilon_0}\right)^2 \frac{NZze^4\pi^3}{m_e v^2} \int_{a_{\min}}^{a_{\max}} \frac{da}{a}$$

$$= \left(\frac{1}{4\pi\epsilon_0}\right)^2 \frac{NZz^2e^4\pi^3}{m_e v^2} \left(\ln \frac{a_{\max}}{a_{\min}}\right) \qquad (3.7)$$

where $a_{\max}$ and $a_{\min}$ are the maximum and minimum impact parameters to be considered in the process.

To estimate the minimum and maximum impact parameters it is necessary to use some concepts of wave mechanics. The reason for this circumstance is that it is not possible to employ the strictly classical approach used here in dealing with atomic phenomena. For example, the minimum impact parameter mentioned in Eq. (3.7) should be zero if the particle model illustrated in Fig. 3.1 were completely correct. The fact is, however, that quantum mechanics requires that the electron can never be localized precisely with respect to the incident particle. Consequently, it makes little sense to say that the impact parameter is smaller than the region of space occupied by the electron. The size of this region is determined roughly by the "wavelength" of the electron as seen by an observer on the incident particle. Therefore

$$a_{\min} \approx \lambda_e \approx \frac{h}{m_e v} \qquad (3.8)$$

where v is the velocity of the incident particle.

It is a little more difficult to estimate the maximum impact parameter, $a_{\max}$. In order to absorb any momentum from the incident particle, it will be assumed that the electron must be freed from the atom. (This assumption is not strictly correct. What is actually required is that the electron make a transition to an unfilled energy level in the atom. Since atomic energy levels have not been considered here, the assumption that the atom is ionized is an acceptable approximation.) The smallest energy which the electron must therefore acquire in the collision is approximately equal to $\bar{\epsilon}$, the average binding energy in the atom. The order of magnitude of the time in which a process occurs is related to energy change in a very crude way by the Heisenberg uncertainty principle:

$$\Delta E \, \Delta t \approx h \tag{3.9}$$

In the ionization process the energy must be specified with at least a precision equal to $\bar{\epsilon}$, hence the maximum uncertainty in the energy ΔE must be $\bar{\epsilon}$. The time which the ionization process can take is thus of the order:

$$\Delta t \approx \frac{h}{\bar{\epsilon}} \tag{3.10}$$

The time interval Δt is determined by the time the incident particle spends in the neighborhood of the electron. The longest time associated with the minimum energy transfer is

$$\Delta t \approx \frac{a_{max}}{v} \approx \frac{h}{\bar{\epsilon}} \tag{3.11}$$

Hence the maximum impact parameter is approximately

$$a_{max} \approx \frac{hv}{\bar{\epsilon}} \tag{3.12}$$

The expressions for a_{min} and a_{max} given in Eqs. (3.8) and (3.12) may now be substituted into Eq. (3.7) to give the following result:

$$-\frac{\Delta E}{\Delta x} = \left(\frac{1}{4\pi\epsilon_0}\right)^2 \frac{NZz^2e^4\pi^3}{m_ev^2} \ln \frac{m_ev^2}{\bar{\epsilon}} \tag{3.13}$$

The energy-loss formula given in Eq. (3.12) has the proper dependence on the parameters Z, z, m_e, and v, even though it does not have precisely the correct numerical factors. The crude assumptions made in the derivation are the reason for this failure to obtain the correct factors. A more precise quantum mechanical calculation[4] for the energy loss yields the formula:

$$-\frac{\Delta E}{\Delta x} = \left(\frac{1}{4\pi\epsilon_0}\right)^2 \frac{4\pi e^4z^2NZ}{m_ev^2} \ln \frac{2m_ev^2}{\bar{\epsilon}} \tag{3.14}$$

which is valid for heavy charged particles with incident energies larger than 0.5 mev and smaller than 20 mev. The failure at low energies is due to the fact that some of the atomic electrons may have binding energies which are comparable to the incident particle energy and are thus either difficult or impossible to remove from the atom. At high energies a relativistic treatment is required if accurate results are desired.

Several features of Eq. (3.13) deserve comment. One is that the energy loss is the same for incident particles of the same velocity even if they have different masses. A second is that the energy loss depends on the square of the charge carried by the incident ion, but only on the first power of the atomic number Z of the material through which the particles pass. The energy loss due to ionization decreases as the velocity (energy) of the incident particle increases. This last statement is not precisely true if relativistic effects are included so that, for very high incident energies, the energy loss increases again, giving rise to a broad minimum in the energy loss curve. Incident particles with energies in this region are usually called "minimum ionizing" particles. Finally, the parameter $\bar{\epsilon}$, which can be determined empirically from energy loss experiments in different elements, turns out to be proportional to the atomic number Z. This quantity is approximately equal to the geometric mean of all the ionization and excitation energies of the atom (see Reference 3).

The purpose of some of the experiments described in subsequent sections of this chapter is to verify the energy-loss formula [Eq. (3.13)] derived in this section.

3.3 SCATTERING OF CHARGED PARTICLES BY ATOMIC NUCLEI

The previous section considered the interaction of the incident particle with the atomic electrons; this section will consider deflection of incident particles by collisions with atomic nuclei. The latter has already been discussed in a qualitative manner. Using methods very similar to those in the previous section, the quantitative results of scattering experiments can be understood. A schematic diagram of the experimental arrangement used by Lord Rutherford and his collaborators (1911) is shown in Fig. 3.3. A radium source, which emits alpha

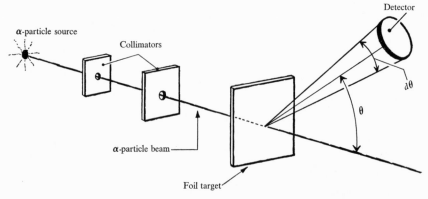

FIGURE 3.3

Thin foil scattering of a collimated alpha particle beam.

38 *Passage of charged particles through matter*

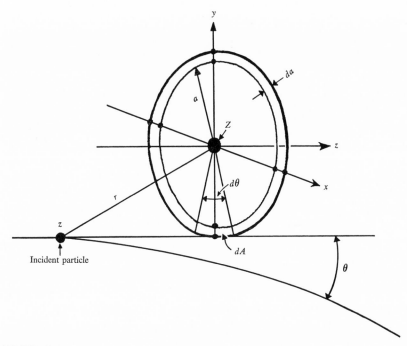

FIGURE 3.4

Rutherford scattering (nuclear scattering) of an alpha particle.

particles with an energy of about 4 mev, was used as a source of high-velocity ions. A beam of particles was produced by means of suitable collimators. These particles were then passed through a metal foil which was sufficiently thin so that the energy loss suffered by the particles is very small compared to the incident energy. A particle detector is placed so as to observe alpha particles scattered through an angle θ away from the axis of the incident beam. The number of scattered particles observed at the detector is

$$n = \Phi_i P(\theta) A \tag{3.15}$$

where Φ_i is the incident flux of particles on the foil, $P(\theta)$ is the probability that a particle is scattered through the angle θ, and A is the area of the detector. The probability $P(\theta)$ must now be evaluated by considering in detail what happens during an individual collision event. Figure 3.4 shows the path of an incident-charged particle passing close to the nucleus. The quantity a in Fig. 3.4 is the same as the "impact parameter" defined in the previous section. In his calculation Lord Rutherford assumed that the force between the nucleus and the incident particle is due only to the electrostatic repulsion

$$\mathbf{F} = \frac{1}{4\pi\epsilon_0} \frac{Zze^2}{r^2} \hat{r} \tag{3.16}$$

A very important implication of this assumption is that both the incident ion and the nucleus have linear dimensions small compared to the impact parameter, so that they may be considered as point particles.

The calculation of $P(\theta)$ is quite complicated, for it requires a relation between the impact parameter a and the scattering angle θ. It can be performed rigorously using the orbit equations for the particle in the force field defined by Eq. (3.16). An approximate solution can be derived more easily using the momentum transfer arguments of the previous section. In the approximation that the deflection angle is small, Eq. (3.4) may be used to calculate the momentum transferred to the incident particle during the collision

$$\Delta p = \frac{1}{4\pi\epsilon_0} \frac{Zze^2\pi}{av} \tag{3.17}$$

where v is the incident particle velocity. The scattering angle is approximately

$$\frac{\Delta p}{p} = \tan \theta \approx \theta \tag{3.18}$$

The relation between the impact parameter and the scattering angle is thus

$$a = \frac{1}{4\pi\epsilon_0} \frac{Zze^2\pi}{mv^2} \frac{1}{\tan \theta} \approx \frac{1}{4\pi\epsilon_0} \frac{Zze^2\pi}{mv^2\theta} \tag{3.19}$$

where m is the mass of the incident particle.

The probability that a particle is scattered through the angle θ can best be evaluated by considering the right half of Fig. 3.4. If the particle is to be scattered into the counter, then it must pass through the area element $a\,da\,d\phi$ shown in the drawing. If the foil has an irradiated area A_I and a thickness t, the number of such area elements is $NA_I ta\,da\,d\phi$, where N is the number of nuclei per cubic centimeter in the foil. The probability that the particle is scattered into the counter is equal to the sum of the area elements $a\,da\,d\phi$ just calculated, divided by the total area of the foil irradiated, A_I,

$$P(\theta) = \frac{NA_I ta\,da\,d\phi}{A_I} = Nta\,da\,d\phi \tag{3.20}$$

Using Eq. (3.19) to evaluate a in terms of θ and substituting into Eq. (3.15) give the following result for the number of particles scattered into the counter:

$$n = \Phi_i N t A \left(\frac{1}{4\pi\epsilon_0} \frac{Zze^2\pi}{mv^2} \right)^2 \frac{d\theta\, d\phi}{\theta^3} \tag{3.21}$$

This result can now be expressed in terms of the scattered flux n/A and the "solid angle" $d\Omega$ subtended by the counter. The solid angle is defined in terms of θ and ϕ as

$$d\Omega = \sin\theta\, d\theta\, d\phi \tag{3.22}$$

Thus, in terms of the solid angle, the scattered flux is

$$d\phi_s = \Phi_i N t \left[\left(\frac{1}{4\pi\epsilon_0} \frac{Zze^2\pi}{mv^2} \right)^2 \frac{1}{\theta^4} \right] d\Omega \tag{3.23}$$

where the approximation that θ is small has again been employed. The quantity shown in brackets in Eq. (3.23) is called the differential scattering cross section. (It has the dimensions (length)^2 and is measured in m^2. The practical unit for measuring cross sections is the barn, which is defined as 1 barn $= 10^{-28}$ m^2.) The differential scattering cross section is

$$\sigma(\theta) = \left(\frac{1}{4\pi\epsilon_0} \frac{Zze^2\pi}{mv^2} \right)^2 \frac{1}{\theta^4} \tag{3.24}$$

As in the case of the stopping power formula, the approximations employed here do not give precisely the correct answer. The differential scattering cross section derived by Lord Rutherford, using the exact orbit equations, is

$$\sigma(\theta) = \left(\frac{1}{4\pi\epsilon_0} \frac{Zze^2}{2mv^2} \right)^2 \frac{1}{(\sin\theta/2)^4} \tag{3.25}$$

The exact derivation of Eq. (3.25) can be found in Reference 2. It can easily be seen that, in the approximation that θ is small, Eqs. (3.24) and (3.25) have the same angular dependence. Both formulas also give the same dependence on z, Z, and the energy of the incident particle. They differ slightly in the numerical factors.

The strong angular dependence of the scattering shown in Eq. (3.25) is typical of coulomb-type interactions. Relatively few particles are scattered through angles larger than $\pi/2$. The factor $(Zze^2/2mv^24\pi\epsilon_0)$ has the dimension of length and is equal to one-quarter of the distance of closest approach in a head-on collision. For the energies usually considered in alpha-particle scattering experiments by heavy nuclei ($Z \approx 80$), this distance is of the order of 10^{-11} cm. The precise experimental confirmation of Eq. (3.25) by Lord Rutherford and his collaborators is very strong proof that the nucleus of the atom must be very small. In fact, the derivation presented here assumes that the nucleus is a point mass carrying a charge Ze. Deviations from the angular dependence given in Eq. (3.25) are observed if nuclei lighter than gold ($Z \approx 50$ rather than $Z \approx 80$) are used to scatter the incident alpha particles. In such experiments the alpha particles have sufficient energy to overcome the coulomb repulsion and actually collide with the nucleus. Such experiments cannot be quantitatively described without taking into account the effect of the finite size of the nucleus and the behavior of nuclear forces.

3.4 EXPERIMENTAL METHODS

Vacuum systems. The first requirement for performing accurate particle scattering experiments is a good vacuum chamber. Charged

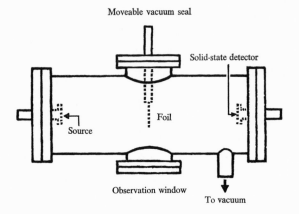

FIGURE 3.5

Experimental vacuum chamber suitable for measuring alpha particle slowing down.

particles lose energy in passing through the air, and if effects due to interactions with the gases in the air are to be minimized, most of the air must be removed from the chamber. Figure 3.5 shows a sketch of a typical chamber used for the performance of scattering experiments. The flanges are removable so that a number of different experimental configurations are available. The over-all source to target distance is of the order of 25 cm. To estimate the operating pressure, the requirement imposed is that the particles emitted by the source should travel the length of the chamber without being scattered by the residual air. This means that the mean free path of the projectile must be longer than the length of the chamber L, or

$$L < \lambda = \frac{1}{n\sigma} \tag{3.26}$$

In Eq. (3.26) n denotes the number of air atoms per cubic centimeter in the chamber and σ is the effective scattering cross section which an air atom presents to the projectile. Since the atomic radius is of the order of 10^{-8} cm, the area will be approximately 3×10^{-16} cm^2. If the length of the chamber L is 25 cm, the density n, which fulfills condition (3.26), is

$$n < \frac{1}{L\sigma} < 1.5 \times 10^{14} \text{ atoms/cc} \tag{3.27}$$

At atmospheric pressure the atomic density is approximately 10^{19} molecules/cc; thus the chamber must be evacuated to approximately 10^{-5} of atmospheric pressure or approximately 10^{-3} torr. (For definitions of the unit torr see Chapter 4.)

Alpha-particle sources. To obtain reasonably reliable results in the scattering experiments it is necessary to use specially prepared sources of alpha particles. Isotopes with atomic numbers (Z) larger than 83 spontaneously emit alpha particles. These particles are monoenergetic, the energy being determined by the mass difference between the initial nucleus and the sum of the alpha particle and final nucleus mass. The energies of the alpha particles emitted by sources range between 4 and 9 mev. If accurate measurements of the alpha-particle energies are to be made, then steps must be taken to ensure that the alpha particles lose only a small amount of their energy in passing through the source itself. Thin sources are produced by evaporating a small amount of radioactive material on a platinum disk. If the specific activity of the sample is high enough, the layer can be made so thin that the alpha particle loses only a few kilovolts of energy in passing through the source layer. If alpha sources are to be used in a vacuum system, it is also necessary to deposit a layer of plastic on top of the source to ensure that none of the alpha-active material spills into the system.

For the purpose of the present experiments, Am[241] sources are recommended. The element americium (Am) is one of the transuranic elements[5] ($Z = 95$) which does not occur in nature. The element must be manufactured with the help of a nuclear reactor or a nuclear accelerator. Most of the artificially produced elements have higher specific activities (i.e., shorter half-lives) than those occurring in nature. For this reason they tend to be more useful for the present purpose. Am^{241} emits alpha particles with an energy of 5.47 mev.

Particle detectors. One of the most interesting features of this experiment is the method used to detect the alpha particles and to measure their energies. Ionization chambers and scintillation counters can be used to detect the charged particles. However, recent developments in solid-state physics have made it possible to produce a new class of very efficient and useful particle detectors.[6] These developments are discussed in Chapter 8 in connection with nonlinear electronic devices. It has already been shown that charged particles cause ionization in passing through matter. The gas ionization counters described in Chapter 5 operate by collecting the charges produced by the ionization. In a gas, this can be done because the charges take a relatively long time to recombine and can therefore be collected before they do so. In principle, an insulating solid could also be used as a particle detector because the fast ionizing particle causes electrons to appear in the conduction band. These electrons could be moved to an electrode by a strong electric field placed across the crystal. The difficulty is that the recombination of the ion pairs in the solid is very rapid. Thus extremely strong electric fields are necessary to move the charges before they recombine. The required fields generally exceed the dielectric strength of the material, and therefore this method for detecting ionizing radiations is impractical.

In spite of the circumstances outlined in the preceding paragraph, it is possible to make "solid-state ionization chambers" by taking advantage of the properties of the *p-n* junctions discussed in Chapter 8. The essential point is that the junction region shown in Fig. 8.9 has a concentration of positive charges (holes) on one side and negative charges (electrons) on the other. A strong "trapped" electric field thus exists inside the junction region, and this field acts to sweep out charges produced in the junction by an ionizing event. A schematic drawing of a *p-n* junction counter is shown in Fig. 3.6. The body of the detector consists of a very pure high-resistivity *p*-type silicon. The surface of the silicon is doped with an impurity (phosphorus for example) which creates a *p-n* junction layer at the surface of silicon. Appropriate electrodes for biasing the junction and collecting the charges liberated by the ionizing event are also provided.

The electron energy level diagram is shown in Fig. 3.7. The *p-n* junction is very close to the surface of the silicon so that charged particles entering the silicon deposit all their energy in the junction region. The electron-hole pairs created by the ionizing event move to the *n*

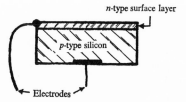

n-type surface layer

p-type silicon

Electrodes

FIGURE 3.6

Cross section of a solid-state diode alpha-particle detector.

and p portions of the detector, respectively, where they are collected by the electrodes. Junction detectors of this type are usually operated with a reverse bias voltage, that is, the surface (n region) of the detector is positively biased with respect to the base (p region). This has the effect of moving the electrons on the right side (p side) of the junction deeper into the silicon, thus increasing the thickness of the junction layer. This layer is often called the "depletion layer" because the electrons of the n-type material have been depleted by the presence of the p-type material and the external reverse bias. In order to be effective as a proportional charged particle detector, the depletion layer must be thicker than the range of the particles so that all the energy of the incident particle is deposited in the layer. This makes it possible to measure the energy of the charged particles because the number of

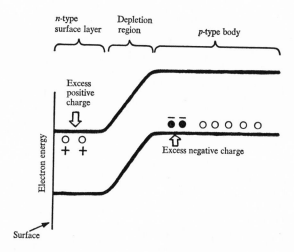

FIGURE 3.7

Electron energy-level diagram of a solid-state diode alpha-particle detector.

electrons liberated is proportional to the energy of the particle. The great advantage of the solid-state detector is that only about 3 electron volts are necessary to produce an electron-hole pair in the solid compared to the 30 electron volts necessary to create an electron-ion pair in a gas counter. This makes it possible to obtain better particle energy resolution because the statistical fluctuations in the total charge collected at the electrodes are smaller by a factor of 3. A typical alpha-particle spectrum is shown in Fig. 3.8. A resolution of 0.5 percent can be obtained. The peak is slightly asymmetric because of the range straggling occurring in the surface layer.

The schematic diagram of the electronic system used with the detector is shown in Fig. 3.9. The preamplifier is of the charge-sensitive type

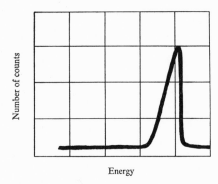

FIGURE 3.8

Energy spectrum of Am^{241} alpha particles as measured by a solid-state detector.

which is used with low-impedance devices such as the *p-n* junction detector. The function of the preamplifier is to drive the long cables which may be necessary between the location of the detector and the recording equipment. For a more detailed description of circuits used with solid-state detection devices, the reader is referred to Reference 5.

Kinematics of particle collisions. In the introduction to this chapter, the conservation of energy and momentum in particle collisions was mentioned briefly. Some of the pertinent equations will now be derived and their consequences will be stated. It will be assumed that the particles in question are uncharged. The existence of a coulomb field between the particles does not change the conclusions concerning energy and momentum conservation, although it does complicate the dynamics of the collision process. It will also be assumed that the

46 *Passage of charged particles through matter*

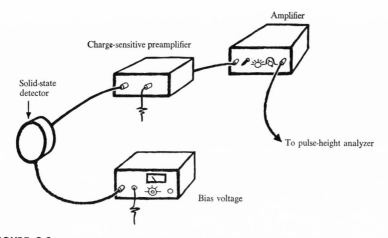

FIGURE 3.9

Instrumentation for measuring alpha particle energy spectrums.

collisions occur in one dimension. This assumption gives the limiting case of maximum momentum transfer while greatly simplifying the equations. The maximum momentum transfer situation is usually the one of greatest physical interest, for it defines the upper limit of what can happen. Figure 3.10 shows the geometry of the problem. Velocities before the collision are denoted by lower-case letters and velocities after the collision by capital letters. The equations of conservation of energy and momentum are

$$\tfrac{1}{2}m_1v_1{}^2 = \tfrac{1}{2}m_1V_1{}^2 + \tfrac{1}{2}m_2V_2{}^2 \tag{3.28}$$

$$m_1v_1 = m_1V_1 + m_2V_2 \tag{3.29}$$

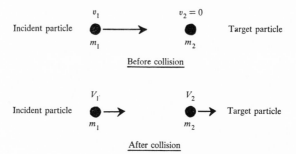

FIGURE 3.10

Kinematics of collisions between particles of mass m_1 and m_2.

These can be solved for the final velocity V_1 of the incident particle by eliminating V_2:

$$V_1 = \frac{v_1(m_1/m_2) - 1}{1 + (m_1/m_2)} = v_1 \frac{(m_1 - m_2)}{(m_1 + m_2)} \tag{3.30}$$

Assume now that $m_1 \gg m_2$. This holds if the target particle is an electron and the incident particle is an alpha particle. In this case m_2 can be neglected in the numerator and denominator of Eq. (3.30), giving

$$V_1 = v_1 \tag{3.31}$$

This equation illustrates the statement made in the introduction that an alpha particle can never lose much energy in a collision with an electron (if the initial and final velocities are equal, the initial and final energies must also be equal). If $m_2 \gg m_1$, which is the case when the alpha particle collides with a heavy nucleus,

$$V_1 = -v_1 \tag{3.32}$$

which means that the alpha particle is scattered in the backward direction (i.e., the new velocity is negative). Equations (3.31) and (3.32) illustrate the important difference between the interaction of the alpha particle with the atomic electrons and with the nucleus. In the first case the alpha particle keeps moving in approximately the same direction, whereas in the second case it is scattered in the opposite direction. It has already been stated that this circumstance makes it possible to distinguish easily between alpha particles which interact only with the atomic electrons and those which have undergone nuclear collisions.

3.5 EXPERIMENTS

Passage of alpha particles through matter. The first experiment is to use the arrangement shown in Fig. 3.5 to determine what happens when alpha particles pass through varying thicknesses of thin foils. The alpha particles should be passed through four aluminum foils of different thicknesses. The pulse height spectrum observed for each of the foils should be plotted as shown in Fig. 3.11. A number of interesting qualitative conclusions can be drawn from this diagram:

1. The alpha-particle energy decreases as it passes through the foil, that is, the position of the peak in the spectrum shifts to a lower channel number.

2. The total number of alpha particles reaching the counter does not change by a very large factor when matter is inserted, that is, most

of the alpha particles pass through the aluminum foils without being deflected through large angles.

3. The alpha-particle peaks in the spectra are broadened, indicating that some of the alpha particles lose more (or less) energy than others in passing through the foils.

The decrease in energy of the alpha particle observed in this experiment can be used to verify the stopping power formula derived in Sec. 3.2. Some care must be taken in interpreting the results. The velocity v appearing in Eq. (3.14) should be considered as the average

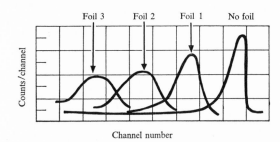

FIGURE 3.11

Energy spectrum of Am^{241} alpha particles after passing through various thicknesses of aluminum foil.

velocity of the alpha particle in traversing the foil

$$\bar{v} = \frac{v_i + v_f}{2} = \frac{\sqrt{2m_\alpha E_i} + \sqrt{2m_\alpha E_f}}{2} = \sqrt{\frac{m_\alpha}{2}} \left(\sqrt{E_i} + \sqrt{E_f} \right) \qquad (3.33)$$

where E_i is the initial energy of the alpha particle and E_f is the final energy measured after the alpha particles have passed through the foil. Using $\bar{v}$, the energy lost, $-\Delta E$, can now be calculated for each thickness Δx. This experiment should also be performed with foils of different elements so that the dependence on Z and N, as predicted in Eq. (3.14), can be verified. The energy lost as a function of thickness for each foil should be plotted on a graph as shown in Fig. 3.12. The relation between $-\Delta E$ and Δx is not quite linear because the factor multiplying Δx increases as Δx is increased (i.e., $\bar{v}$ decreases as Δx increases). It is also interesting to determine the behavior of $-\Delta E/\Delta x$ as a function of alpha-particle energy. This experiment can be done by using two foils, one to determine the initial alpha-particle energy and the second to measure the energy loss at that energy. The results should be displayed as shown in Fig. 3.13.

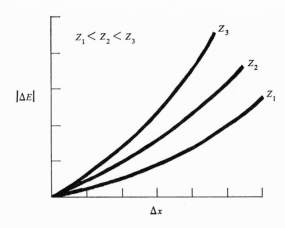

FIGURE 3.12

Energy-loss curves for materials of different atomic number.

The second observation is very easy to understand. The probability that an alpha particle is scattered through a large angle by a nuclear collision is quite small. It will be shown in the following section that, for the foils considered here, the probability of scattering through angles larger than 45 degrees is of the order of 1 percent. Therefore most of the alpha particles will pass through the foil without being strongly deflected, and hence no great change in the counting rate should be observed.

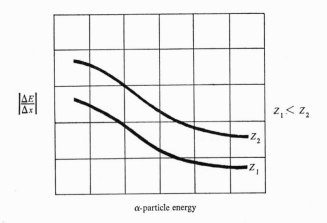

α-particle energy

FIGURE 3.13

Alpha-particle energy-loss rate $(-\Delta E/\Delta x)$ as a function of the alpha-particle energy.

50 *Passage of charged particles through matter*

The broadening of the peaks observed in the spectrum is caused by straggling. This fact is a statistical phenomenon due to the large number of possible ways in which the incident alpha particle can interact with an atom. The numbers derived in the foregoing sections pertaining to energy loss per atomic interaction are average values. For example, it is possible for the alpha particle to lose much more (as many as three order of magnitude) energy than the quoted average if it ionizes a K-shell electron in a heavy atom which may have a binding energy up to 80 kev. Thus some alpha particles may lose more energy than the average and some may lose less. The result is the observed broadening of the peaks shown in Fig. 3.11.

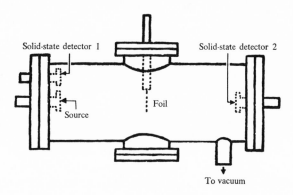

FIGURE 3.14

Experimental vacuum chamber suitable for measuring Rutherford scattered alpha particles.

Scattering of alpha particles by nuclei. In order to verify the nuclear scattering formula [Eq. (3.25)], a number of small changes must be made in the apparatus shown in Fig. 3.5. Another counter must be placed on the same side of the foil as the source. The new arrangement is shown in Fig. 3.14. The first important measurement is to determine the ratio of the number of alpha particles observed in counters 1 and 2. The counting rate in counter 2 must be determined with the foil removed, otherwise small-angle scattering will affect the result. Note also that the geometry of the experiment is so arranged that the alpha particle must travel the same distance to reach counters 1 and 2. It is therefore unnecessary to make corrections for different solid angles subtended by the source at the two counters. Rather long counting times will be necessary, for the ratio is quite small.

A very approximate estimate of the upper limit of the size of the nucleus can be obtained from this measurement. Assume that the nuclei in the foil appear to the alpha particles as disks. Assume also that, in order to be scattered in a backward direction, the alpha particle must strike one of the disks. The number of alpha particles scattered by the foil is given by

$$N_\alpha = \Phi_\alpha N \pi r^2 \tag{3.34}$$

where N is the number of disks per unit area, the quantity (πr^2) is the effective area of each disk or the scattering cross section, and Φ_α is the number of alpha particles incident on the target material. The ratio of the counting rates in counters 1 and 2 must now be calculated in terms of the scattering cross section. Let S be the effective source strength, D the distance between the source and the target foil, and A_1, A_2, and A_F the effective areas of counter 1, counter 2, and the target foil. The observed counting rate in counter 2 is

$$C_2 = \frac{SA_2}{4\pi(2D)^2} \tag{3.35}$$

and the counting rate in counter 1 is

$$C_1 = \frac{N_\alpha A_1}{2\pi D^2} \tag{3.36}$$

where N_α is the effective alpha-particle source strength of the foil given in Eq. (3.34). Note that the factor 2π appears in the denominator rather than 4π, since we have assumed that πr^2 is the cross section for scattering only in the backward (i.e., $\theta > 90°$) direction. To evaluate Eq. (3.36), Eq. (3.34) is used together with the definition of Φ_α:

$$\Phi_\alpha = \frac{SA_F}{4\pi D^2} \tag{3.37}$$

Thus

$$C_1 = \frac{SA_F A_1 N(\pi r^2)}{(4\pi D^2)(2\pi D^2)} \tag{3.38}$$

The ratio of the two counting rates is therefore

$$\rho = \frac{C_1}{C_2} = \frac{2A_F A_1}{A_2 D^2} N(\pi r^2) \tag{3.39}$$

The factor depending on the counter areas can be further simplified, for $A_1 = A_2$. Therefore

$$\rho = \frac{2A_F}{D^2} N(\pi r^2) \tag{3.40}$$

The number of "disks" per unit area in the target foil is just equal to the number of atoms (i.e., nuclei) per unit volume n multiplied by the thickness of the foil t:

$$N = nt \qquad (3.41)$$

Thus the final expression for the ratio ρ in terms of measured or calculable quantities is

$$\rho = \frac{2A_F}{D^2}\,(nt)(\pi r^2) \qquad (3.42)$$

The value of r can be determined from the measurement of ρ with the help of Eq. (3.42). It should be about 10^{-12} cm^2. The scattering nuclei are thus very small compared to atoms, having a radius which is approximately 10^4 times smaller than the radius of the atom.

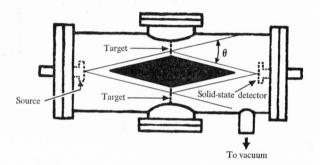

FIGURE 3.15

Experimental vacuum chamber suitable for approximate measurement of the nuclear radius.

The angular dependence of the scattering can also be determined, although this is a more difficult experiment to perform with the weak alpha sources available in student laboratories. The experimental arrangement is shown in Fig. 3.15. The alpha-particle source is placed at the left end of the chamber and an annular foil of the material from which the alpha particles are to be scattered is mounted as shown in the middle of the chamber. The solid-state detector is mounted on the right-hand side. A brass shield is placed between the counter and the detector to prevent unscattered alpha particles from reaching the detector. It can easily be seen that only alpha particles scattered through a small range of angles around θ in the foil will be detected. The angle θ can be varied by changing the distance D between the source and the detector. By measuring the counting rate for different distances and making the appropriate estimates of the solid angle $d\Omega$, the angular dependence shown in Eq. (3.25) may be verified.

Nuclear recoil motion. The solid-state detectors employed in this experiment have sufficiently high resolution so that the effects of the nuclear recoil motion can be easily observed. Equation (3.30) gives the recoil velocity V_1 of the alpha particle as a function of the masses of the target and alpha particle. The recoil energy of the alpha particle is

$$E_R = \frac{1}{2}\, m_1 V_1{}^2 = \left(\frac{m_1 - m_2}{m_1 + m_2}\right)^2 E_1 \qquad (3.43)$$

If the ratio m_1/m_2 is much smaller than unity, the preceding expression

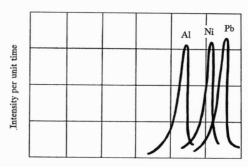

Energy of backscattered α particle

FIGURE 3.16

Energy spectrum of alpha particles backscattered from various materials.

can be simplified as follows:

$$E_R = \left(1 - \frac{2m_1}{m_2}\right)\left(1 - \frac{2m_1}{m_2}\right)E_1 \qquad (3.44)$$

or

$$E_R = E_1 - \frac{4m_1}{m_2}\, E_1 \qquad (3.45)$$

Now the difference between initial energy and the recoil energy is

$$\Delta E = E_1 - E_R = \frac{4m_1}{m_2}\, E_1 \qquad (3.46)$$

This equation can be verified by measuring the energy of the backscattered alpha particles from a number of different foil materials. The resulting pulse height spectra are shown in Fig. 3.16. This method can be used under certain circumstances to obtain an analysis of the nuclear species in certain materials. The energy of the backscattered alpha particles will depend on the nuclear mass of the target. The primary difficulty with using this method in practice is that very large source strengths are necessary to give sufficiently high counting rates.

The counting rates observed in this experiment should decrease as the square of the atomic number. This is in agreement with Eqs. (3.42) and (3.45) and should also be verified experimentally.

REFERENCES

1. Becquerel's papers appear in *Compt. Rend.*, vol. 122, 1896.
2. Rutherford, E.: *Phil. Mag.*, **21**, 669, 1911.
3. Evans, R. D.: "The Atomic Nucleus," McGraw-Hill Book Company, New York, 1955.
4. Bethe, H. A.: *Ann. Physik*, **5**, 325, 1930.
5. Seaborg, G., J. Katz, and W. Manning: The Transuranium Elements: Research Papers. National Nuclear Energy Series IV, vol. 14B, McGraw-Hill Book Company, New York, 1949.
6. Dearnaley, G., and D. Northrop: "Semiconductor Counters for Nuclear Radiations," John Wiley & Sons, Inc., New York, 1963.

GENERAL BIBLIOGRAPHY

1. Bethe, H., and J. Ashkin: Passage of Radiations Through Matter, Part II of "Experimental Nuclear Physics," edited by E. Segrè, John Wiley & Sons, Inc., New York, 1953.
2. Fermi, E.: "Nuclear Physics," University of Chicago Press, Chicago, 1949.
3. Kaplan, I.: "Nuclear Physics," Addison-Wesley Publishing Company, Inc., Reading, Mass., 1955.

Chapter 4 | **VACUUM TECHNOLOGY**

4.1 INTRODUCTION

Most of the important discoveries in modern atomic and nuclear physics would not have been possible without a well-developed vacuum technology. The fundamental facts about atmospheric pressure have been known for a long time; even the ancients knew some practical facts when they devised pumps for irrigation and other purposes.

They also knew some qualitative rules which were usually stated in terms such as the famous dictum that "Nature abhors a vacuum." One of the earliest demonstrations of the magnitude of atmospheric pressure was the famous experiment carried out in Magdeburg, Germany, in the year 1654, in which it was shown that two partially evacuated hemispheres held together only by atmospheric pressure could not be pulled apart by two teams of horses. Also in the seventeenth century, the pressure of the atmosphere was determined quantitatively by Torricelli and others. With the advent of the atomic theory (Dalton), the work of Lavoisier on the chemical nature of various gases, and, finally, the quantitative gas laws, a true understanding of the situation was attained. A gas consists of a very large number of atoms or molecules which are constantly in random motion, colliding with each other and with the walls of the container. Once this was realized, the methods which had to be applied to obtain low pressures were clear.

The first quantitative application of vacuum technology was in the famous series of experiments in which the electrical properties of gases were investigated as a function of pressure. To do this properly, electrical machinery had to be available with which continuously operating mechanical pumps could be operated. These experiments subsequently led to the discovery of electrons, X rays, and many of the other important experiments in modern atomic and nuclear physics.

Today there are a great many important uses of high-vacuum technology. These range from the enormous high-energy accelerators designed to produce ultrahigh-energy particle beams to the very large environmental test chambers used to subject spacecraft to conditions similar to those they will experience in actual use. Three important points will be discussed in the following sections: An elementary treatment of the kinetic theory of gases will be presented, a description of the methods employed for measuring low pressures will be given, and, finally, an enumeration of techniques used to obtain low pressures will be presented.

4.2 THE KINETIC THEORY OF GASES

At the end of the eighteenth century a series of experiments were performed which laid the foundation of the kinetic theory of gases. It was discovered that, when certain gases at atmospheric pressure and ambient temperature are made to react, the gases always combine in the same volume by proportion. For example, if oxygen and hydrogen are made to combine, then they combine in such a way that two volumes of hydrogen molecules always combine with one volume of oxygen molecules to give two volumes of water molecules. Other gases also obey similar rules. In addition, it was found that the same weight is always associated with each of the combining values of gas. Some common examples of this are

$$2H_2 + O_2 \rightarrow 2H_2O$$
$$N_2 + 3H_2 \rightarrow 2NH_3 \qquad (4.1)$$
$$H_2 + F_2 \rightarrow 2HF$$

Each reaction has characteristic weights associated with it as follows:

$$2H_2 + O_2 \rightarrow 2H_2O$$
$$4 \text{ gm} + 32 \text{ gm} \rightarrow 36 \text{ gm}$$
$$N_2 + 3H_2 \rightarrow 2NH_3$$
$$28 \text{ gm} + 6 \text{ gm} \rightarrow 34 \text{ gm} \qquad (4.2)$$
$$H_2 + F_2 \rightarrow 2HF$$
$$2 \text{ gm} + 18 \text{ gm} \rightarrow 20 \text{ gm}$$

These experiments provided some of the very strong early evidence for the atomic theory because the facts can be explained if it is assumed that the gases consist of a large number of small, identical particles. Obviously, if this assumption is correct, two molecules of hydrogen always combine with one molecule of oxygen to form two molecules of water. Furthermore, the weights of the volumes are related to the weights of the molecules, since each volume of gas at the same pressure contains the same number of molecules.

The lightest gas is hydrogen. If it is assumed that the atomic weight of hydrogen is one unit, then one mole of hydrogen gas is defined as one gram of gas. Actually, it is known that the hydrogen gas "atom" actually contains two atoms and hence is called a hydrogen molecule. Thus one mole of hydrogen actually weighs 2 grams. Each mole of gas is always found to occupy the same volume (22.4 liters at standard temperature and pressure) and contains the same number of molecules (or atoms). This number, Avogadro's number, has been measured and has the value:

$$N_A = 6.02 \times 10^{23} \text{ molecules/mole} \qquad (4.3)$$

The number of molecules per cubic centimeter of a gas at room temperature (20°C) and atmospheric pressure is

$$N = \frac{6.02 \times 10^{23}}{22.4 \times 10^3} \approx 3 \times 10^{19} \text{ molecules/cc} \qquad (4.4)$$

This number at atmospheric pressure is very large indeed. The best working vacuum which can be obtained with present methods is 10^{-14} times atmospheric pressure. Even at this pressure, the number of molecules per cubic centimeter is still as large as 10^5. Hence even the best vacuum which can be obtained contains many molecules per cubic centimeter. These laboratory vacuums might be compared with interplanetary space, where the gas density is roughly 10^3 atoms/cc, or with intergalactic space, where the density is of the order of one atom/cc.

Another concept which will be used very often when working with vacuum systems is that of the collision mean free path. The atoms in a gas are always in random motion, and, for many experiments, it is necessary to know how far a molecule travels, on the average, before it

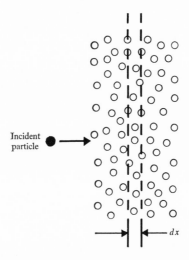

FIGURE 4.1

An atom incident upon an assembly of gas atoms.

makes a collision with another molecule. The mean free path can best be defined in terms of the attenuation of a beam of gas atoms passing through a region occupied by other atoms of the same kind.

Consider an atom incident from the left on an assembly of gas atoms as shown in Fig. 4.1. The probability that the atom is scattered in passing through the thickness element dx is equal to the number of atoms in the layer multiplied by the effective scattering area σ of each of the atoms. If the density of atoms is n per cubic centimeter and the area considered is one square centimeter, then the probability of being scattered is

$$P = n\sigma\,dx \tag{4.5}$$

Equation (4.5) is valid only if the probability is very small, that is, if most of the atoms incident on the layer pass through. If an incident beam is considered instead of a single atom, the number of atoms scattered in the layer dx is

$$-dN = PN = Nn\sigma \, dx \tag{4.6}$$

The negative sign is necessary because fewer particles emerge from the layer than are incident on it. Equation (4.6) can be integrated to obtain the number of atoms emerging after traversing a distance x

$$N = N_0 e^{-n\sigma x} \tag{4.7}$$

where N_0 is the number of incident atoms.

The mean free path is defined as the length in which the beam is attenuated to $1/e$ of its initial value. Thus the mean free path λ is

$$\lambda = \frac{1}{n\sigma} \tag{4.8}$$

It can be shown that the mean free path is also the average distance between collisions. The mean free path increases as the gas molecule density decreases, which is the same as saying that the mean free path increases as the pressure decreases.

The radius of a typical gas molecule is approximately 3×10^{-8} cm, so that the effective scattering area (or total cross section) σ is

$$\sigma = \pi r^2 = 3 \times 10^{-15} \, \text{cm}^2 \tag{4.9}$$

The mean free path at standard pressure and temperature is therefore

$$\lambda = \frac{1}{n\sigma} = \frac{1}{10 \times 10^4} \approx 10^{-5} \, \text{cm} \tag{4.10}$$

where Eq. (4.4) has been used to evaluate the atom density n. From this it can be seen that if the mean free path is to be made as large as the dimensions of an average vacuum vessel ($\sim$100 cm), the density must be

$$n \approx \frac{1}{\lambda\sigma} \approx \frac{1}{100 \times 3 \times 10^{-15}} \approx 3 \times 10^{12} \, \text{molecules/cc} \tag{4.11}$$

and the corresponding pressure is thus approximately one ten-millionth of an atmosphere.

A few words should be said about the units which are commonly employed to measure pressure. In the previous paragraph, the pressure has been defined in terms of "atmospheres." An atmosphere of pressure is defined as 1,013,250 dynes/cm² and very closely approximates the average gas pressure existing at sea level at 0°C. A gas at a pressure of one atmosphere and 0°C is commonly referred to as a gas at "standard temperature and pressure" (STP). The "atmosphere" is also a unit used in high pressure physics and is usually referred to as the "bar." (For example, a megabar is one million times atmospheric pressure.)

For low pressure work, the most frequently used unit is the "millimeter of mercury." This unit refers to the height of a column of mercury which can be supported by the pressure of the gas in an enclosure. The height of a column of mercury supported by the atmosphere at sea level is approximately 760 mm (see Fig. 4.2). Therefore 760 mm of mercury corresponds to a molecular density of approximately 3×10^{19} molecules/cc. In these units the pressure at which the

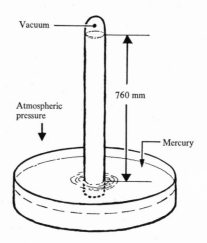

FIGURE 4.2

Simple barometric gauge illustrating the magnitude of atmospheric pressure.

mean free path of the atom is 100 cm is computed as follows:

$$\frac{P(\text{in mm of Hg})}{0.3 \times 10^{13}} = \frac{760 \text{ mm}}{3 \times 10^{19}} \tag{4.12}$$

or $\quad P \text{ (in mm of Hg)} = 0.760 \times 10^{-7} \approx 7.6 \times 10^{-5} \text{ mm of Hg} \quad (4.13)$

To avoid large exponents it is sometimes convenient to express the pressure in terms of microns of mercury. (One micron $= 10^{-6}$ meter $= 10^{-3}$ mm). The pressure corresponding to the density 3×10^{12} atoms/cc is therefore 0.076 microns of mercury. Note that the height of a column of mercury of one micron cannot be directly measured; nevertheless, this unit or millimeters of mercury are still the two most commonly used in spite of the fact that they have no physically measurable meaning.

To avoid the awkward expression "millimeters of mercury," a new convention has been introduced. A pressure of one millimeter of mercury has been defined as one torr. The name of the unit is derived from the name of the seventeenth century Italian physicist, Evangelista Torricelli, who invented the barometer shown in Fig. 4.2.

Finally, one more result of the kinetic theory of gases is often used in the design of vacuum systems—the "average" velocity of the gas molecules. Molecules moving at random in a gas do not all have the same velocity, but their velocities are distributed according to the so-called Maxwell-Boltzmann distribution, which can be derived from very general statistical considerations. It is the most probable distribution of velocities in a gas, subject to the constraints that the total number of particles contained in the volume and the total energy of all the molecules in the container are both constant.

Consider a molecule moving with a velocity v making a collision with the wall of the container. Assume that the velocity is perpendicular to the wall, then in colliding with the wall and bouncing back, the molecule transfers a momentum of 2 mv to the wall. If the opposite wall of the container is a distance l away and the molecule bounces back and forth between the walls, it will make $v/2l$ collisions per second with the wall. The total momentum transferred per second is therefore mv^2/l. The total force on the wall is thus obtained by multiplying the momentum transfer for one molecule by the average number of molecules moving toward the wall, $N/3$, where N is the total number of molecules in the volume. (Isotropic reaction of the molecules is assumed.) The force on each wall is thus

$$F = \frac{Nmv^2}{3l} \tag{4.14}$$

The pressure on the wall is defined as the force on the wall per unit area. If the volume under consideration is a cube with side l, the pressure p is

$$p = \frac{F}{l^2} = \frac{Nmv^2}{3l^3} \tag{4.15}$$

Since l^3 is equal to the volume of the box V, the product pV is

$$pV = \frac{Nmv^2}{3} \tag{4.16}$$

The energy of each molecule is

$$\epsilon = \tfrac{1}{2}mv^2 \tag{4.17}$$

so that, in terms of the energy,

$$pV = \tfrac{2}{3}N\epsilon \tag{4.18}$$

Under many conditions, both the pressure and the volume of a gas are known to be proportional to the temperature when the other variable is held constant. Thus the "equation of state" for such a gas (usually called an ideal gas) is

$$pV = \nu RT \tag{4.19}$$

where ν is the number of moles of gas and R is the gas constant. Therefore the energy is

$$\epsilon = \frac{3}{2}\frac{\nu RT}{N} \tag{4.20}$$

It should be pointed out that the "derivation" outlined above is a simplified one. Obviously the "velocity" used in the equations is an average of the molecular velocity distribution. Furthermore, all molecules do not move in the same direction, so that in a more detailed derivation, the vector components of the velocity must be used. In any event, Eq. (4.20) is obtained even if the more detailed steps mentioned here are included.

The average molecular velocity can now be computed using Eq. (4.20). The constant $\nu R/N$ is called Boltzmann's constant k and has the value 1.38×10^{-16} ergs/°K. Hence

$$\bar{\epsilon} = \tfrac{1}{2}m\bar{v}^2 = \tfrac{3}{2}kT \tag{4.21}$$

or

$$\bar{v} = \sqrt{\frac{3kT}{m}} \tag{4.22}$$

At room temperature ($T = 300°$K), therefore, the average molecular velocity is approximately 10^5 cm/sec. Thus in a vacuum system with linear dimensions of the order of 100 cm, operating at a pressure of 10^{-6} atm, the molecules make of the order of 10^3 traversals of the chamber per second. It is important to note that average velocity is independent of the pressure and the volume of the chamber and that it depends only on the temperature and the mass of the molecules.

The situation outlined in the foregoing paragraphs is, of course, greatly oversimplified. The definition of an "average" velocity depends on the existing velocity distribution. Great care must be taken to make certain that the average velocity defined in Eq. (4.21) can actually be shown to be the quantity which determines the momentum transfer to the wall of the enclosure. The Maxwell-Boltzmann velocity distribution is given as

$$n(v)\, dv = 4\pi v^2 \left(\frac{m}{2\pi kT}\right)^{3/2} e^{-mv^2/2kT}\, dv \tag{4.23}$$

where $n(v)\, dv$ is the number of molecules per unit volume having

The kinetic theory of gases **63**

velocities in the interval between v and $v + dv$. (A detailed derivation of Eq. (4.23) is given in Appendix II.) The behavior of the Maxwell-Boltzmann distribution function at several different temperatures is shown in Fig. 4.3. It is now possible to define several different "average" velocities which may have interesting physical properties. The mean velocity for the velocity distribution given in Eq. (4.23) can be defined as

$$\bar{v} = \frac{\int_0^\infty v n(v)\,dv}{\int_0^\infty n(v)\,dv} \tag{4.24}$$

Using Eq. (4.23) to evaluate these integrals, the mean velocity becomes

$$\bar{v} = \frac{2}{\sqrt{\pi}}\sqrt{\frac{2kT}{m}} \tag{4.25}$$

This expression is not the same as the one obtained from elementary

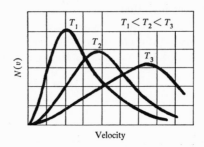

FIGURE 4.3

Maxwell-Boltzmann distribution function for various gas temperatures.

considerations [Eq. (4.21)]. The reason for this is evident from Eq. (4.15). The total pressure is obtained by computing an average not of the mean velocity but of the mean-squared velocity. Thus

$$\bar{v}^2 = \frac{\int_0^\infty v^2 n(v)\,dv}{\int_0^\infty n(v)\,dv} \tag{4.26}$$

which leads to the desired result. The "average" velocity in Eq. (4.15) is therefore really the so-called root-mean-squared velocity

$$v_{rms} = \sqrt{\bar{v}^2} = \sqrt{\frac{3kT}{m}} \tag{4.27}$$

Another "average" velocity which is sometimes useful is the "most

64 *Vacuum technology*

probable velocity." This quantity is defined operationally as the position of the velocity interval dv, which contains more molecules than any other interval. This interval of maximum occupation is located at the velocity for which

$$\frac{dn(v)}{dv} = 0 \qquad (4.28)$$

The most probable velocity determined in this fashion is

$$v_{mp} = \frac{2kT}{m} \qquad (4.29)$$

It is of interest to note that all three of these "average" velocities have roughly the same magnitude and that the mean velocity and the root-mean-squared velocity are both slightly larger than the most probable velocity

$$\bar{v} = \frac{2}{\sqrt{\pi}} v_{mp} \qquad (4.30)$$

and

$$v_{rms} = \tfrac{3}{2} v_{mp} \qquad (4.31)$$

4.3 VACUUM PUMPING SYSTEMS

The results derived in Sec. 4.2 can now be applied to describe the methods employed to evacuate gases from closed systems. A number of pumping systems will be described and their uses will be discussed. Vacuum pumps fall into three large categories. There are the mechanical pumps which operate by creating a void space which is then repeatedly "exposed" to the system to be evacuated so that a portion of its gas is allowed to flow into the void. The second group consists of the diffusion pumps (and other molecular or ionic flow devices) which operate by creating streams of particles in such a way that residual gas molecules are dragged along with the stream and swept out of the system. Finally, there are the gas absorption and adsorption pumps which operate by absorbing or adsorbing material into or onto a cooled surface.

Mechanical pumps. Most mechanical pumps are of the eccentric rotary types shown in Fig. 4.4. Most commonly, these are driven by an ordinary electric motor at approximately 360 rpm. The pump unit consists of two cylinders with displaced centers. The outer cylinder forms the body of the pump. The inner cylinder is slotted and has two spring-loaded vanes (Gaede pump) mounted in such a way that the intake and exhaust volumes are isolated from each other. When one of the vanes passes the intake, the volume enclosed between the vane, the pump body, and the rotor is quite small. This volume increases rapidly as the rotor moves until the second vane closes off the intake. During the open period, gas from the system flows rapidly into the volume created by the moving vane. As soon as the first vane passes the exhaust opening, the gas is expelled. The Cenco Hyvac pump, also shown in Fig. 4.4, operates on a similar principle. Here the rotor is mounted on an eccentric shaft, and there is only one stationary spring-loaded vane which divides the intake and the exhaust chamber.

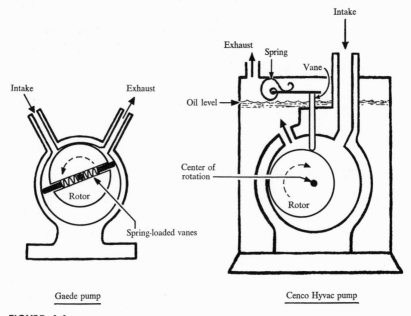

Gaede pump   Cenco Hyvac pump

FIGURE 4.4

Schematic illustration of two common mechanical vacuum pumps.

Both pumps operate at very high compression ratios ($\sim$700:1) in order to obtain as high an intake efficiency as possible. A low vapor pressure oil that serves as both a lubricant and a vacuum seal is constantly supplied to the bearing surfaces. Three important effects determine the lower pressure limits which can be reached by means of a mechanical pump:

1. The vapor pressure and purity of the pump oil
2. The efficiency of the gas discharge on the exhaust cycle
3. The effectiveness of the seals which prevent the passage of gas from the high-pressure to the low-pressure side of the pump

In practice, these effects limit the pressures which can be reached with mechanical pumps to the region around 10^{-3} torr.

Another type of mechanical pump which has lately come into use is based on the turbine principle. These blowers are used primarily for applications where very high pumping speeds are desired.

Diffusion pumps. In order to reach pressures below 10^{-3} torr, it is necessary to use pumps based on an entirely different principle. The diffusion pump is based on the principle that when the pressure is low

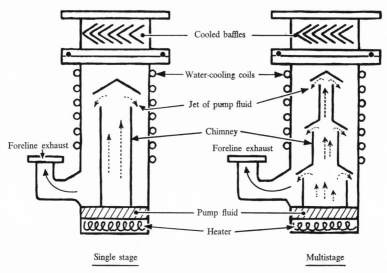

Single stage   *Multistage*

FIGURE 4.5

Cross section of a single and a multistage diffusion pump.

enough so that the mean free path of a molecule is of the same order of magnitude as the dimensions of the vacuum system, then the molecules diffusing from the chamber to be evacuated into the pump opening will be swept away by a jet of molecules flowing past the opening. The configuration of a typical diffusion pump is shown in Fig. 4.5. The pump liquid is placed at the bottom of the pump and heated to boiling by the electric heater. The vaporized liquid passes up the chimney of the pump, where it is then deflected downward by the deflector on top of the chimney. A downward-directed stream or jet of gas molecules is thus formed. The barrel of the pump is water cooled so that the jet of vaporized pump fluid is condensed and flows back to the bottom of the pump. The pump is also equipped with cooled baffles which prevent uncondensed pump fluid vapors from back streaming into the vacuum system. The molecular jet formed at the top of the chimney collides with gas molecules which diffuse into the throat of the pump. In the collisions, some of the gas molecules acquire a velocity directed down toward the region behind the jet. This is a region of pressure higher than that above the jet, the pressure difference being maintained by the jet. This region of higher pressure is then evacuated by a mechanical forepump. This pumping mechanism is a phenomenon related to the Bernoulli effect in fluid flow. Obviously the diffusion pump cannot operate until the pressure in the barrel is low enough so that the jet can be established. (The mean free path must be much longer than the distance between the top of the chimney and the barrel wall.)

If the pump is operated at a pressure which is too high, the jet will not be established and the pump fluid will pass up through the pump barrel by convection and will eventually condense on the baffles, choking the pump. Care must therefore be taken not to operate the pump at too high a pressure.

The primary requirement on the pump fluid is that it have a relatively low vapor pressure and that it be stable so that it does not decompose when heated. Mercury and special silicon-hydrocarbon oils are commonly employed as the pumping fluids. Ordinary single-stage diffusion pumps of the kind shown in Fig. 4.5 have an ultimate limiting pressure of the order of 10^{-6} to 10^{-7} torr. The limiting factor in determining the pressures which can be reached by a diffusion pump is usually the vapor pressure of the working fluid and how well the pump is baffled to prevent back streaming of the fluid into the system. Some types of diffusion pumps can, under special circumstances, reach lower pressures. Multistage or multijet (Fig. 4.5) pumps with the proper baffles can go as low as 10^{-10} or 10^{-11} torr. In these pumps the pressure differential across each stage is considerably less than that across the entire pump. Diffusion pumps are operated with a mechanical pump on the foreline to reduce the pressure to approximately 10^{-3} torr before the diffusion pump is turned on. Very large diffusion pumps (32 in. in diameter) have been constructed to achieve very high pumping speeds.

The ability of vacuum pumps to remove gas molecules from a chamber is usually measured by specifying a "pumping speed." The pumping speed is equal to the number of gas molecules the pump will remove from the system per unit time. Obviously this is a pressure-dependent property, so that pumping speeds are usually presented on graphs plotted as a function of pressure. The most common unit of pumping speed is the liter per second, where the liter means the number of gas molecules in a one-liter volume at the pressure for which the pumping speed is specified.

Absorption or getter pumps. Many substances have the capacity to absorb very large quantities of gas on their surface layers. For example, at 800°C tantalum will absorb seven hundred times its own volume of hydrogen. This principle has been used to build the vacuum pump shown in Fig. 4.6. In this case titanium is used as a "getter" or absorbing material. A strip of titanium metal is resistance heated until it vaporizes. This vaporized titanium is then condensed on the wall of the chamber. The constantly renewed layers of titanium absorb gases contained in the volume. Absorption pumps of this type must first be properly evacuated by a diffusion pump so that the evaporation-condensation process can be carried out. The major drawback of the

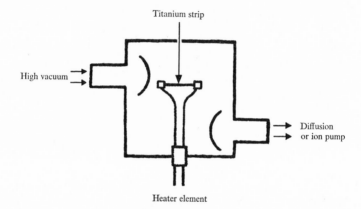

FIGURE 4.6

Titanium-sublimation type of vacuum pump.

getter pump is that not all gases are equally well absorbed by the getter material. Magnesium, calcium, tungsten and aluminum have also been used as getter materials.

Ion pumps. Another type of pump used in the pressure region between 10^{-7} and 10^{-11} torr is the ion pump. One way of removing gas molecules from an enclosure is to ionize them and then accelerate them to a negatively charged electrode. If the potential is of the order of a few kilovolts, the ions penetrate the surface to a sufficient depth so that they are entrapped in the metal and are thus effectively removed from the volume. A typical ion pump configuration is shown in Fig. 4.7. The electrons are drawn from the cathode by field emission and are accelerated to the anode. To increase the electron path length, and hence the probability of making an ionizing collision, a magnetic field is placed transverse to the electron path. The ions produced in the collisions are drawn to the cathode. The cathode is made of titanium, which is a metal that can absorb many gas molecules without substantially changing its properties. The use of titanium as a cathode material has the added advantage that any cathode material eroded by the incident ions (sputtering) plates out on the anode and there acts as as an absorption pump.

Ion pumps have the advantage that they require no cryogenic baffles, for they have no pumping fluid. Also, once they are started, they require no backing pumps. Of course, as in the case of the getter pumps, they must be evacuated with a good forepump to approximately 10^{-3} torr before they can be operated. Two disadvantages are

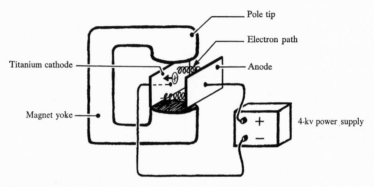

FIGURE 4.7

Geometrical arrangement of electrodes and magnets illustrating the operating principle of the sputter ion pump.

inherent in their operation. One is that they cannot handle large gas loads; thus they are best suited for operation at pressures of 10^{-7} torr and lower. The other is that they do not pump all gases at the same rate because of differences in the ionization probability. For example, if water vapor is pumped at a certain rate, hydrogen will be pumped at twice that rate, whereas helium and argon would be pumped at only one-tenth of the water vapor rate.

Cold traps. A very important feature of all high-vacuum systems is the cold trap. One function of the cold trap is to remove the water vapor and other condensable vapors from the vacuum system as it is being pumped down. When the pressure in the system reaches 10^{-3} torr or better, gases absorbed on the surfaces of the various parts of the container begin to be evolved at a significant rate. This process is called outgassing. Often, condensable vapors are outgassed from the surfaces in the system and are then adsorbed onto the cold traps. Finally, the traps also condense out diffusion pump fluids and mechanical pump oil which stream back into the system.

4.4 PUMPING SPEEDS AND MOLECULAR FLOW

To design a good vacuum system requires more than placing pumps of the necessary capacity on the chamber. It is also essential to provide proper apertures through which the gas can be pumped and to design

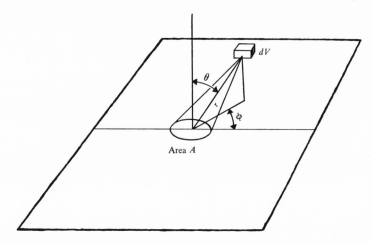

FIGURE 4.8

Geometrical considerations for calculating the pumping speed of a hole in a plane.

a piping system which does not unnecessarily impede the flow of gas. By considering the flow of gas molecules through pipes at low pressures, that is, when the mean free path is large compared to the dimensions of the pipe, appropriate design criteria can be established. This pressure region is usually called the molecular flow region.

Consider a region of gas at pressure p separated by a plate from a region in which there is no gas at all, as shown in Fig. 4.8. If the plate has a hole of area A cut in it at some point, gas will flow through this aperture at a well-defined rate. The "pumping speed" of the aperture, defined as its ability to pass molecules from the pressure region to the void, can be determined in the molecular flow approximation by calculating the rate at which gas atoms escape through the aperture. Consider the volume element shown in Fig. 4.8 at the point r, θ and ϕ

Pumping speeds and molecular flow **71**

above the hole of area A in the plane. The number of molecules having speeds between v and $v + dv$ in the volume element dV is

$$d^4N = [n(v)\,dv]\,dV \tag{4.32}$$

where the function $n(v)$ is the velocity distribution of the particles, which, in this case, is a Maxwell-Boltzmann distribution. The fourth-order differential in Eq. (4.32) indicates that the right side of the equation is a product of four differentials (three space dimensions and one speed). The volume element in polar coordinates is

$$dV = r^2\,dr \sin\theta\,d\theta\,d\phi \tag{4.33}$$

The fraction of particles moving in the proper direction to pass through the hole is obtained by multiplying Eq. (4.32) by $A \cos\theta/4\pi r^2$. The numerator of this fraction is the area of the opening projected onto a plane perpendicular to r, and the denominator is the area of the whole sphere of radius r. Thus

$$d^4N_f = n(v)\,dv\,r^2\,dr \sin\theta\,d\theta\,d\phi\,\frac{A\cos\theta}{4\pi r^2} \tag{4.34}$$

is the number of particles from dV which pass through A. The rate at which particles from the volume element dV pass through the aperture is given by dividing d^4N_f by dt:

$$\frac{d^4N_f}{dt} = A n(v)\,dv\,\frac{dr}{dt} \cos\theta\,d(\cos\theta)\,d\phi$$
$$= A n(v)v\,dv\,d(\cos\theta) \cos\theta\,d\phi \tag{4.35}$$

To calculate the rate at which molecules from the entire region above the plane pass through the aperture, Eq. (4.35) must be integrated over the upper half of the sphere:

$$\frac{dN_f}{dt} = \frac{A}{4\pi} \int_0^\infty v n(v)\,dv \int_0^{2\pi} d\phi \int_0^{\pi/2} \cos\theta\,d(\cos\theta) \tag{4.36}$$

or
$$\frac{dN_f}{dt} = \frac{1}{4} A \int_0^\infty v n(v)\,dv \tag{4.37}$$

This integral can be evaluated using the Maxwell-Boltzmann distribution discussed in Sec. 4.2. If $n(v)$ is the Maxwell-Boltzmann distribution function, the integral in Eq. (4.37) can be expressed in terms of the average velocity $\bar{v}$ defined in Eq. (4.24):

$$\int v n(v)\,dv = \bar{v} \int n(v)\,dv = \bar{v} N_0 \tag{4.38}$$

In Eq. (4.38) N_0 is the total number of atoms per cubic centimeter in the gas. Therefore the number of atoms striking the area A per second is

$$\frac{dN_f}{dt} = \frac{1}{4} A N_0 \bar{v} \qquad (4.39)$$

The rate at which gas leaks through the aperture is usually expressed in units of liters per second. Here the volume measure "liters" means the number of molecules contained in a liter at the pressure at which the leak rate is being measured. In this way Eq. (4.39) can be written in a form independent of N_0, the atomic density (or pressure) of the gas. The total number of atoms N in the volume is related to the atomic density N_0 and the volume through

$$N = N_0 V \qquad (4.40)$$

Thus
$$\frac{dN_f}{dt} = N_0 \frac{dV}{dt} \qquad (4.41)$$

and therefore the leakage rate in units of cm³/sec is

$$\frac{dV}{dt} = \frac{1}{4} A \bar{v} \qquad (4.42)$$

It is instructive to evaluate the constant factors in Eq. (4.42) and to express the results in terms of the temperature and the molecular weight of the gas. By using Eq. (4.25), the appropriate values for the Boltzmann constant and the nucleon mass, Eq. (4.42) results in the following expression for the pumping speed:

$$\frac{dV}{dt} = 3.62 A \sqrt{\frac{T}{m}} \text{ liters/sec} \qquad (4.43)$$

For an aperture with an area of one square centimeter at room temperature and assuming $m = 29$ (for air), the pumping speed computed from Eq. (4.43) is 11.7 liters/sec. This number is often referred to as the "black-hole" pumping speed of an aperture. It is a good approximation, under many circumstances, to consider the pumping speed of a fast diffusion pump as the black-hole pumping speed, 11.7 liters/sec multiplied by the aperture area of the pump.

Another important consideration is to perform a similar computation for the vacuum pipes which lead from the pumps to the vacuum chamber. This is considerably more complicated, and only the result will be discussed here.

If M_0 is the pumping speed of the pump and M is the pumping speed at the other end of the vacuum line, the conductance μ of the pipe is defined as

$$\frac{1}{\mu} = \frac{1}{M} - \frac{1}{M_0} \tag{4.44}$$

For a straight cylindrical pipe of length l and diameter d (with l not too much larger than d), the conductance is

$$\mu = \frac{3.75 \sqrt{T}}{\sqrt{m}} d^3 \left(\frac{1}{l + \frac{4}{3}d}\right) \text{liters/sec} \tag{4.45}$$

where T is the absolute temperature and m is the molecular weight of the gas. For air at 20°C,

$$\mu = 12.1 d^3 \left(\frac{1}{l + \frac{4}{3}d}\right) \text{liters/sec} \tag{4.46}$$

For long pipes, where $l \gg d$, the second term in the denominator can be neglected, so that

$$\mu = 12.1 \frac{d^3}{l} \text{liters/sec}$$

$$\simeq 100 \frac{r^3}{l} \text{liters/sec} \tag{4.47}$$

where r is the radius of the pipe.

It should be noted that all these formulas must be modified if traps or baffles are placed in the line.

4.5 VACUUM–MEASUREMENT METHODS

The methods of producing a high vacuum have been discussed in some detail. However, it is important that, as pumping methods are improved, methods of measuring the pressures of gases with very small molecular densities must also be improved. A great many different gauges operating on a variety of principles are in use, and not all of them can be discussed in detail here. Consequently, only three gauges which are commonly used in three different pressure ranges will be considered.

McLeod gauge. The simplest vacuum gauge is based on the hydrostatic principle illustrated in Fig. 4.2. It relies on measuring the height of a column of mercury held between atmospheric pressure and the pressure in the vacuum system, as shown in Fig. 4.9. This gauge can be employed successfully to measure pressures down to approximately one centimeter of mercury (10 torr). For lower pressures, it is not possible to measure d, the height of the mercury column, with sufficient accuracy. Also, the pressure of the atmosphere is usually not known with sufficient accuracy to compute precisely the pressure in the vacuum system.

To measure pressures lower than one centimeter of mercury, another mercury gauge is often used, the so-called McLeod gauge. This gauge is illustrated in Fig. 4.10 and operates on the following principle: The vacuum system is attached at point A and the mercury reservoir is attached by a flexible rubber hose to point B. At the beginning of the measurement, the reservoir is lowered so that the mercury level is below the point C. The bulb is then raised until the mercury level reaches the point D in the right tube. Point D is equal in height to the top of the capillary tube E. As the mercury rises, the gas in bulb F,

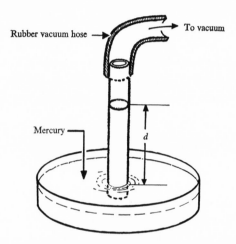

Rubber vacuum hose

To vacuum

Mercury

d

FIGURE 4.9

Mercury manometer for measuring vacuums relative to atmospheric pressure.

which has a known volume V, is trapped. The rising mercury then compresses the gas in the volume and forces it into the top level of the capillary tube E. If the cross section of the capillary tube is a, then the gas pressure originally in the bulb can be computed using the gas law:

$$PV = P'V' \qquad (4.48)$$

The volume V' is equal to ah and the pressure P' is equal to the head of mercury h compressing the volume. Thus the pressure in the vacuum system can be determined directly in millimeters of mercury by making the appropriate substitutions in Eq. (4.48):

$$P = \frac{ah^2}{V} \qquad (4.49)$$

Vacuum-measurement methods **75**

The McLeod gauge is useful for measuring pressures down to 10^{-6} torr with good accuracy. It is often used to calibrate other gauges operating in the same pressure region. However, the laboratory use of the McLeod gauge is limited because it is cumbersome to use.

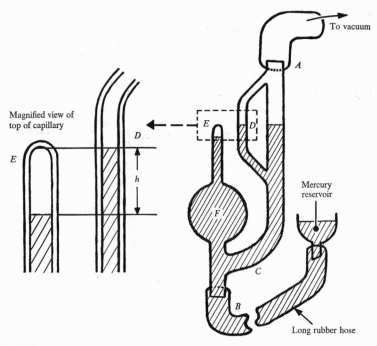

FIGURE 4.10

A McLeod-gauge type of manometer useful for making pressure measurements down to 10^{-6} torr.

Thermocouple gauge. A gauge that is widely employed for pressure measurements in the range of 1 torr to 10^{-3} torr is the thermocouple gauge. Its principle of operation is based on the change in the convective heat-transfer properties of a gas with changes in pressure.

The device consists of a bimetallic thermocouple attached to the center of a resistance heater filament which is heated by a constant-current power supply. At higher pressures the number of molecules striking the filament is greater than at lower pressures, so that the filament will be cooler at the high-pressure end of the operating range than at the lower end. The thermocouple is used to measure the filament temperature and, once calibrated, is a direct measure of the pressure.

Thermocouple gauges are insensitive to pressure changes above 1 torr because the thermal conductivity of gases is essentially constant at these pressures. The lower limit of 10^{-3} torr is set because the gas density is so low that collisions with the filament are rare. In fact, at 10^{-3} torr convective heat transfer accounts for only about 1 percent of the total heat transferred; the rest is by radiation.

The most important use of thermocouple gauges is to measure the pressure in forelines used to back diffusion pumps.

Ionization gauges. To measure pressures below 10^{-3} torr with a compact and simple unit, ionization gauges are used. An ionization

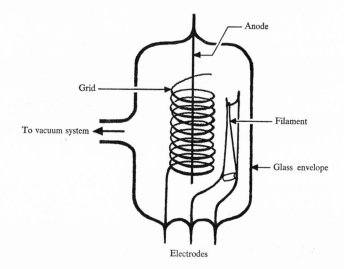

FIGURE 4.11

Glass envelope ion gauge.

gauge is a triode which operates as follows: Electrons are emitted from a hot filament and are accelerated to a grid at a positive potential. In their passage through the gas, the electrons ionize some of the gas atoms in the enclosure. These ions are then collected at a negatively biased anode where the ion current is measured. This anode ion current is a function of the pressure and, therefore, a direct measure of the pressure. A commonly used electrode configuration for ion gauges is shown in Fig. 4.11, and the electrical circuit used to operate ion gauges is shown in Fig. 4.12.

The grid is usually operated at about $+200$ volts, which is sufficient to cause ionization of the gas molecules. The anode is kept at a smaller, negative potential to draw the ions to this electrode. The collected ions are returned to ground through a microammeter whose reading, when calibrated, is a direct measure of the pressure. The filament emission current is variable in steps which correspond to the different pressure ranges over which the gauge operates. Low-filament emission currents (1 ma) are used at the high-pressure end (10^{-3} torr) and high-filament emission currents (10 ma) are used at the low-pressure end (10^{-5} torr and lower). Ion gauges can be used to obtain pressure readings down to 10^{-11} torr. Below this pressure the gauge itself begins to operate as an ion pump (see Sec. 4.3), thus affecting the pressure in the vacuum system.

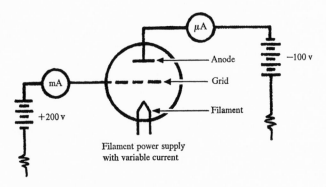

FIGURE 4.12

Circuit diagram of ion gauge.

4.6 LEAK HUNTING, OUTGASSING, AND GASKETS

An essential part of vacuum technology is concerned with the detection of small leaks in high-vacuum systems. Almost all leak detection methods involve spraying the suspected region of the system with a volatile substance and observing the resultant pressure rise in the system in an appropriate way. For large leaks (i.e., system in the thermocouple pressure region), acetone, ketone, or some other high-vapor pressure solvent is employed. When the leak is flooded with one of these liquids, the thermocouple gauge jumps quite rapidly. If the leak is small (i.e., below 10^{-3} torr), a helium leak detector is generally used. This instrument is a small mass spectrometer set so that it is sensitive to helium ions. It is attached to the foreline of the vacuum system and detects the helium introduced into the system through the leak.

A phenomenon of great importance in vacuum technique is the

outgassing of surfaces. All materials adsorb gas molecules on their surfaces. When the pressure is lowered, these adsorbed gas molecules slowly escape. These gases may take a long time to be removed from the system, causing the pressure to remain high. This situation is sometimes referred to as a virtual leak. Outgassing can usually be speeded by heating the surface. If a system is outgassed by heating, great care must be taken to ensure that the gaskets employed in the various pipe joints of the system survive the heating procedure. Most vacuum gaskets are made of rubber and other organic synthetics. Usually a low-vapor pressure grease is used to lubricate these gaskets to make tighter seals. More recently, metal gaskets made of indium, gold, copper, or aluminum have been used in systems designed for bake out at high temperatures. Systems equipped with metal gaskets and baked out for many hours at high temperatures (up to 400°C) have been pumped down to pressures as low as 10^{-12} torr.

4.7 EXPERIMENTS

A great many experiments are possible to demonstrate the principles outlined in the foregoing sections. The operation of various vacuum gauges can be demonstrated. The pumping speeds of various apertures and tubes should also be measured in order to verify the formulas derived in Sec. 4.4.

A useful vacuum system for performing these experiments is illustrated schematically in Fig. 4.13. For maximum versatility, the components can be mounted on a mobile cart.

The system should include the following features: The foreline should have a bypass line to the vacuum chamber so that experimental changes can be made without having to forepump through the diffusion pump, which therefore does not have to be cooled off. There should be an auxiliary valve on the high-vacuum flange. This valve allows the system to pump on vacuum chambers that are not readily adaptable to the high-vacuum flange. The high-vacuum flange in this case can be blanked off with a plate. The auxiliary high-vacuum valve also provides a convenient means for letting the vacuum system up to atmospheric pressure.

The vacuum gauges are placed in such a way that the pressures throughout the system can be monitored at all times.

Pumping speeds of apertures. The pumping speeds of various apertures are measured by using a special vacuum chamber which can be attached to the vacuum pump cart shown in Fig. 4.13. This chamber is divided into two separate volumes with a hole in the partition between them. The hole can be coupled by opening a suitable valve. Thermocouple and ionization gauges are provided for each side of the chamber so that the pressure can be measured on each side. The rate of gas flow through the hole can be determined by first keeping the

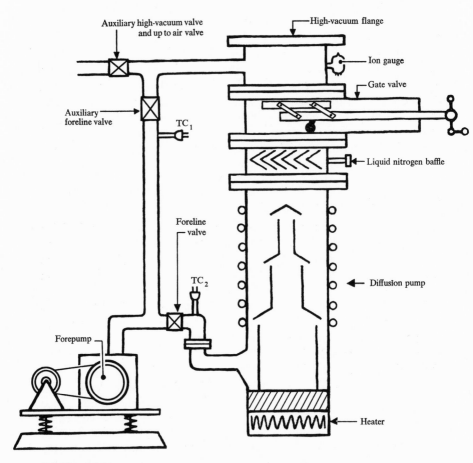

FIGURE 4.13

Typical valving and pump-location scheme for a student laboratory high-vacuum system.

chambers at different pressures, opening the aperture and measuring the time necessary for the pressures to equalize. A schematic diagram of this vacuum chamber is shown in Fig. 4.14. The size of the aperture between the chambers is variable, so that the dependence of the pumping speed of the aperture on the aperture radius can be determined. It is also of interest to show how the pumping speed of the gas varies as a function of the molecular weight of the gas in the chamber. This can be done by introducing another gas into the chamber through the bleeder valve and using the vacuum system to adjust the pressure properly. Helium, neon, and xenon are good gases for this purpose, for they all have molecular weights substantially different from air. The pumping speed should depend on the square root of the molecular weight.

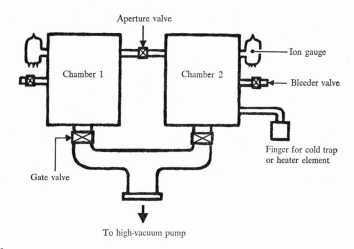

FIGURE 4.14

Student laboratory vacuum chamber arrangement suitable for illustrating vacuum techniques.

Outgassing. The evolution of gas from a surface can also be determined using the vacuum chamber shown in Fig. 4.14. One of the chambers is evacuated and the finger is heated with a heating tape. The pressure in the chamber will rise as the gas is driven off the surface.

Cryogenic pumping. Another interesting experiment which should be done is to show how gas may be absorbed by certain substances when they are cooled. Activated charcoal can be used for this purpose. The material is placed into one of the fingers and the finger is cooled using a liquid nitrogen dewar. When the charcoal is cooled, the pressure in the chamber should decrease rapidly. When the finger is warmed, the gas will be driven off again and the pressure will rise accordingly.

GENERAL BIBLIOGRAPHY

1. Steinherz, H. A., and P. A. Redhead: *Scientific American*, **206,** 78, 1962.

2. Barrington, A. E.: "High Vacuum Engineering," Prentice-Hall, Inc., Englewood Cliffs, N.J., 1963.

3. Yarwood, J.: "High Vacuum Technique," John Wiley & Sons, Inc., New York, 1961.

4. Guthrie, A., and R. K. Wakerling: "Vacuum Equipment and Technique," McGraw-Hill Book Company, New York, 1949.

5. Steinherz, H. A.: "Handbook of High Vacuum Engineering," Reinhold Publishing Corporation, New York, 1963.

6. Turnbull, A. H., R. S. Barton, and J. C. Riviere: "An Introduction to Vacuum Technique," John Wiley & Sons, Inc., New York, 1962.

7. Dushman, S.: "Scientific Foundations of Vacuum Techniques," John Wiley & Sons, Inc., New York, 1949.

8. Pirani, M., and J. Yarwood: "Principles of Vacuum Engineering," Reinhold Publishing Corporation, New York, 1961.

Chapter 5

THE DETECTION
AND MEASUREMENT
OF IONIZING RADIATIONS

5.1 INTRODUCTION

Ionizing radiations are charged particles or electromagnetic quanta sufficiently energetic so that they
can ionize the atoms of the material through
which they pass. These radiations are divided into
three general categories:

1. *Heavy particles*. This group contains protons, deuterons, alpha particles, and other charged

particles of nuclear mass. They ionize matter by colliding with atomic electrons, causing them to leave the atom. Neutrons and other uncharged nuclear fragments do not ionize matter, for they do not interact with the atomic electrons.

2. *Light particles.* These are the positrons, electrons, and some of the light mesons. They differ from the heavy particles in that their masses are much smaller. They ionize matter in the same way as the heavy charged particles.

3. *Gamma rays and X rays.* These are electromagnetic radiations of very high frequencies. Gamma rays are emitted by nuclei and X rays by atoms. This difference refers only to the origin of the radiation, not to its nature. Electromagnetic radiations interact with (and ionize) atoms in three important ways. One is the photoelectric effect, in which a gamma rays is absorbed by an atomic electron which leaves the atom carrying away the energy of the gamma ray. The second interaction is the Compton process, in which the gamma ray collides with an electron and is scattered. The scattered gamma ray and the recoil electron share the initial energy of the gamma ray, and energy and momentum are conserved exactly as if the gamma ray were a particle. Finally, if the energy of the gamma ray exceeds twice the electron rest energy, an electron-positron pair may be produced.

The detection of ionizing radiation is generally accomplished by using the ions and electrons produced by the radiations. These charged particles can be used to generate electrical signals as in ionization chambers, or they cause secondary effects, such as fluorescence, which can then be detected. The devices most widely used today for the detection of ionizing radiations are scintillation counters and gas-filled counters of various types. In the experiments described in this chapter, attention is restricted to gamma rays, positrons, and electrons. The heavy particles were discussed in Chapter 3.

5.2 RADIATION DETECTORS

Scintillation counters. The purpose of any counting system is to detect the presence of a high-energy particle and to convert this event to a useful signal. Some counting systems produce a signal due to a radiation flux or the average of a large number of particles. There are also counters which are sensitive to individual particles and gamma rays. Most scintillation counters are used as single-particle detectors.

A scintillation counting system consists of a transducer or detector in which the incident radiant energy is converted to light, an amplifying system, and a scaler. The detector in this case is a fluorescent substance, the amplifying system is a photomultiplier tube plus an electronic pulse amplifier, and the pulses produced are counted by an electronic scaler. A schematic diagram of such a system is shown in Fig. 5.1.

When the radiations strike the scintillator, a very small light flash is produced. This flash strikes the photocathode of a photomultiplier tube, producing a small number of electrons inside the tube by photoelectric emission. The number of photoelectrons is then multiplied by a factor of 10^6 to 10^7 in the dynode structure of the photomultiplier tube. The light flashes are thus converted to electrical signals which appear

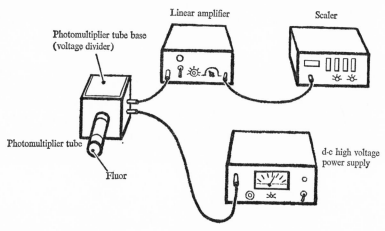

FIGURE 5.1

Instrument arrangement for pulse counting of radiations detected by a scintillation counter.

at the photomultiplier-tube anode. The pulses at the output of the photomultiplier tube, which have amplitudes of the order of millivolts, are further amplified with an electronic amplifier so that signals of the order of a volt appear at the scaler input. A typical oscilloscope display of such a pulse is shown in Fig. 5.2.

The most important feature of scintillation counters is that the intensity of the light produced in the scintillator is proportional to the energy of the incident radiation.[1] Each voltage pulse produced at the output of the photomultiplier tube has an amplitude proportional to the energy of the incident radiation. If the voltage distribution of the pulses is measured, some information about the energy spectrum of the initial radiations can be determined. The voltage distribution of the output pulses is measured by a pulse-height analyzer. Pulse-height analyzers, as the name implies, measure the voltage of the input pulses and then distribute them according to voltage among a number of different scalers. Each scaler corresponds to a definite voltage increment (usually called the channel width) centered around some mean voltage. By calibrating the system with a radiation source of known energy, the pulse voltages sorted into various channels by the pulse-height analyzer can be related to the energy of the radiation. The schematic diagram with a pulse-height analyzer system is shown in Fig. 5.3.

The mechanism by which the energy of the incident ionizing radiation is transformed to light by the scintillator is still not well under-

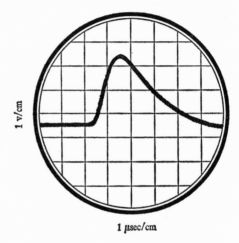

1 v/cm

1 µsec/cm

FIGURE 5.2

Typical oscilloscope display of a pulse from the photomultiplier.

stood.[2] In any event, a certain number of light quanta (or photons) are produced for every ion pair created in the scintillating material. The ion pairs themselves are created by charged particles passing through the scintillator. The charged particles are either directly incident on the detector or are produced by gamma rays which liberate fast electrons in the scintillator by photoemission or by Compton scattering.

The photomultiplier tube used to convert the light pulse to an electrical signal operates on the following principle. The light flash from the scintillator produces a small number of electrons at a photosensitive surface deposited on the glass face of the tube. These photoelectrons are then accelerated by an electric field to a small metal plate called a dynode. The plate is coated with a material which emits proportionally more electrons when it is struck by fast electrons. (It multiplies the electrons, hence the name photomultiplier.) The electrons from the first dynode are accelerated again and strike a second dynode, where they are again multiplied. This process is continued through ten or more stages depending on the type of photomultiplier tube employed. The accelerating potentials on the dynodes are supplied by the high-voltage power supply and a resistance voltage divider.

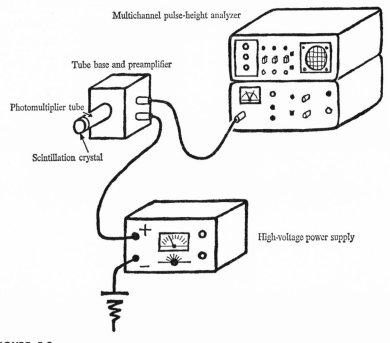

FIGURE 5.3

Instrument arrangement for pulse-height analysis of the scintillator pulses.

Gas-filled counters. For many years the most common radiation detection devices were the gas-filled counters. Although still in wide use, they have been replaced for many purposes by the scintillation detectors described in the previous section.

In a gas-filled counter, the ionization of the gas caused by a high-energy particle or gamma ray is measured directly. In most cases this is done by placing the counter gas in an electric field so that the ion pairs are separated, the electrons moving toward the anode and the ions toward the cathode. The currents caused by the collected charges are measured and related to the radiations which caused the ionizing

Radiation detectors **87**

events. A typical gas-filled counter is shown in Fig. 5.4. The cylindrical volume is filled with the counter gas. The case is grounded and the thin center wire is kept at a high positive potential, usually between 300 and 3000 volts, with respect to the case. When an ionization event occurs in the gas, the electric field causes the electrons and ions to move away from each other, preventing recombination. Since the electrons have a very much larger average drift velocity in the gas than the ions, all of the current observed comes from electron motion. The electrons may be prevented from reaching the center wire unless the proper gas is used. Certain molecules, oxygen for example, form negative ions when they collide with electrons. This process, known as electron attachment, causes the appearance of negative ions which

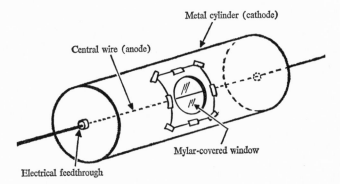

FIGURE 5.4

Simple gas-filled radiation detector.

move much more slowly than the electrons and thus are more difficult to detect at the center wire. A current amplifier is usually necessary to observe ionization currents in gases having large electron attachment probabilities. The inert gases—mostly neon and argon—are the best counter gases because they do not form negative ions.

As the electrons move toward the center wire of a cylindrical counter, they experience a stronger electric field ($E \sim 1/r$). If the potential of the center wire is sufficiently high, there is some distance, r, from the wire at which the electrons will gain enough energy between collisions to cause secondary ionization. Thus more electrons are produced in a region where they in turn can cause additional ionization. Much larger currents (or current pulses) are therefore observed at the center wire under these conditions. This phenomenon is called gas multiplication, and it amplifies the size of the signal observed at the center wire.

Amplification factors between 10^2 and 10^4 are quite common, and they may be much higher under certain conditions.

Gas counters may be operated either as flux detectors (ionization chambers) or as single-pulse counters (proportional counters and Geiger-Müller counters). In the former case, the voltage is usually kept low enough so that there is no gas multiplication. The current measured in this case comes only from electrons directly produced in primary ionizing events. The current is measured by using the system

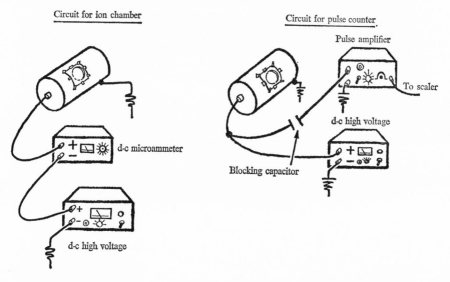

Circuit for ion chamber

Circuit for pulse counter

Pulse amplifier

To scaler

d-c high voltage

d-c microammeter

Blocking capacitor

d-c high voltage

FIGURE 5.5

Wiring arrangement for using gas-filled counters as a current-producing detector (ion chamber) or as a voltage-pulse detector (proportional counter or Geiger-Müller counter).

shown in Fig. 5.5 and is read on a microammeter or recorded on a strip chart. Most radiation survey meters are operated in this way, and the microammeter is usually calibrated directly in terms of radiation dose rates.

The circuit necessary for operation as a pulse counter is also shown in Fig. 5.5. In this case the blocking capacitor is charged by the electron pulse arriving at the center wire. This signal is then amplified by a fast amplifier and recorded by a scaling system similar to the one described for use with scintillation counters.

When gas counters are used as single-event detectors, the center wire potential is usually large enough so that gas multiplication occurs.

Figure 5.6 shows the gas multiplication as a function of voltage on the center wire. There are three important operating regions. In the ionization region there is no gas multiplication; the number of electrons at the center wire is small and equal to the number of ion pairs produced by the primary radiations in the chamber. The next region is the proportional region. Here there is gas multiplication, but the number of electrons observed at the center wire for each ionizing event remains proportional to the number of primary ion pairs produced by the

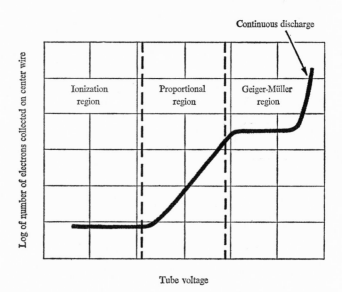

FIGURE 5.6

Response of gas-filled radiation detectors indicating various regions of possible operation.

incident particle. Counters operated in this region are especially useful because the pulse size observed is proportional to the energy deposited by the incident particle in the counter gas. They are called proportional counters and are often used as particle or gamma ray spectrometers. Proportional counters commonly have a gas multiplication of the order of 10^3. When the center wire potential is increased beyond the proportional region, the output pulse voltage is independent of the number of primary ion pairs produced by the incident particle. This occurs because each ionizing event causes a discharge which spreads along the entire length of the center wire. The number of electrons collected therefore depends on the structure of the counter alone. Gas counters operated in this manner are called Geiger-Müller counters. Finally, if the center wire voltage is increased beyond the Geiger-Müller region, no ionizing event is required to initiate a discharge. A continuous discharge exists in the counter under these conditions, initiated by random free electrons in the counter volume.

It should be pointed out that the curve shown in Fig. 5.6 is a strong function both of the gas pressure and the type of gas used to fill the counter. The general features (i.e., the three regions of operation) are preserved, but the voltage ranges over which the counter works in a particular mode are changed. Depending on the purpose, gas counters can be operated at pressures ranging from 10 cm of mercury to several atmospheres. Most of the common detectors are, for the sake of simplicity, run at atmospheric pressure. Particular care must be taken in choosing the proper gas mixture in the case of proportional counters. Pure inert gases do not work well because the electrons tend to gain too much energy between collisions, and thus the "proportional" region of operation is limited to a small range of voltages. A quenching gas such as methane is usually introduced to solve this problem. A common gas mixture is 90 percent argon (or neon) and 10 percent methane. In proportional counters, great care must also be taken to prevent poisoning of the gas mixture with impurities. Small amounts of organic impurities, for example, may change the gas multiplication factor enough to change the output voltage by a factor of two or more. The counter windows and the electrical leads should therefore be mounted in such a way that no solder flux or sealing compound is inside the active volume of the counter. A common method of maintaining the purity of the counter gas is to bleed fresh gas from a reservoir through the counter continuously so that the gas in the active volume is always being replaced. Proportional counters of this type are said to work in the "flow mode."

5.3 EXPERIMENTS

A large number of experiments can be performed using the radiation detectors described in Sec. 5.2. A few of the more important ones are described below.

Detection of electrons. Energetic electrons (or *beta particles* as they are sometimes called) are usually detected by scintillation counters using organic fluors (scintillators) which are relatively insensitive to gamma rays. Organic fluors are either pure stilbene or anthracene crystals or plastic materials saturated with these substances.

The first step is to detect the electrons and the second is to show that they are indeed electrons. The electrons used in this experiment are emitted by a cesium-137 (Cs^{137}) source. This isotope emits monoenergetic electrons with an energy of approximately 630 kev (see Fig. 5.16). (An electron volt is the energy of an electron which has been accelerated through a potential difference of one volt. Measured in ergs, one electron volt equals 1.6×10^{-12} ergs.) The source is now placed about 5 cm from the counter, mounted on a scale as shown in Fig. 5.7, and the pulse-height spectrum is determined. The spectrum observed should look like the curve shown in Fig. 5.8. In this graph

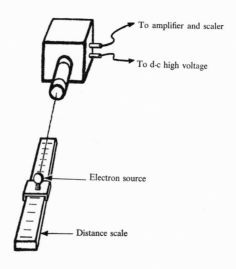

FIGURE 5.7

Method for measuring energy degradation and range of energetic electrons in air.

the counting rate is plotted against the channel number. The observed peak is due to the pulses caused by the monoenergetic electrons striking the scintillator. If the distance between the counter and the source is changed, the position of the peak changes. Specifically, the energy of the electrons decreases as the source-to-counter distance is increased. This can be verified by observing that the voltage of the pulse group corresponding to the electrons decreases. The energy change is due to the energy loss suffered by the electrons in passing through the air and the counter window. The counter window is necessary in this case to keep light from the sensitive surface of the photomultiplier tube. It is obviously important to minimize the window thickness when detecting charged particles so that energy losses of this kind are as small as possible. A number of experiments concerning the passage of electrons through matter should now be performed. Specifically:

1. Determine the energy as a function of distance and plot the energy loss per centimeter of air.

2. Determine the energy loss as a function of thickness of a number of foils placed between the counter and the source (mylar, nickel, aluminum, tantalum, and gold).

3. Plot energy as a function of thickness for all these materials and describe any regularities that may be observed.

4. Express the results in terms of energy loss per atom passed by the electron by performing the appropriate calculations.

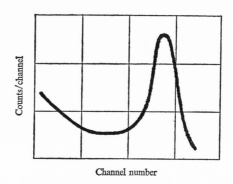

Channel number

FIGURE 5.8

Energy spectrum of monoenergetic electrons emitted from the decay of Cs^{137}.

The mechanism by which electrons lose energy has been discussed in more detail in Chapter 3.

To prove that the observed pulses are caused by energetic electrons, a number of deflection experiments can be performed. Electrons are charged particles and can thus interact with electric and magnetic fields. The simplest experiment is to observe what happens when a strong magnet is placed between the counter and the source. The magnetic field should deflect the electrons and the counting rate should be lowered. The experimental geometry is shown in Fig. 5.9. Verify from the effects observed in this experiment that electrons are negatively charged.

Detection of gamma rays. The problem of detecting gamma rays with a scintillation counter is fundamentally different from that of detecting electrons. When an electron passes through matter, it ionizes the atoms. In the scintillator this causes light bursts. A gamma ray on passing through matter does not ionize all the atoms in its path. It interacts with one electron in the material either by the photoelectric effect, Compton scattering, or pair production. The electron then carries off all or part of the energy of the gamma ray. This electron ionizes the atoms in the scintillator, causing light flashes to appear. In the case of gamma rays, the ionization is a secondary effect. It is possible for a gamma ray to pass through matter without interacting at all, whereas this cannot happen with a charged particle. It will be

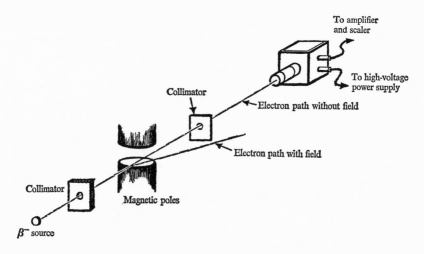

FIGURE 5.9

Experiment for verifying the sign of and the charge of beta particles.

shown later that the probability of photoelectric emission increases as the atomic number (Z) of the material increases. The Compton collision probability is roughly independent of Z but does depend on the electron density in the material. Pair production occurs only when the incident gamma ray energy exceeds twice the electron rest mass (1.02 mev). This process is important only for gamma rays with energies above 5.0 mev because the cross section for pair production near the threshold is small. To detect gamma rays, scintillators with high Z and large numbers of electrons are more efficient. The most popular of these are crystals of sodium iodide (NaI) and cesium iodide (CsI). The iodine has an atomic number of 53 which provides electrons for Compton collisions, and, furthermore, this material has a large photoelectric cross section.

A gamma ray counter has the same schematic diagram as the electron counter shown in Fig. 5.3. The organic fluor is replaced by a sodium iodide or cesium iodide scintillation crystal. The pulse-height spectrum observed when a monoenergetic gamma ray strikes the crystal is shown in Fig. 5.10. The peak in the spectrum is due to photoelectric absorption, and the continuous distribution arises from Compton collisions. In the case of the photoelectric effect, all the energy of the gamma ray is deposited in the crystal so that the position of the peak corresponds to the energy of the gamma ray. In this way the counter can be used as a gamma ray spectrometer.

The first experiment is to expose a number of sources which emit gamma rays with known energies to the crystal. A plot of the photo-

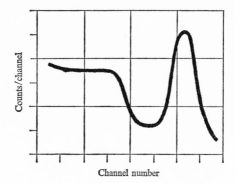

FIGURE 5.10

Gamma ray energy spectrum measured for the decay of Cs^{137}.

peak channel number (or the pulse voltage) against the energy should be made to show that the spectrometer is linear. The linearity of the plot demonstrates that the light produced by the crystal is proportional to the gamma ray energy. In addition, the passage of gamma rays through matter can be investigated by repeating the experiments which were performed with electrons. In contrast to the electron case, the gamma ray peak does not shift in position (energy) as the absorber thickness is increased. This is consistent with the statement that some of the gamma rays can pass through matter without interacting. The counting rate decreases because some of the gamma rays are absorbed or scattered by the electrons in the absorber material. The counting rate as a function of absorber thickness should be determined, and an effective interaction probability per atom should be computed. These calculations should be done for various materials with differing atomic numbers.

An important question to be considered when dealing with gamma ray spectrometers is resolution. In general, the resolution is a measure of how well the spectrometer can distinguish between gamma rays of differing energies. Ultimately, the resolution depends on the width of the photo peak in Fig. 5.10. This peak is very much wider than the natural width (or energy spread) of the gamma rays emitted by the source. The resolution ρ is defined as

$$\rho = \frac{\Delta V}{V} \tag{5.1}$$

where ΔV is the width of the gamma ray peak at half maximum and V is the position of the peak on the voltage scale. The value of ρ for the 661-kev gamma ray shown in Fig. 5.10 is approximately 0.05 (this means that the resolution of the spectrometer is 5 percent). The spectrometer can thus distinguish between two gamma rays with an energy difference of 5 percent in the 600-kev region. The width of the peak is statistical in nature and arises from the fluctuation in the number of electrons produced at the photosensitive surface of the photomultiplier tube. The number of primary photoelectrons produced determines the resolution. The statistical relation between the number of photoelectrons N and the resolution is

$$\frac{\sqrt{N}}{N} = \frac{1}{\sqrt{N}} = \rho \tag{5.2}$$

Thus, in the case of the 661-kev gamma ray,

$$\rho = 0.05 = \frac{1}{\sqrt{N}} \quad \text{and} \quad N = \frac{1}{25 \times 10^{-4}} = 400 \tag{5.3}$$

Therefore 400 electrons are produced at the photosensitive surface for every 661-kev gamma ray captured in the crystal by a photoelectric process. For a gamma ray spectrometer of this type, it is approximately true that one or two photoelectrons are produced for every kiloelectron volt of energy deposited in the crystal. An important consequence of this argument is that the resolution of the spectrometer becomes worse as the energy of the incident photon is decreased. At 100-kev energy, for example, the number of photoelectrons produced is 100; hence the resolution is

$$\rho = \frac{1}{\sqrt{100}} = \frac{1}{10} = 0.10 \text{ or } 10\% \tag{5.4}$$

To verify this relation, measure the widths of the peaks observed with gamma rays of various energies. Show that the resolution of the spectrometer is inversely proportional to the square root of the gamma ray energy. Similar arguments apply in the case of the proportional gas counters mentioned in Sec. 5.2, p. 90.

Measurement of the beta-decay spectrum. Certain radioactive nuclei emit electrons when they decay. This process is called beta decay. When a source containing beta-active nuclei is placed in front of the electron counter shown in Fig. 5.7, the pulse-height spectrum shown in Fig. 5.11 is observed. The electron-energy distribution is continuous, not single valued. That is, electrons of all energies up to some maximum energy are emitted by the source. The most probable energy

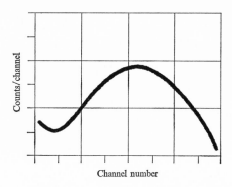

FIGURE 5.11

Typical beta decay energy spectrum.

of an emitted electron corresponding to the peak shown in Fig. 5.11 is approximately 0.3 E_{max}.

The continuous nature of the beta-decay spectrum is one of the most important effects in nuclear physics. It led to the discovery of a new particle, the neutrino,[3] whose existence was verified experimentally only a few years ago.[4] The existence of the neutrino can be inferred from the continuous spectrum by the following argument: The energy available for the particles involved in the decay is fixed by the mass difference between the radioactive nucleus and its daughter:

$$\Delta E = (M_1 - M_2)c^2 \tag{5.5}$$

If the electron were the only particle emitted in the decay process, conservation of energy and momentum would require that all the decay electrons have the same energy. Experimentally, this is not observed. Since it is unlikely that energy and momentum conservation is invalid, the most plausible explanation is that a second particle is emitted in the decay process. In this event, the decay energy is shared between the electron and the second particle, and the amount of energy carried off by the electron depends on the angles between the two particles and the recoil nucleus (see Fig. 5.12). If all angles θ are equally probable, that is, if the angular distribution of the neutrino with respect to that of the electron is isotropic, an energy distribution of the kind shown in Fig. 5.11 will be observed.

Two conclusions can be drawn about the second particle emitted in the process. It must be uncharged and must not interact strongly with matter, for it would otherwise be easy to observe. It must also be very light, for the maximum electron energy observed in the decay is very nearly equal to the maximum energy available in the nuclear decay. Very little of the decay energy goes into the rest mass of the neutrino.

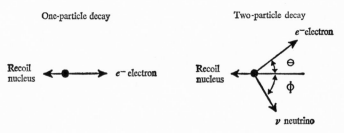

FIGURE 5.12

The two possible methods of beta decay.

It is for this reason that Enrico Fermi, who, along with W. Pauli, first suggested the existence of this particle, called it the neutrino—meaning the "little neutral one" in Italian.

A number of other experiments and calculations should be performed. Methods similar to those described in Sec. 5.3, p. 93 should be employed to verify that beta particles are actually electrons. Also, the effect of the finite resolution of the electron spectrometer on the observed electron spectrum should be estimated.

The Compton effect. One of the most striking experiments in modern physics is the scattering of gamma rays by electrons.[5] The reason for the importance of this experiment is that it graphically demonstrates the particle nature of electromagnetic waves. This wave-particle duality is one of the important results of quantum mechanics. Specifically, the prediction is that light waves, if they have high enough frequencies, behave as if they were particles with the following relation between energy and momentum:

$$E = pc \tag{5.6}$$

Furthermore, the relation between the energy of such a light "particle" (or photon) and the frequency of the corresponding wave is

$$E = h\nu \tag{5.7}$$

Thus the relation between the momentum and the wavelength of the light particles is

$$p = \frac{h}{\lambda} \tag{5.8}$$

Consider next what happens when a light particle collides with an electron at rest. The vector diagram in Fig. 5.13 shows the momentum

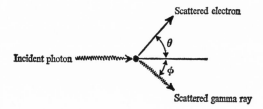

FIGURE 5.13

Kinematics of Compton scattering of a gamma photon from an electron.

vectors of the two particles in the collision. If p_e is the momentum of the scattered electron, the following relations are obtained from the conservation of energy and momentum:

$$h\nu + m_e c^2 = h\nu' + (p_e^2 c^2 + m_e^2 c^4)^{1/2} \qquad \text{Energy conservation}$$

$$\left.\begin{array}{l} p_e \sin \theta = \dfrac{h\nu'}{c} \sin \phi \\[2mm] \dfrac{h\nu}{c} = \dfrac{h\nu'}{c} \cos \phi + p_e \cos \theta \end{array}\right\} \qquad \text{Momentum conservation} \quad (5.9)$$

In these equations ν is the frequency of the incident photon and ν' is the frequency of the scattered photon. Notice also that the rest energy of the electron, $m_e c^2$, must be included in the conservation of energy calculation. If p_e and the angle θ are eliminated between these equations, the energy change in the light particle (photon) is

$$\Delta E = h\nu - h\nu' = h\nu - \frac{h\nu}{1 + (h\nu/m_e c^2)(1 - \cos \phi)} \tag{5.10}$$

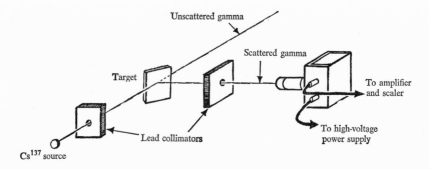

FIGURE 5.14

Experimental arrangement for verifying the energy loss [Eq. (5.10)] of a Compton scattered gamma photon.

Notice that the maximum energy change occurs when the scattering angle ϕ is 180 degrees.

The energy change predicted by Eq. (5.10) can easily be verified experimentally. The gamma ray counter described in Sec. 5.3, p. 95 is used along with the Cs^{137} source. The experimental setup is shown in Fig. 5.14. The gamma rays are collimated by the lead bricks and allowed to strike a target. The counter is placed at a 90° angle to the incident gamma ray beam. The spectrum of the scattered gamma rays is measured and compared to the original Cs^{137} spectrum. The result is shown in Fig. 5.15. The energy shift ΔE is also shown. This shift should be measured as a function of the scattering material. If Eq. (5.10) is correct, ΔE should depend only on ϕ and not on the material,

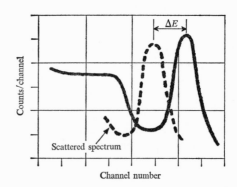

FIGURE 5.15

Energy spectrum for an unscattered and a Compton scattered Cs^{137} gamma ray.

that is, it should depend only on the properties of the electron. The relative intensity of the peak should increase as the electron density in the scatterer increases. Both statements should be verified experimentally. Energy shifts for other scattering angles should also be measured to verify Eq. 15.10).

Internal conversion processes. Another interesting investigation deals with the origin of the monoenergetic electrons emitted by the Cs^{137} source. They cannot be ordinary beta-decay electrons because these would not have the observed monoenergetic spectrum. The monoenergetic electrons arise from the decay of a nuclear energy level. The decay scheme of this isotope is shown in Fig. 5.16. The Cs^{137} nucleus decays by beta-particle emission (β^-) to an excited level in the daughter nucleus Ba^{137}. This energy level then decays to the ground state of Ba^{137} with the emission of a 661-kev gamma ray. Sometimes the level can also decay by transferring the nuclear excitation energy (661 kev)

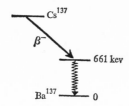

FIGURE 5.16

Decay scheme of Cs^{137} to Ba^{137}.

to one of the electrons in the atom. When this occurs, the electron is emitted with a kinetic energy of 661 kev minus the binding energy of the atomic shell from which the electron originated (i.e., K, L, M, etc., shells).

The first experiment is to determine the energy difference between the gamma ray and the electron emitted by the isotope. Careful calibration of the detectors is necessary because the energy difference between the two is approximately 30 kev. This energy corresponds to the binding energy of an electron in the K shell of barium. The existence of a group of monoenergetic electrons having the correct energy shows that the postulated process, called internal conversion, actually occurs.

Positrons and annihilation radiation. One of the most fascinating stories in modern physics is the discovery of the positron or positive electron. The positron is a particle with a rest mass equal to that of the electron, but with a positive rather than a negative charge. The existence of a positron was first predicted by P. A. M. Dirac[6] in order to resolve a dilemma which he encountered when he formulated relativistic quantum mechanics. Dirac discovered that the solution of his equation required the energy spectrum for electrons shown in Fig. 5.17. Electrons can exist in states where their total energy is larger than $m_e c^2$ (the electron energy) or less than $-m_e c^2$. The physical interpretation of the positive energy states presents no difficulties, for all electrons encountered in normal situations have positive energies, the rest energy plus some kinetic energy. If the electron is bound to an atom, it has some potential energy which is negative; however, this does not substantially change the argument, for the total energy, including the rest energy, is always positive. The allowed negative energy states pose a problem which is more difficult to solve. It is not at all clear how such

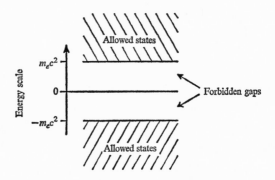

FIGURE 5.17

Possible energy states (both positive and negative) available to electrons.

a particle should behave. If an electron were in the uppermost (i.e., least negative) level, nothing would prevent it from making transitions to even lower energy levels, and eventually it would acquire an infinite negative kinetic energy! This is clearly nonsense. To evade this situation, Dirac postulated that *all* the negative energy levels are already filled, so that the problem of "falling through the floor" of the energy diagram never occurs. If this interpretation is accepted, then the energy diagram must be modified in the way shown in Fig. 5.18.

Dirac then asked what would happen if an electron from the filled negative energy levels were lifted to an allowed positive state. The electron in the positive energy state behaves like a normal particle, but what about the "hole" in the negative energy level which is left when the electron is lifted to a positive level? This "hole" behaves as if it were an electron with a positive charge. It is easy to see this from the following consideration. Suppose an electric field is applied to the region near the hole. All the negative electrons move past the hole in the appropriate direction. The hole thus has a relative velocity with respect to the negative electrons which is precisely the same as that which a positively charged particle would acquire in the presence of an applied electric field.

If Dirac's explanation is accepted, the holes should behave like positive electrons or positrons. In addition, the positrons should have another important property which is implicit in Dirac's model. If such a hole comes close to an electron in a positive energy level, the electron will jump through the gap and fill the hole. In this process the energy which the electron loses in the transition is emitted in the form of electromagnetic radiation, usually called annihilation radiation. The

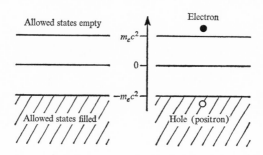

FIGURE 5.18

Electron energy-level diagram illustrating the creation of a negative energy hole or positron.

second prediction, then, is that the holes, or positrons, should not be able to exist very long in an environment containing matter, since they will soon be "filled." Thus positrons should not be very common, and this is indeed the case.

The Dirac theory of holes (or antiparticles as they are usually called) has a number of flaws, the most significant being the difficulty of visualizing physically the infinite "sea" of electrons in negative energy levels. A more complete picture has been provided by modern relativistic field theory in which a complete symmetry between particles and antiparticles is postulated. This is not true of Dirac's theory. This symmetry has led to speculations that there may be galaxies in which the roles of matter and antimatter are reversed. To test this notion, a gamma-ray counter telescope was placed aboard a launched satellite and set to observe the characteristic annihilation radiations emitted by electrons, protons, and other heavier particles. A number of experiments will now be described which demonstrate that positrons behave as predicted by the Dirac theory.

The most convenient method of producing positrons is to use a positron-emitting radioactive source such as Na^{22}. These isotopes are very similar to the electron emitters, the only difference being that they have a proton excess rather than a neutron excess to make them unstable. The first experiment is to establish that positrons carry a charge opposite in sign to that carried by electrons. This is most easily accomplished by using the equipment described in Sec. 5.3, p. 93 which was used to establish the sign of the electron charge (see Fig. 5.9). The positrons will simply be bent in the opposite direction by the magnetic field, proving that they carry the opposite charge.

A more difficult series of experiments is to establish the existence and to determine the properties of annihilation radiation. A positron, in passing through matter, behaves just as an electron does in that it

$$E = m_e c^2 \qquad\qquad E = m_e c^2$$

$$P = -\frac{h\nu}{c} \qquad\qquad P = +\frac{h\nu}{c}$$

FIGURE 5.19

Annihilation radiation — the result of the combination of an electron and a positron.

ionizes the atoms in its path giving up its energy and eventually coming to rest. The electron, when it comes to rest, loses itself in the material; however, the positron always comes close enough to an electron (remember, the two attract each other, since they are oppositely charged) that it disappears. The two particles "annihilate" each other, and the energy contained in their rest masses is given off in the form of gamma rays. Conservation of energy and momentum determines how the gamma rays are emitted. If the annihilation process occurs when both the positron and the electron are at rest, then the total energy available is $2m_e c^2$ and the total momentum is zero. The momentum conservation requires that more than one gamma ray be emitted in the annihilation process. Gamma rays always possess a momentum equal to $h\nu/c$, where ν is the frequency. Thus momentum can only be conserved if all the momentum vectors of the emitted gamma rays have a vanishing sum. The most likely event is that two gamma rays are emitted going in opposite directions from the annihilation region, each carrying half the available energy (see Fig. 5.19).

The first experiment is to establish the existence of gamma rays with

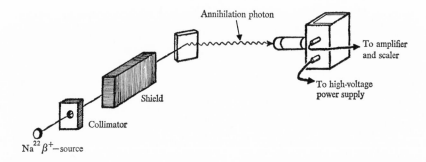

FIGURE 5.20

Method for measuring the energy spectrum of the annihilation photon.

an energy equal to the electron rest mass. The gamma ray counter described in Sec. 5.3, p. 95 is used as shown in Fig. 5.20. The positrons from the Na²² source are passed through a collimator and are allowed to strike a target. The positrons are annihilated in the target and produce gamma rays. Since the rest energy of each electron (and positron) is 0.511 mev, gamma rays of this energy should be observed.

The next step is to show that each of the gamma rays observed in the previously described experiment is accompanied by another one of equal energy going in the opposite direction. To do this, a device called a coincidence counter is used.[2] A coincidence counter is a system which gives an output whenever two signals appear simultaneously at the

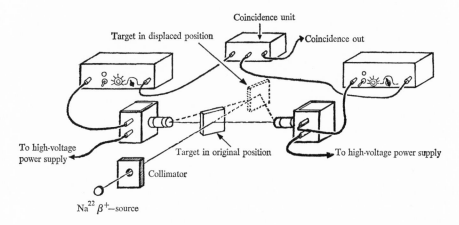

FIGURE 5.21

Experimental arrangement for verifying the existence of the two annihilation photons and the fact that they have opposite directions.

appropriate inputs. The signals are usually electrical voltage pulses. There are a number of ways in which such coincidence circuits can operate. A common method is to add the two input signals linearly and then pass the sum pulse through a discriminator circuit, which is adjusted to trip only if the input signal exceeds the voltage of a single-input pulse. With such a system, only the sum pulses are observed. (For an actual coincidence circuit see Chapter 8.) The experimental arrangement is shown in Fig. 5.21. Each of the counters is set to observe the 0.511-mev gamma ray. In the arrangement shown in Fig. 5.21, a high coincidence rate should be observed. If the target is now slightly displaced as shown, the counting rate at each counter output should not change substantially because the geometry has not been altered very much. The coincidence rate, on the other hand, should almost disappear, because the companion of any gamma ray observed in one counter cannot appear in the other. These experiments confirm the hypotheses which were made about the nature of annihilation radiation.

REFERENCES

1. Hofstadter, R.: *Nucleonics*, **4**, 4, 2; **4**, 5, 29, 1949.
2. Price, W. J.: "Nuclear Radiation Detection," McGraw-Hill Book Company, New York, 1958.
3. Fermi, E.: *Z. Physik*, **88**, 161, 1934.
4. Reines, F., and C. L. Cowen: *Phys. Rev.*, **90, 492**; **92, 831**, 1953.
5. Compton, A. H.: *Phys. Rev.*, **22**, 409, 1923.
6. Dirac, P.A.M.: *Proc. Roy. Soc.* (*London*) **117**, 610; **118**, 351, 1928.

GENERAL BIBLIOGRAPHY

1. Richtmyer, F. K., E. H. Kennard, and T. Lauritsen: "Introduction to Modern Physics," McGraw-Hill Book Company, New York, 1955.
2. Halliday, D.: "Introductory Nuclear Physics," John Wiley & Sons, Inc., New York, 1955.
3. Kaplan, I.: "Nuclear Physics," Addison-Wesley Publishing Company, Inc., Reading, Mass., 1955.
4. O'Kelley, G. D.: "Detection and Measurement of Nuclear Radiation," Office of Technical Services, Department of Commerce, Washington 25, D.C., 1962.
5. Korff, S. A.: "Electron and Nuclear Counters," D. Van Nostrand Company, Inc., Princeton, N.J., 1955.

X–RAY SPECTROSCOPY AND X–RAY ANALYSIS

Chapter 6

6.1 INTRODUCTION

X rays are electromagnetic radiations that originate outside the nucleus. The convention is to place the lower quantum energy limit of the X-ray spectrum at roughly 1 kev or just above the ultraviolet spectrum. There are two major processes for X-ray production which are quite different and which lead to different X-ray spectra.

Characteristic X rays. If electrons striking a target are sufficiently energetic to ionize some of the inner electron shells of the target atoms, the atoms themselves emit electromagnetic radiations in the X-ray energy region when the holes in the inner shells are filled. The X rays produced in this manner are monochromatic, that is, they exhibit a line spectrum just as the visible (optical) spectra emitted by atoms. These X rays are characteristic of the target atoms, hence the name "characteristic X rays."

Bremsstrahlung. Electromagnetic radiations are also produced when electrons are decelerated upon passing through matter. (Bremsstrahlung is a German word meaning deceleration radiation.) These X rays are characterized by a continuous spectrum. The maximum quantum energy of the X rays emitted is equal to the maximum energy of the electrons.

One of the important characteristics of X rays is that they are penetrating, that is, they pass through matter with relative ease. Thus it is necessary to measure the absorption of X rays by various materials as a function of the quantum energy of the X rays. These measurements yield information about the structure of the atom and also about the interaction of electromagnetic radiation and atoms.

X rays can also be used to study other properties of matter. So far only the incoherent scattering of X rays has been considered in the experiments on absorption. However, if the scattering centers (atoms) are arranged periodically, as in a crystal, the X rays can be scattered coherently. The pattern of the scattered X rays obtained from such experiments allows a complete determination of the structure of many crystals.

An elementary description of X-ray diffraction was given by Friedrich, Knipping, and Laue[1] and by W. L. and W. H. Bragg[2] in 1912. It was pointed out that the wavelengths of X rays are of the same order of magnitude as the dimensions of an atom and therefore that a regular array of atoms (as in a crystal) should behave much like an optical diffraction grating. Just as there is a relation between the slit width and the wavelength of light in an optical grating, there will be a similar relation between the lattice spacing of the crystal and the X-ray wavelength. The geometry of the situation is illustrated in Fig. 6.1, where the horizontal rows represent the crystal planes. Assume that a collimated beam of X rays is directed at the crystal surface, making an angle θ with the surface. The X rays will interact with the electrons of the crystal lattice and will be scattered. Some will suffer a change in frequency (Compton scattering) and thus will be lost from the coherent beam, but most of the photons in the region of a few kiloelectron volts quantum energy are scattered without change in frequency (Rayleigh scattering). Since the electrons in the crystal (i.e., electrons belonging to the lattice atoms) are arranged in an ordered manner, coherent Rayleigh scattering can be observed. The condition for a diffraction maximum is that the path difference between rays 1 and 2 in Fig. 6.1 is an integral number of wavelengths. This is expressed by

$$n\lambda = 2d \sin \theta \qquad (6.1)$$

where λ is the wavelength, d is the lattice spacing, and n is an integer.

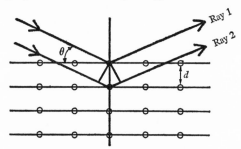

FIGURE 6.1

Bragg reflection from two crystallographic planes.

This condition is known as Bragg's law and is the fundamental relation used in X-ray analysis to measure crystal lattice spacings. The condition in Eq. (6.1) will be used to determine the symmetry properties of the crystal.

6.2 EXPERIMENTAL METHODS

Production of X rays. X rays are produced by bombarding matter with energetic electrons. Two types of X-ray tubes are in common use, the cold-cathode and the hot- or filament-cathode type. The operation of the cold-cathode tube is shown in Fig. 6.2. This tube is operated at a pressure of about 10^{-2} to 10^{-3} torr. When the potential is applied to the tube, some of the residual gas atoms are ionized and, since they are positively charged, will drift to the cathode. When they strike the cathode, each will have sufficient energy to liberate a few electrons by local heating. These electrons are then accelerated across the tube to the anode, where they produce X rays when they are stopped.

The more common method of producing X rays is to use a hot-filament tube as shown in Fig. 6.3. Such tubes are evacuated to 10^{-6} or 10^{-7} torr so that the probability of electrons colliding with the residual gas is very small. The electrons are produced by heating a tungsten

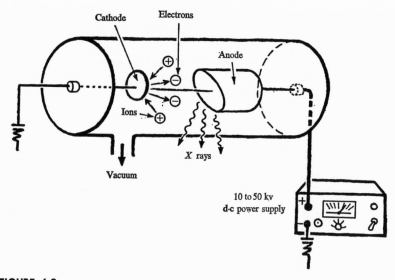

FIGURE 6.2

Cold-cathode type of X-ray tube.

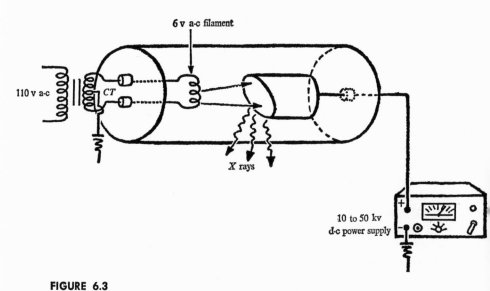

FIGURE 6.3

Hot-filament type of X-ray tube.

wire to incandescence. They are then accelerated to strike the anode where the X rays are produced. Both hot-filament and cold-cathode tubes are available as sealed-off units so that no external vacuum systems are necessary. In general, hot-filament tubes are more commonly used, but the cold-cathode tubes are used in certain special applications.

Detection of X rays. X rays can be detected using methods similar to those described for the detection of gamma rays. The major difference in the two methods is that single quantum detectors are much more important for gamma rays than they are for X rays. For X-ray detection, integrating flux meters or count-rate devices are usually more useful because of the lower quantum energy of the X rays. Perhaps the most widely used X-ray detector is photographic film. These usually are fast, coarse-grained emulsion films which give very high sensitivity and good contrast. Films are used in many configurations, sometimes flat and sometimes curved to intercept the reflected X-ray beams in crystal diffraction experiments. There are many good books describing the techniques used to expose and to read photographic films.[3]

Fluorescent and other scintillating screens are also employed for the detection of X rays. These screens usually consist of layers of a scintillating material, such as zinc sulfide, glued to stiff cardboard or plastic backings. Such fluorescent screens are sometimes used to determine X-ray beam optics in diffraction experiments and also in the familiar fluoroscopes used in many medical applications.

Another important group of detectors used extensively in X-ray work are the ionization chambers. Ionization chambers belong to the class of gas-filled counters described in Chapter 5. In X-ray diffractometers, gas-filled counters are often used to detect scattered X rays because of their high efficiency in the region of quantum energies around 10 kev. The counter and its collimating system are generally mounted on a rotating arm as shown in Fig. 6.4. The crystal sample is mounted in a fixed position at the center of the circle. The counter is rotated, and the counting rate is determined as a function of the scattering angle. Maxima in the counting rate are observed whenever the angle θ in Fig. 6.4 fulfills the Bragg condition (Eq. 6.1). Many of the more modern X-ray diffractometers of this type have automatic recording devices which plot the counting rate as a function of angle and sometimes even prepare the data for computer analysis.

X-ray diffraction and crystal structure. In order to give a qualitative description of the phenomenon observed when X rays are dif-

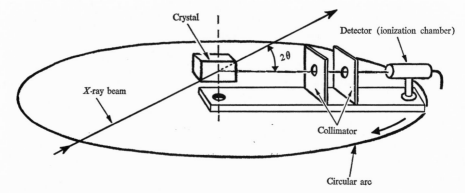

FIGURE 6.4

X-ray diffractometer used for scanning various crystallographic planes.

fracted by crystals, a short discussion of crystal structure is necessary. Crystals are ordered, three-dimensional arrays of atoms. There are a large number of basic symmetry groups (230) into which the atoms can arrange themselves. The fundamental unit is called the "unit cell." This unit repeats itself over and over again to make up the crystal. As was shown in Sec. 6.1, X rays can be coherently reflected from crystal planes. Each crystal has a very large number of such planes which must somehow be catalogued. To illustrate the indexing scheme, consider the cubic lattice shown in Fig. 6.5. The x and y axes are assumed to be in the plane of the paper and the z axis is perpendicular

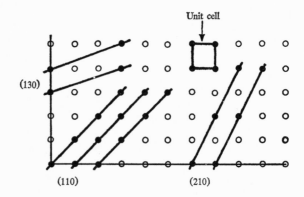

FIGURE 6.5

Various crystallographic planes and the unit cell for the simple cubic structure.

112 *X-ray spectroscopy and x-ray analysis*

to the paper. Various crystal planes are shown and the appropriate indices are indicated. These are usually called "Miller" indices. The index of a plane is written as $(\bar{x},\bar{y},\bar{z})$, where each symbol represents the reciprocal of the distance between the planes along the principal axis. These distances are written as multiples of the lattice constant a. Also, rather than writing $(\bar{x},\bar{y},\bar{z})$ as fractions, it is customary to multiply the expression by the smallest multiple which will make them all integers. The index $\bar{z} = 0$ for all the planes indicated in Fig. 6.5 shows that each

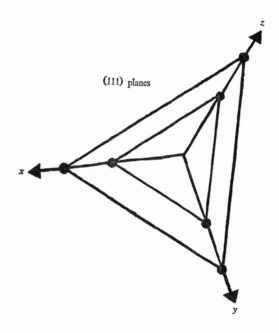

FIGURE 6.6

(111) planes for the simple cubic structure.

of the sets of planes is parallel to the z axis. Planes which are not parallel to the z axis have a $\bar{z}$ different from zero. This is illustrated by the planes in Fig. 6.6, which are the (111) planes. The distance between the planes, usually called the d spacing, is given by

$$d = \sqrt{\bar{x}^2 + \bar{y}^2 + \bar{z}^2} \tag{6.2}$$

This is the quantity used in the Bragg equation [Eq. (6.1)]. In order to calculate the intensity of the X rays reflected from each of these planes, more detailed information about the electron density along each of the crystal planes must be available. It is *not* necessarily true that the planes with the lowest indices give the most intense reflections. Note also that the situation is considerably more complicated if the lattice is not cubic. For example, the lattice spacing is no longer given correctly by Eq. (6.2).

6.3 EXPERIMENTS

End-point energy of the bremsstrahlung spectrum as a function of the tube voltage. The bremsstrahlung process has been described qualitatively in the introduction as radiation emitted when electrons are decelerated in passing through matter. The mechanism is illustrated in Fig. 6.7. An electron with kinetic energy E comes close to a nucleus and is deflected by the coulomb field of the nucleus. The electron is accelerated (and decelerated) in the scattering process, and

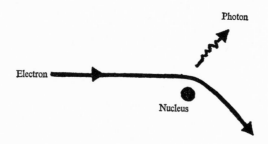

FIGURE 6.7

Trajectory of an electron passing near a nucleus and the resultant bremsstrahlung or slowing-down radiation.

radiation may thus be emitted. The spectral distribution of this radiation was first calculated by Kramers,[4] who obtained the following expression for the intensity of the radiation as a function of frequency:

$$I_\nu \, d\nu = K \frac{e^2 h^2}{mc^3} Z(\nu_0 - \nu) \, d\nu \qquad (6.3)$$

where K is a numerical constant approximately equal to one, Z is the atomic number of the target material, and e, h, m, and c are, respectively, the charge on the electron, Planck's constant, the mass of the electron, and the velocity of light. The intensity I_ν is defined as the energy radiated per electron impact. The frequency of the radiation is ν. The frequency ν_0 represents a maximum frequency which will be discussed shortly. The observed bremsstrahlung spectrum should therefore appear as shown in Fig. 6.8. An important feature of the spectrum is that no radiation appears with frequencies larger than ν_0. The purpose of the present experiment is to measure the frequency ν_0 and to relate it to the other relevant parameters of the experiment. To do this, scintillation counters or gas-proportional counters may be used. Since these counters measure the number of photons and the energy of each photon (i.e., they are single-particle detectors), Eq. (6.3) must be rewritten. (Kramers' formula contains intensity and frequency as factors, whereas single-photon counters measure the number of photons and the energy of each photon.)

The frequency of the electromagnetic radiation is related to the photon (or quantum) energy by

$$E = h\nu \tag{6.4}$$

This is the fundamental law which relates the particlelike properties of

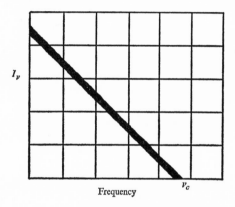

FIGURE 6.8

X-ray photon intensity versus photon frequency as predicted by Kramers [Eq. (6.3)].

electromagnetic radiations (energy E) with their wavelike properties (frequency ν). The intensity I_ν, which is the radiant energy in the frequency interval from ν to $\nu + d\nu$, is related to the number of photons in the frequency interval by

$$h\nu N_\nu = I_\nu \tag{6.5}$$

Thus, in terms of the number of photons, Eq. (6.3) is

$$N_\nu \, d\nu = K \frac{Ze^2 h}{mc^3} \left(\frac{\nu_0}{\nu} - 1 \right) d\nu \tag{6.6}$$

or, using Eq. (6.4) to eliminate ν, is

$$N_E \, dE = K \frac{Ze^2}{mc^3} \left(\frac{E_0}{E} - 1 \right) dE \tag{6.7}$$

Experiments **115**

where N_E is the number of photons observed in the energy range between E and $E + dE$. Again, as in Eq. (6.3), the energy spectrum given in Eq. (6.7) has a maximum energy E_0 beyond which no photons are observed. The shape of the energy spectrum is shown in Fig. 6.9.

Two important approximations are usually made in bremsstrahlung problems. If $E \ll E_0$, then the first term in Eq. (6.7) is the dominant one, so that

$$N_E \sim \frac{1}{E} \tag{6.8}$$

which is a familiar approximation in many situations. If $E \approx E_0$, then

$$N_E \sim E_0 - E \tag{6.9}$$

The first step in the experiment is to measure the spectrum emitted by the X-ray tube when operated at a potential of approximately

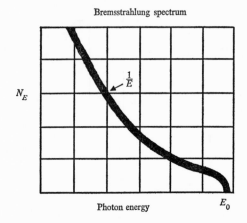

Bremsstrahlung spectrum

FIGURE 6.9

X-ray photon intensity versus photon energy as predicted by Eq. (6.7).

30 kev. A plot of the experimental results should be similar to the illustration shown in Fig. 6.10. The decrease in the spectrum at low energies is caused by absorption in the glass of the tube, the air, and the counter window. The counter is calibrated with some known radioactive sources, and the energy E_0 is measured. The voltage across the X-ray tube is varied, and the end-point energy E_0 is measured again. Plotting E_0 against the tube voltage gives a curve similar to that shown in Fig. 6.11. This result implies that

$$E_0 \sim V \tag{6.10}$$

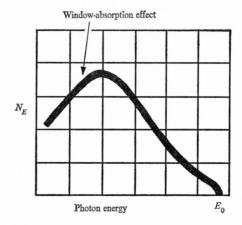

FIGURE 6.10

X-ray spectrum measured experimentally to verify prediction of Eq. (6.7).

The maximum quantum energy of the spectrum is equal to the accelerating voltage of the X-ray tube. The explanation for this behavior is that in the scattering event shown in Fig. 6.7 a fraction of the kinetic energy of the electron is given off in the form of electromagnetic radiation. The maximum energy the emitted photon can have is just equal to the incident kinetic energy of the electron, that is, the electron is completely stopped in the collision. The energy of the electron is equal to the product of the voltage across the tube and the electron charge.

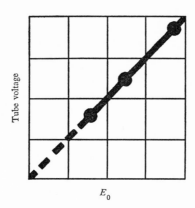

FIGURE 6.11

Experimental verification that the maximum photon energy equals the X-ray tube voltage.

Hence the proportionality in Eq. (6.10) is established, and therefore

$$E_0 = eV \qquad (6.11)$$

where V is the X-ray tube potential. This experiment is important, for it confirms the mechanism by which bremsstrahlung is produced.

Absorption of X rays in matter. Much of the information on atomic structure in the literature[5,6] has been obtained by performing X-ray absorption experiments. To understand the principal results of these experiments, it is necessary to describe briefly the fundamental features of atomic structure. The alpha-particle scattering experiments

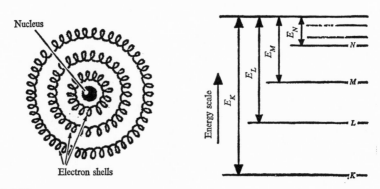

FIGURE 6.12

Energy-level diagram for atomic electrons.

performed by Rutherford and his collaborators (see Chapter 3) demonstrated without question the existence of atomic nuclei. The work of Bohr[7] and later of W. Pauli[8] made it possible to understand how atoms are constructed and how the periodic table of elements comes about. The picture of a complex atom based on these ideas is shown in Fig. 6.12. There is a small, massive nucleus around which electrons move in stable orbits. These orbits are *not* orbits in the sense that the earth has an orbit around the sun. They are regions of space to which electrons are confined by the nature of the coulomb force field and the laws of quantum mechanics. Each of these "orbits" has a well-defined binding energy, that is, the electrons in each of the various shells K, L, M, N, etc., require that a certain amount of energy be absorbed by the atom if they are to be moved to outer orbits or removed from the atom. A very common way of supplying this energy is by the use of electromagnetic radiation, and the process by which the electrons are liberated from the atoms is called the photoelectric effect.

It has already been stated that the relation between the quantum energy of a photon and the frequency of an electromagnetic wave is $E = h\nu$ [see Eq. (6.6)]. When an atom is irradiated with electromagnetic waves of frequency ν, it can absorb the energy contained in the waves only by absorbing photons, each having an energy $h\nu$. The conservation of energy then requires that

$$E = h\nu = E_{K,L,M} + \epsilon \qquad (6.12)$$

where $E_{K,L,M}$ is the appropriate binding energy of the electron and ϵ is the kinetic energy of the liberated electron. The Eq. (6.12) is called

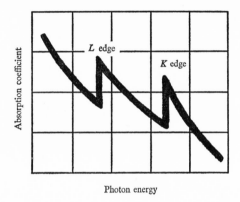

FIGURE 6.13

X-ray absorption coefficient representative of all materials indicating K and L edges.

Einstein's photoelectric absorption law and has several important consequences. The first is that all the energy of the photon is absorbed by the atom. In the photoelectric process, most of the energy of the photon is carried off by one of the atomic electrons which is ejected from the atom. Finally, and most important, the absorption event occurs as if the photon were a particle colliding with the bound electron in which the remainder of the atom absorbs the recoil momentum.

The probability that a given atom absorbs a photon as a function of photon energy is shown in Fig. 6.13. The steps in the curve occur whenever the incident photon energy exceeds the electron binding energy ($E_{K,L,M}$, etc.) for a given atomic shell. The absorption probability increases when such an absorption edge is passed. Below the absorption edge, fewer electrons in the atom are available for a photoelectric process because the photon energy must exceed the electron binding energy if an electron is to be liberated from the atom. As an absorption edge is passed, the electrons in this shell become available for photoelectric interaction and thus an increase in the absorption probability is observed. It is clear from Figs. 6.12 and 6.13 that measurements of the positions of various atomic absorption edges serve to determine the energy level diagram of the atom.

The absorption edge experiment is carried out in two steps. The voltage applied to the X-ray tube is set at approximately 15 kev. A

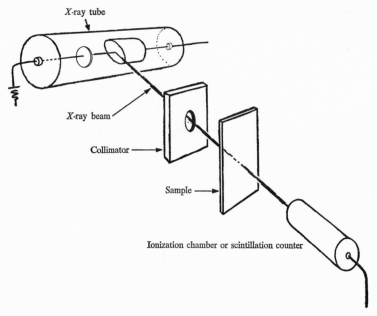

FIGURE 6.14

Experimental arrangement for measuring X-ray absorption of various materials.

molybdenum anode is used for these experiments. At this voltage a substantial fraction of the radiation is reasonably monochromatic, since mostly characteristic X rays from the molybdenum target are produced. The relative absorption of a number of different materials is then measured using the geometry shown in Fig. 6.14. The intensity ratio I/I_0 is determined, where I is the counting rate with the sample and I_0 is the counting rate without the sample in place. The results must now be expressed in terms of an absorption coefficient per atom.

The normal relation between transmitted intensity and absorber thickness, x, is

$$\frac{I}{I_0} = e^{-\mu x} \tag{6.13}$$

where μ is the absorption coefficient. The absorption coefficient is usually rewritten as follows:

$$\mu = \rho \mu_M \tag{6.14}$$

where ρ is the density of the material and μ_M is called the mass absorption coefficient. The quantity μ_M depends only on the nature of the atoms in the absorbing material and has the dimensions cm^2/gm.

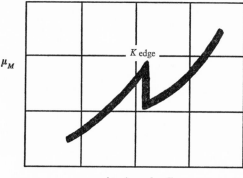

Atomic number, Z

FIGURE 6.15

Mass absorption coefficient of monoenergetic X rays for materials of various atomic numbers.

Figure 6.15 shows μ_M as a function of the atomic number of the absorbing materials for a monoenergetic incident beam. The mass absorption coefficient first increases and then, as the K edge of the material corresponding to the quantum energy of the incident beam is passed, decreases again. The results obtained from the experiment (see Fig. 6.15) imply that variation of the X-ray energy will produce the result shown in Fig. 6.13. The reason for not following the latter procedure (i.e., varying the X-ray energy and keeping the absorber material constant) is that tubes with variable target materials are difficult to obtain. The results obtained in Fig. 6.15 also show, as is expected, that the binding energy of the K electrons increases as a function of atomic number.

X-ray diffraction. In the previous experiments stress was placed on the particle nature of X rays (and electromagnetic radiations in general). In the diffraction experiments described below, the wavelike nature of X rays is demonstrated and is used to obtain information about crystal structure. The first X-ray diffraction experiments were carried out by M. von Laue about fifty years ago. Using the continuous X-ray spectrum and the geometry shown in Fig. 6.16, he obtained a picture containing a pattern of spots, each of which corresponds to

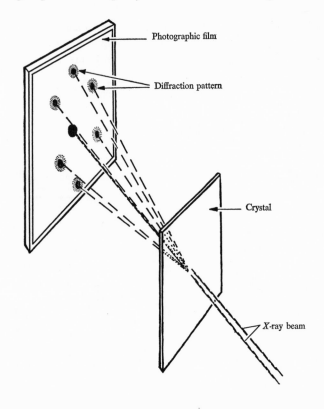

FIGURE 6.16

Transmission X-ray diffraction pattern.

coherent reflection of the X-ray beam from one set of the crystal planes. This experiment is a striking demonstration of the wave nature of X rays. The pattern of the spots was characteristic of the crystal structure of the material being examined. In the case of Laue diffraction a continuous spectrum is used to irradiate the crystal; thus *every* crystal plane contributes to the diffraction pattern, since it picks out the proper frequency (wavelength) component in the initial beam which satisfies the Bragg condition [Eq. (6.1)]. This situation is illustrated in Fig. 6.17. Each of the reflected beams will be monochromatic,

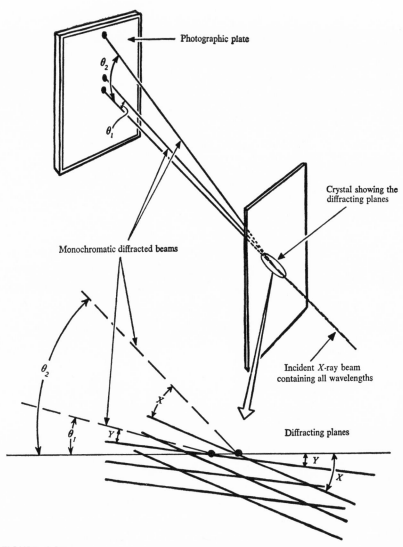

FIGURE 6.17

Schematic representation of various crystallographic planes contributing to X-ray diffraction.

with a wavelength determined by the d spacing of the particular planes. Also, the angles θ_1 and θ_2 and the symmetry pattern of reflections on the photographic plate make it possible to deduce whether cubic, hexagonal, or other crystal structures exist in the sample.

Another method which is sometimes useful in X-ray diffraction experiments is the back reflection method. In this case the film is placed between the X-ray tube and the sample as shown in Fig. 6.18. A hole is cut in the film to allow the incident beam to pass through the film. The back reflection method has the advantage that the sample need not be thin enough to transmit the X rays. Therefore less careful

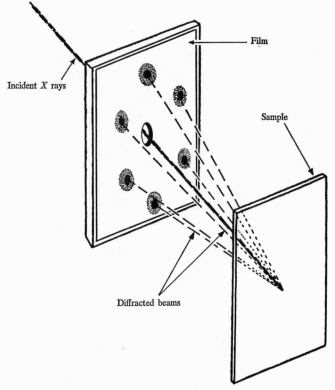

FIGURE 6.18

Back-reflection method of X-ray diffraction.

sample preparation is required if this method is employed; otherwise it is exactly the same as the Laue method.

The Laue and back reflection methods just described can be used to show the qualitative differences between the crystal structure of salt (NaCl) and mica. Salt has a cubic lattice so that Laue spots should exhibit a symmetry axis around 90 degrees, whereas mica has a hexagonal structure and thus should exhibit symmetry around 120 degrees, that is, the pattern should be invariant with respect to a rotation through 120 degrees.

Another method of obtaining information about the structure of a material using X-ray diffraction is the powder (Debye-Scherrer) method.[6] In many cases it is not possible to obtain single crystals which are suitable for X-ray work; yet the material does possess a crystal structure. In such cases it is possible to obtain some information about the material by preparing a thin sample of the material in a powder form and using a geometry similar to that shown in Fig. 6.16. However, instead of a continuous X-ray spectrum, it is necessary to use monochromatic X rays. Since the crystal planes are now randomly oriented, the resulting pattern will not show Laue spots but rather a set of rings, each ring corresponding to the diffraction cone created by one set of planes. A typical powder pattern is shown in Fig. 6.19. If the

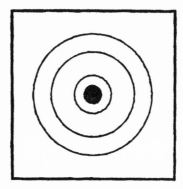

FIGURE 6.19

Debye-Scherrer rings obtained from a powder sample.

powder method is used, then all information about the symmetry group of the crystal is lost, but the crystal plane spacing d may still be calculated from Eq. (6.1). To do this, the frequency (wavelength) of the incident radiation must be known. The frequency can be obtained either by varying the X-ray tube voltage and measuring the potential at which a given ring appears or by passing the initial X-ray beam through suitable filters so that an approximately monochromatic beam is obtained. The "powder" method is a very important tool in X-ray analysis, since most materials have a strong reflection for a characteristic d spacing. The appearance of the appropriate ring in the X-ray photograph of an unknown sample therefore indicates the presence of the material.

In the previous paragraphs, the discussion has centered around crystalline materials because these give well-defined coherent reflections, that is, they behave like optical gratings. However, X-ray

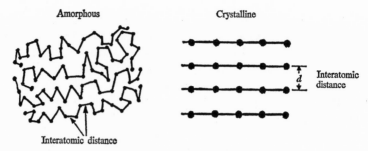

Amorphous   Crystalline

Interatomic distance

Interatomic distance

FIGURE 6.20

Characteristic interatomic spacings in both amorphous and crystalline materials.

diffraction can also be used to obtain valuable information regarding the structure and properties of noncrystalline (amorphous) materials. Such materials, like organic plastics (mostly C_nH_{2n}) and glasses (mostly SiO_2) do not have regular crystalline structures, but they do have chemical bonds (such as C—C or Si—O) which have characteristic interatomic distances (see Fig. 6.20). The interatomic distances play much the same role as the crystal "d" spacings in a powder diffraction picture. Rings similar to those shown in Fig. 6.19 are observed except that the rings are not sharp but diffuse. The reason is that the interatomic distances are not as nearly constant as the interplane spacings in a crystal.

A typical amorphous-structure pattern is shown in Fig. 6.21. The interatomic distance characteristic of the material can be measured just as the crystal d spacing is measured using the Bragg relation.

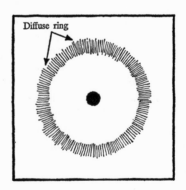

Diffuse ring

FIGURE 6.21

Diffuse ring diffraction pattern from an amorphous material.

126   *X-ray spectroscopy and x-ray analysis*

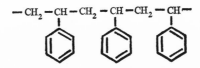

FIGURE 6.22

Chemical structure of the polymer molecule polystyrene.

An interesting application of X-ray diffraction is its use in determining the physical structure of certain organic polymers.[9] A polymer molecule is a very large organic molecule made of repeated structures of the same unit. Common natural polymers are cellulose, rubber, paraffin, and certain sugars. There are also many artificial polymers, such as polystyrene, polyvinyl chloride, and polyethylene. The chemical structure of a typical polymer molecule (polystyrene) is shown in Fig. 6.22. Under certain circumstances molecular weights of the order of 10^5 to 10^6 may be obtained for such materials. The characteristic distance of these materials is the C—C bond distance. The question which must be answered is how polymer molecules arrange themselves in various materials. In most cases they are simply randomly coiled. There are, however, certain materials (both natural and artificial) in which several physical states are possible. Rubber is a good example of such a polymer. In its "natural" unstretched state, the rubber molecules are randomly coiled just as they are in a natural polymer. These molecules have a structure which allows them to slip by each other.

Randomly coiled molecules
in unstretched rubber

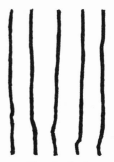

Oriented molecules
in stretched rubber

FIGURE 6.23

Relative orientation of polymer molecules in stretched and unstretched rubber.

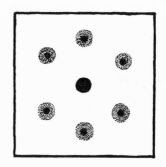

Unstretched rubber   Stretched rubber

FIGURE 6.24

Diffuse diffraction patterns from stretched and unstretched rubber.

When the rubber is stretched, the molecules are oriented until the elastic limit is reached. The situation is pictured in Fig. 6.23. That the foregoing theory of rubber elasticity is correct can be demonstrated using X-ray diffraction. A picture of the unstretched rubber is very similar to the picture obtained from an amorphous sample. When the rubber is stretched, a pattern of diffuse spots is obtained. This result would be obtained if the stretched rubber has the structure shown in Fig. 6.23. The spots are characteristic of the crystal-like structure obtained when the polymer molecules are aligned (see Fig. 6.24). This experiment is a good example of how X-ray diffraction is used to obtain information about the structure of amorphous materials.

REFERENCES

1. Friedrich, W., W. P. Knipping, and M. Laue: *Bayer. Akad. Wiss.*, 1912, *J. Phys. Radium*, **10,** 47, 1913.
2. Bragg, W. L.: *Proc. Cambridge Phil. Soc.*, **17,** 43, 1912.
3. Sproull, W. T.: "X Rays in Practice," McGraw-Hill Book Company, New York, p. 173, 1946.
4. Kramers, H. A.: *Phil. Mag.*, **46,** 836, 1923.
5. Allison, S. K., and A. H. Compton: "X Rays in Theory and Experiment," D. Van Nostrand Company, Inc., Princeton, N.J., 1935.
6. Clark, G. L.: "Applied X Rays," McGraw-Hill Book Company, New York, 1955.
7. Bohr, N.: *Phil Mag.*, **26,** 1, 1913.
8. Pauli, W.: *Z. Physik*, **31,** 765, 1925.

9. Mark, H. F., and A. V. Tobolsky, High Polymers, vol. II, 2d ed., "Physical Chemistry of High Polymeric Systems," Interscience Publishers, Inc., New York, 1950.

GENERAL BIBLIOGRAPHY

1. McLachlan, D.: "X-ray Crystal Structure," McGraw-Hill Book Company, New York, 1957.
2. Cullity, B. D.: "Elements of X-ray Diffraction," Addison-Wesley Publishing Company, Inc., Reading, Mass., 1956.
3. Clark, G. L.: "Applied X Rays," McGraw-Hill Book Company, New York, 1955.
4. King, H. P., and L. E. Alexander: "X-ray Diffraction Procedures," John Wiley & Sons, Inc., New York, 1954.

Chapter 7	# PROPERTIES OF NEUTRONS AND THEIR INTERACTIONS WITH MATTER

7.1 INTRODUCTION

The discovery of the neutron was one of the most important steps in the development of modern physics. This step opened the way to understanding the structure of nuclei and also provided the key for the practical applications of nuclear power.

The first nuclear reactions were identified by co-workers of Lord Rutherford.[1] They discovered that the air in the sample tubes which held their alpha-particle sources contained trace amounts of elements (fluorine for example) which are not normally present in air. The only explanation for their presence was that the alpha particles caused certain transformations in the nitrogen and oxygen nuclei of the air. When it became obvious that this explanation was indeed correct, many other people began to use the alpha particles emitted by naturally radioactive sources to bombard various materials. In due course beryllium was bombarded, and it was discovered that very highly penetrating radiations were emitted.

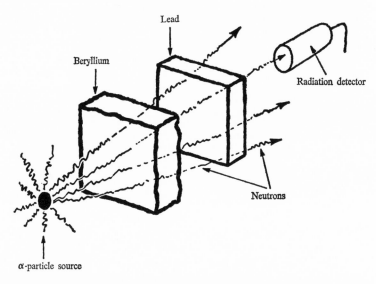

FIGURE 7.1

First experimental geometry used to produce and detect neutrons.

During 1931 and 1932, Frederic Joliot[2] and his wife, Irene Curie, daughter of the famous Marie Sklodowska Curie, carried out a number of experiments to determine the properties of the secondary radiations emitted by the beryllium. Using the experimental geometry shown in Fig. 7.1, they measured the ability of the secondary radiations to penetrate various thicknesses of lead. The Joliots assumed that the radiations they had discovered were electromagnetic in nature, and they were able to calculate the mean quantum energy of the radiations from their measured penetrating power in lead. These calculations showed that the quantum energy was approximately 50 million ev. It was extremely difficult to understand this result because there was apparently no source for the production of quanta with such high energies. The energies of the incident alpha particles and the associated nuclear binding energies were of the order of 5 mev—about one order of magnitude smaller than the calculated energy of the observed "gamma" rays.

This dilemma was finally resolved by James Chadwick[3] of Cambridge University (England), also in 1932. Chadwick pointed out that the ionization chambers used as a detector by the Joliots are sensitive to *any* particle producing secondary ionization and that the assumption that the observed radiations were electromagnetic in nature was not necessarily true. He then postulated that the radiations were neutral particles having the same mass as the proton. The existence of such particles had previously (1920) been suggested by Lord Rutherford for a different reason. Rutherford searched for these "neutrons," as he called them, but failed to find any evidence that they actually occur in nature. Neutral particles would be extremely penetrating because they would not interact with the atomic electrons but only with the very small nuclei at the center of the atoms. Chadwick estimated the mass of the neutron by measuring the energy of recoil particles produced by the high-energy neutrons. From this he found that the postulate that the neutron and proton masses were equal was quite reasonable. The apparent existence of the neutron also helped to explain the phenomenon of isotopes. If a neutral particle having the same mass as the proton really did exist, then it would be easy to understand how nuclei having the same atomic number (i.e., nuclear charge) could have a number of different isotopes having different mass numbers.

Chadwick's hypothesis has stood the test of time and has since been confirmed by a large number of independent experiments.[4] The results may be summarized as follows: The neutron is a particle about 0.05 percent heavier than the proton, so that for all practical purposes the original assumption of equal masses was quite good. It carries no electric charge, but it does possess a magnetic moment about two thirds as large as that of the proton and pointing in a direction opposite to the intrinsic spin of the particle. The spin has a value of $\hbar/2$. The neutron is also unstable, decaying into a proton by emitting an electron and a neutrino with a half-life of approximately 12 minutes.

7.2 NUCLEAR REACTIONS

In order to understand fully the production and the detection of neutrons, it is necessary to develop some elementary ideas about nuclear reactions. This topic will be discussed again in greater detail in Chapter 12 in connection with ion accelerators. Suppose that a nucleus A is bombarded by a particle x, producing a nucleus B and another particle

y. This reaction can be written as

$$A + x \rightarrow B + y + Q \qquad (7.1)$$

where Q is the amount of energy given off in the reaction. If Q is positive, the reaction is exoergic and energy is released in the reaction, whereas if Q is negative, the reaction is endoergic, and it is necessary to supply a minimum amount of energy to make the reaction go. Thus endoergic reactions have a threshold energy below which the process cannot occur. To complete the nomenclature, A is called the target nucleus, x the bombarding particle, B the product nucleus, and y the product particle. An alternative notation often employed for the reaction (7.1) is

$$A(x,y)B \qquad (7.2)$$

In the study of nuclear reactions, it is most important to be able to predict the value and the sign of Q. This can be done by using Einstein's mass-energy relation. The energy associated with a mass m is

$$E = mc^2 \qquad (7.3)$$

The energy Q is then given by the difference in the total mass of the initial particles and the final particles

$$Q = M_A c^2 + m_x c^2 - (M_B c^2 + m_y c^2) \qquad (7.4)$$

If the masses of the particles in a nuclear reaction are known, it is possible to calculate Q, the energy given off in the reaction or the energy necessary to cause the reaction to occur.

A few words should also be said about the structure of nuclei. Nuclei are made of neutrons and protons in roughly equal numbers until the mass number A reaches approximately 40. Beyond this point neutrons are more abundant, that is, there is a neutron excess. This neutron excess is necessary to overcome the mutual electrostatic repulsion of the protons in the nucleus. On the average, the energy necessary to remove a nucleon from a nucleus is of the order of 8 mev. Some important exceptions to this statement, especially among the lighter nuclei, will be mentioned shortly. The nucleus of the normal hydrogen atom consists of a single proton and is the simplest of all nuclei. The proton carries a charge e, equal to that of the electron but opposite in sign, and has an intrinsic angular momentum (spin) of $\hbar/2$. The next heavier nucleus is the deuteron, which is the heavy, stable isotope of hydrogen. It consists of a neutron and a proton bound together by the nuclear force with a binding energy of 2.225 mev. The deuteron thus has a mass nearly equal to the sum of the masses of the proton and the neutron

$$M_D = M_p + M_n - \frac{2.225 \text{ mev}}{931 \text{ mev(AMU)}^{-1}} \qquad (7.5)$$

The intrinsic angular momentum of the deuteron is $\hbar$, that is, the total spin of the deuteron is the sum of the spins of the neutron and the proton. More complex nuclei are then built up by further additions of protons and neutrons as shown in Fig. 7.2. Tritium, the heaviest known isotope of hydrogen, is unstable, having a half-life of 12 years. It decays to a light isotope of helium by emitting an electron and a neutrino. The most abundant isotope of helium has four nucleons, two

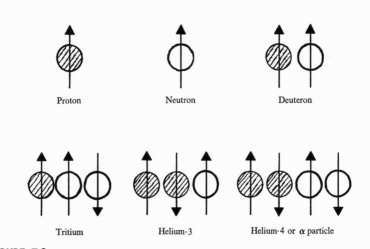

FIGURE 7.2

Construction of various nuclei from combinations of protons and neutrons.

neutrons and two protons, and is a particularly stable nucleus. It has a total binding energy of 28 mev. This nucleus is commonly called the alpha particle.

The nomenclature used to describe nuclear isotopes is that the atomic number, or nuclear charge, Z, is placed on the lower left side of the atomic symbol, and the mass number A is placed on the upper right. This convention is illustrated by the following examples:

Proton $-$ $_1H^1$
Deuterium $-$ $_1H^2$ or D
Tritium $-$ $_1H^3$ or T
Helium-3 $-$ $_2He^3$
Helium-4 $-$ $_2He^4$ or alpha particle

134 *Neutrons and their interactions with matter*

7.3 EXPERIMENTAL METHODS

Neutron sources. Neutrons are commonly produced by one of the three following methods: alpha-particle beryllium sources, particle accelerators, and nuclear reactors.

The alpha-particle beryllium sources use the reaction

$$\alpha + Be^9 \rightarrow n + C^{12} + 5 \text{ mev} \tag{7.6}$$

The alpha particles usually have an incident energy of the order of 4.0 to 5.5 mev. The neutrons are emitted at a somewhat higher energy than the incident alpha-particle energy, since the reaction is exoergic.

The sources are made by intimately mixing the alpha-active material with the beryllium. The alpha particles then have a good chance of striking a beryllium nucleus before they are stopped in the material of the source. Sources emitting up to 10^9 neutrons/sec can be made in this manner. A number of disadvantages are inherent in the use of alpha-particle beryllium sources. One is that the neutrons emitted are not monoenergetic. There are two reasons for this fact. First, the final nucleus (C^{12}) in the reaction has several excited levels. If C^{12} is left in one of these levels after the reaction, the neutron does not emerge with the total kinetic energy available, but with some smaller portion thereof. The remainder of the energy remains as excitation energy of the C^{12} nucleus and is eventually given off as gamma radiation. The second reason that the emitted neutrons are not monoenergetic is that some alpha particles pass through more matter than others before causing the (α,n) reaction. Thus the energy of the incident alpha particle is not always the same, causing an energy spread among the emitted neutrons. Another important difficulty with alpha-particle sources is that they also emit large numbers of X rays and gamma rays which contribute to background effects. On the other hand, these sources have the great advantage that there are no moving parts, electrical circuits, or fissionable materials which are present in other neutron sources.

Particle accelerators are also important as sources of neutrons. Neutron-producing reactions may be induced by protons, deuterons, and alpha particles. These particles are usually accelerated to energies between 0.100 and 10.0 mev and then focused on a target to produce the neutrons. The most widely used proton-induced reactions are

$$Li^7 + p \rightarrow Be^7 + n - 1.646 \text{ mev} \tag{7.7}$$
$$Be^9 + p \rightarrow B^9 + n - 1.85 \text{ mev} \tag{7.8}$$
$$H^3 + p \rightarrow He^3 + n - 0.765 \text{ mev} \tag{7.9}$$

These reactions are all endoergic, so that the neutrons are always emitted with energies smaller than the initial proton energy. These reactions also give neutrons of a well-defined energy, provided that the initial energy of the proton is well defined and a thin target is employed.

The most common deuteron-induced reactions are

$$H^2 + H^2 \rightarrow He^3 + n + 3.27 \text{ mev} \qquad (7.10)$$
$$H^2 + H^3 \rightarrow He^4 + n + 17.6 \text{ mev} \qquad (7.11)$$
$$H^2 + Be^9 \rightarrow B^{10} + n + 4.35 \text{ mev} \qquad (7.12)$$

Reactions (7.10) and (7.11) are the so-called fusion reactions. These

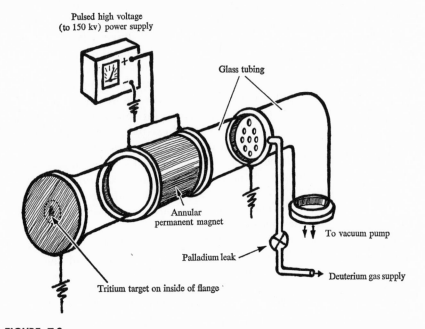

FIGURE 7.3

Omnitron pulsed neutron generator.

are important because they are highly exoergic and comparatively easy to initiate. The incident deuteron energy necessary to make these reactions go with a large probability is of the order of 30 to 50 kev.

The fusion reactions (7.10) and (7.11) can be produced using a relatively simple and compact device such as the "omnitron."[5] A schematic drawing of the omnitron is shown in Fig. 7.3. The device consists of a cylindrical vacuum chamber with a high-voltage terminal in the center, separated from the ends of the tube by cylindrical glass insulators. The tube is evacuated through one end. A high-vacuum diffusion pump system is used for this purpose. This end also contains a gas supply line through which deuterium is bled into the system when the generator is operating. A palladium leak controls the gas flow. The center high-voltage terminal is connected to a pulsed high-voltage supply which periodically raises the center electrode to a positive 100 kv with respect to the grounded ends. An annular permanent magnet is mounted inside the high-voltage terminal to produce an axial magnetic field in the region.

The target at which the neutrons are produced is mounted at the left end of the tube shown in Fig. 7.3. The targets employed in neutron generators of this type are usually occluded-gas targets. These are made by evaporating a thin layer of titanium on a tantalum backing. The titanium-tantalum disk is then heated to a few hundred degrees centigrade in a tritium atmosphere. The titanium absorbs the tritium gas, and at the surface the ratio of tritium to titanium atoms is roughly one to one.

The neutron generator is operated under the following conditions. The glass chamber is first evacuated to 10^{-5} or 10^{-6} torr by the diffusion pump. This is to remove as many nondeuterium atoms and molecules as possible. The diffusion pump is then valved off and deuterium bled into the glass chamber. The deuterium pressure should be adjusted to a pressure of about 15 microns using a palladium adjustable leak. To achieve this equilibrium the forepump should pump out the excess gas. (See Chapter 4 for a more detailed description of vacuum systems.) When the terminal is pulsed, ions are produced because stray electrons in the gas are rapidly accelerated into the high-voltage electrode. The axial magnetic field causes the electrons to spiral, increasing their path length, which in turn causes them to make more ionizing collisions. The ions produced in the central region are repelled from the high-voltage terminal region, and half of them move toward the tritium target. When they reach the target, they have an energy roughly equal to the terminal voltage (100 kv), since the pressure is adjusted so that a mean free path is approximately equal to the distance between the terminal and the target. At this energy, the reaction $H^3(d,n)He^3$ occurs, producing 14-mev neutrons. Since the 100-kv pulses are about one microsecond long, the neutrons are also generated in microsecond pulses. About 10^8 to 10^9 neutrons are produced per pulse. Pulsed neutron generators of this type are particularly useful for neutronics experiments in which the neutron transport properties of materials are investigated. These experiments are described in greater detail in Sec. 7.4, p. 146.

Fission reactors are also important neutron sources. The fission reaction of U^{235} produces, on the average, 2.5 neutrons per fission event. The mean neutron energy is 2 mev. In a nuclear reactor these neutrons are slowed down to thermal energies ($\sim$ 0.025 ev). Large fluxes of thermal neutrons thus exist in the reactor core, usually of the order of 10^{12} to 10^{13} neutrons/(cm²)(sec). These neutrons can be brought out of the reactor and collimated into thermal neutron beams. Reactors are also used to produce large quantities of radioactive isotopes.

Detection of neutrons. Neutron detection is difficult because neutrons are not charged and thus lose little energy in passing through matter. To observe neutrons, nuclear reactions involving the neutron must be employed which produce secondary charged particles. These charged particles are then detected using ordinary methods. In order to do this, suitable reactions must be found. The most useful processes are exoergic reactions in which the charged products leave with high kinetic energies and are thus easy to observe. Among these reactions are

$$B^{10} + n \rightarrow Li^7 + \alpha + 2.3 \text{ mev} \qquad (7.13)$$
$$Li^6 + n \rightarrow H^3 + \alpha + 4.78 \text{ mev} \qquad (7.14)$$

Both processes are exoergic and produce strongly ionizing particles. The $B^{10}(n,\alpha)$ reaction is employed by using BF_3 gas to fill a proportional counter. (The concentration of B^{10} in natural boron is approximately 19 percent, so that BF_3 gas enriched in B^{10} is usually used as the filler gas.) The alpha particles emitted in the (n,α) process ionize the counter gas and produce the usual voltage pulses arising from charged particles. Since the cross section for the $B^{10}(n,\alpha)$ reaction is a rather complex function of neutron energy,[6] it is difficult to compute the efficiency of the counter for the detection of neutrons with differing energies or for the detection (and measurement) of neutron fluxes containing particles with many different kinetic energies (see Fig. 7.4). A common procedure is to surround the counter with a cylinder of paraffin. The paraffin thermalizes the neutrons so that the only cross section of importance is the (n,α) cross section at thermal energies. A BF_3 counter operated in this manner is called a "long" counter.[7] The long counter has the important property that its response or detection efficiency is nearly independent of the neutron energy. Of course, this counter is not sensitive to the energy of the incident neutrons and therefore is not a spectrometer.

Another neutron counter which has come into use more recently depends on the scintillation principle. Lithium iodide crystals are good scintillating materials, so that if a lithium iodide crystal is placed in a neutron flux, the $Li^6(n,\alpha)$ reaction can occur inside the crystal. The charged alpha particles and H^3 ions produced in the reaction cause scintillations in the crystal just as other charged particles cause scintillations, and these are detected by the usual methods (see Chapter 5). Lithium iodide counters have the advantage that they are more efficient than BF_3 counters, since the solid crystals contain more nuclei per unit volume in which (n,α) reactions can occur.

Neither of the counters just described is useful for measuring the energy of the neutrons. The reason is that the energy of the secondary alpha particle is usually much greater than the initial neutron energy.

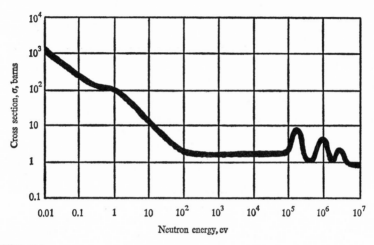

FIGURE 7.4

Energy dependence of $B^{10}(n,\alpha)$ cross section.

The output pulse magnitude observed is therefore not strongly dependent on the energy of the neutron causing the (n,α) reaction. The (n,α) reactions are readily initiated by thermal neutrons, whereas the outgoing alpha particles have energies in the million electron volt region. If the (n,α) reactions are initiated by fast neutrons, the alpha particles produced have greater energies, but these energies are related to the incident neutron energy in a rather complex way. Therefore, except for very special circumstances, counters operating on this principle are not useful as neutron spectrometers.

One of the important problems in neutron physics is to devise methods of measuring neutron energies. The difficulty is, of course, that the neutrons, being uncharged, do not lose energy in passing through matter which can then be turned into a detectable signal. One method of determining the neutron energy is to make the neutron collide elastically with charged particles and then to measure the recoil energy of the charged particles. Counters operating on this principle are called proton recoil counters. If the neutron makes a head-on collision with the proton, all the energy of the neutron is given to the proton. Other than head-on collisions will produce protons of smaller energies, so that the counter is still not a good spectrometer, that is, neutrons with a single energy do not give output signals of a single size. Recoil counters are usually used with the counter biased, so that only the largest pulses observed are counted. A typical pulse-height spectrum and a bias setting are shown in Fig. 7.5. This diagram

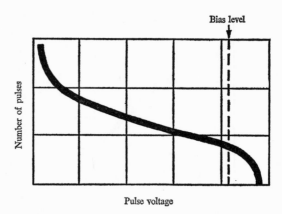

FIGURE 7.5

Proton recoil spectrum produced by monoenergetic neutrons.

shows the recoil spectrum observed when neutrons of a single energy are used.

Recoil counters are of two types, hydrogen-filled proportional counters and plastic scintillation counters. The gas counters are usually quite slow, as are the other gas-filled counters mentioned previously. The plastic scintillators give very short pulses (of the order of 10^{-8} sec compared to 10^{-6} sec for gas counters) and can therefore be readily applied to the most important method of measuring neutron energies, that is, time-of-flight measurement. A neutron with a kinetic energy of one million electron volts has a velocity given by

$$\beta = \frac{v}{c} = \left(\frac{2E}{mc^2}\right)^{1/2} \approx (2 \times 10^{-3})^{1/2} \approx 4.5 \times 10^{-2} \quad (7.15)$$

so that $$v \approx 10^9 \text{ cm/sec} \quad (7.16)$$

In one microsecond, the neutron thus moves 10 meters. Since plastic scintillators can produce pulses as short as 10^{-8} sec, it is possible to measure the energies of neutrons in the million electron volt region to 1 percent using flight paths of the order of one meter. To use time-of-flight methods effectively, pulsed neutron sources are required. These can be produced by using charged particle accelerators. An example of this method of producing pulsed neutrons is the omnitron, as are several other commercially available pulsed neutron generators.

Another method of detecting neutrons which is sometimes used for specialized purposes is the activation method. Neutrons can be used to produce radioactive isotopes, which can then be detected by their characteristic radiations. Gold foils are often used to detect thermal neutron fluxes because gold (Au^{197}) has a reasonably large cross section for activation by thermal neutrons and is readily available in thin foils. The most important reason for employing gold foils is that the unstable isotope Au^{198} emits a β particle and a gamma ray in coincidence. It is thus possible to determine very accurately the absolute activity of the foil by a β-γ coincidence counting technique. From this known activity, the weight of the foil and the time of exposure, the thermal neutron flux it was exposed to can be calculated. Indium (In^{115}) is also useful because it has an excited level at 250 kev, which is easily produced by inelastic scattering of fast neutrons. Indium foils are a good example of the so-called "threshold" detectors, for they cannot be excited to the 250-kev isomeric level by neutrons with a kinetic energy less than 250 kev. In^{115} can also capture neutrons to produce the active isotope In^{116}. There is no threshold for this process, and this effect must be taken into account. Fortunately, both the energy and the half-life of the 250-kev isomeric level of In^{115} are sufficiently characteristic of this isotope that it is feasible to use indium foils as threshold detectors.

7.4 EXPERIMENTS

Neutron absorption measurements. The interaction of neutrons with nuclei is usually very complicated. The neutron absorption cross sections are rapidly varying functions of the kinetic energy of the incident neutron. In order to obtain interpretable results, the first experiment deals with measuring interaction cross sections of thermal neutrons. These measurements determine the average interaction cross section for neutrons in the thermal energy region. This cross section will be a property of the material being bombarded.

Thermal neutrons, which are neutrons in thermal equilibrium with their surroundings, can be produced by passing neutrons through materials containing a high concentration of light nuclei. A high-energy neutron making a collision with a light nucleus will lose a good fraction of its initial kinetic energy to the recoil nucleus of the target, as shown in Fig. 7.6. Quantitatively, the average energy of the neutron after the collision with a target nucleus of mass number A is given by

$$E = E_0 \frac{A}{A + 1} \qquad (7.17)$$

where E_0 is the energy before the collision. It is obvious from Eq. (7.17) why light nuclei (small A) are most effective in slowing down or moderating high-energy neutrons. In the present experiment, a polyethylene block is used as a neutron moderator. This material is rich in hydrogen ($A = 1$), and thus the neutron loses roughly one-half of its

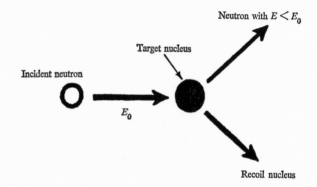

FIGURE 7.6

Kinematics of a neutron scattered elastically from a target nucleus.

initial energy in each collision. In this moderator, the neutrons are thermalized after an average of about 20 collisions.

The neutron absorption experiments are performed using the arrangement shown in Fig. 7.7. The neutron source (alpha particle-beryllium type) is placed in the center of a paraffin or water drum with removable beam port plugs. The outside of the drum is lined with cadmium. The hydrogen serves to thermalize the neutrons while the cadmium, which has a large thermal neutron capture cross section, prevents any neutrons from escaping through the sides of the tank. The only neutrons leaving are those from the beam port. If the plug is in, the neutrons will be collimated and have thermal energy. If the plugs on both sides are removed, the beam will be neutrons of the source energy.

The counting rate at the BF_3 counter should be determined for a number of different absorbing materials. Large differences should be observed for various materials, for thermal neutron interaction cross sections are strongly dependent on the particular nucleus being studied. The total interaction cross section, σ_t, is defined as follows in terms of the measured attenuation:

$$\frac{I}{I_0} = e^{-n\sigma_t x} \tag{7.18}$$

where n is the number of atoms per cubic centimeter in the sample and

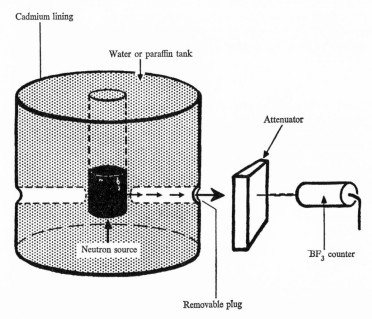

Cadmium lining

Water or paraffin tank

Attenuator

Neutron source

BF_3 counter

Removable plug

FIGURE 7.7

Experimental geometry for obtaining beams of fast and slow neutrons for cross-section measurements.

x is the thickness of the sample. Thus

$$\sigma_t = \frac{1}{nx} \ln \frac{I_0}{I} \tag{7.19}$$

where I_0 is the counting rate with no material and I is the counting rate with a material of thickness x.

The absorption experiments outlined here should be performed using a number of different materials. From these, a list of the cross sections should be compiled The attenuation experiments should then be repeated without the moderator in place (i.e., the plug removed) and a similar cross section list should be compiled for the same materials. The most important result is that the thermal cross sections are almost always considerably larger than the so-called "fast" neutron cross sections. (The neutrons emitted by the source have energies of the order of a few million electron volts.) This is not hard to understand if it is assumed that the probability of an interaction with the nucleus depends directly on the time which the neutron spends in the vicinity of the nucleus

$$\sigma \sim t \sim \frac{2r_0}{v} \tag{7.20}$$

where r_0 is the nuclear radius and v is the velocity of the neutron. Therefore

$$\sigma \sim \frac{1}{\sqrt{E_n}} \tag{7.21}$$

Calculations should be made to verify the behavior of the cross section predicted by Eq. (7.21). Assume that the average energy of the neutrons emitted by the source is about one mev and the thermal energy is 0.02 ev.

Production of radioactive isotopes. One of the more important discoveries in modern physics is the production of isotopes (both radioactive and stable) by the capture of neutrons. In this experiment, the activation of a number of materials will be demonstrated.

The experimental arrangement is very simple. The neutron source is placed inside the paraffin container used in the last experiment. Activation cross sections also obey the Eq. (7.21) and are thus larger for small neutron energies. The sample foils to be activated are placed toward the outside of the beam plug as shown in Fig. 7.8. After neutron irradiation, the foils are removed from the neutron flux and the induced activity is counted using scintillation techniques.

As an example, the case of gold foils will be discussed in some detail to illustrate the principles. Gold is a monoisotopic element consisting of nuclei with $Z = 79$ and $A = 197$. When a neutron is captured, an unstable isotope of gold is produced according to the reaction

$$\mathrm{Au}^{197} + n \to \mathrm{Au}^{198} + \text{gamma rays} \tag{7.22}$$

The gamma rays serve to carry off the binding energy of the extra neutron. Au^{198} is unstable, since it has too many neutrons. One of these changes into a proton by emitting an electron and a neutrino. This process is called beta decay (see Chapter 5). The nucleus remaining after the decay process has one more proton ($Z = 80$) than gold and

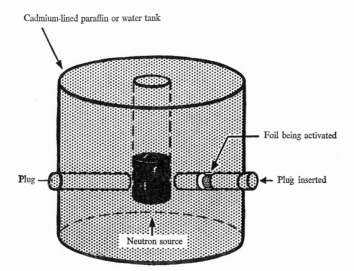

Cadmium-lined paraffin or water tank

Foil being activated

Plug

Plug inserted

Neutron source

FIGURE 7.8

Neutron-moderating assembly for producing radioisotopes.

is thus an isotope of mercury, Hg^{198} The decay process occurs as

$$Au^{198} \rightarrow Hg^{198} + \beta^- + \text{neutrino} + \text{gamma rays} \qquad (7.23)$$

The presence of the unstable isotope Au^{198} can be detected by looking for the gamma rays associated with the decay process. In this particular case, a strong gamma ray with a quantum energy of about 410 kev is emitted in the process. The decay scheme is shown in Fig. 7.9. The origin of the gamma ray is clear from the picture. The beta-decay

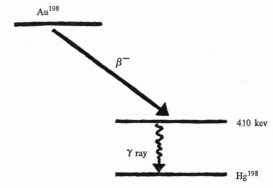

Au^{198}

β^-

410 kev

γ ray

Hg^{198}

FIGURE 7.9

Decay scheme of Au^{198}.

process results in an excited level of the product nucleus, which immediately decays to its ground state by the emission of a gamma ray. The energy of the radiations and the half-life (64.8 hr) of the process are used to determine which isotope has been produced.

The characteristic feature of a radioactive decay process is that a constant fraction of the material decays in every time interval dt. The mathematical statement is

$$\frac{dN}{N} = -\lambda \, dt \tag{7.24}$$

where λ is the "decay" constant. Integrating Eq. (7.24) gives the fraction of active atoms which remain after a time t:

$$\frac{N}{N_0} = e^{-\lambda t} \tag{7.25}$$

where N_0 is the number of radioactive atoms originally in the sample and N is the number present at time t. The half-life of the isotope is defined as the time $t_{\frac{1}{2}}$ at which N/N_0 is equal to one-half. Thus

$$t_{\frac{1}{2}} = \frac{\ln 2}{\lambda} \cong \frac{0.693}{\lambda} \tag{7.26}$$

Another quantity which is often used is the mean life, which is defined as the time at which N/N_0 equals $1/e$. Therefore

$$\tau = \frac{1}{\lambda} \tag{7.27}$$

Neutron capture is by far the most useful process for making radioactive isotopes. The primary reason is that neutrons are uncharged and consequently are not repelled by the nuclei which are being bombarded. Thermal neutrons can thus be used to produce isotopes very effectively because the cross sections generally tend to increase with decreasing energy according to Eq. (7.21). It is also relatively easy to produce large fluxes of low-energy neutrons in nuclear fission reactors. These are, at present, the principal source of the radioactive isotopes used for industrial and scientific purposes.

Moderating fast neutrons. The slowing-down process for neutrons has been described in the section on thermal neutron cross sections. The purpose of the present experiment is to investigate the slowing-down mechanism in greater detail and to demonstrate that the recoil mechanism proposed in Fig. 7.6 is correct. The method used to prove this is indirect, for no single scattering event is observed. In this experiment the average time $\bar{\tau}$ necessary for a 14-mev neutron to slow down to thermal energies in a hydrogenous material is measured. This average time is then computed, using the recoil model, and compared with the experimental results.

In order to measure time intervals, some signal must be obtained which identifies the production of a fast neutron. This is not possible

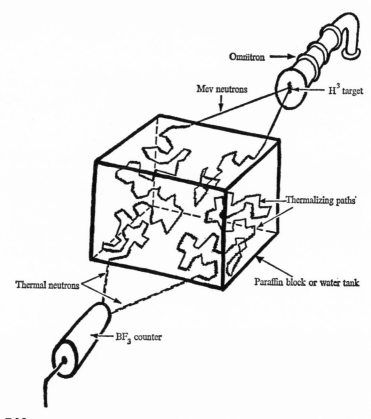

FIGURE 7.10

Thermalization paths of neutrons produced by the Omnitron.

using the usual (α,n) neutron sources, for it is impossible to predict precisely when a given radioactive nucleus will decay. To obtain a signal at the birth of a neutron a pulsed accelerator is used. The Omnitron described in Sec. 7.3, p. 136 is employed for these experiments. The high-voltage pulse of the Omnitron serves as the trigger signal. The experimental arrangement is shown in Fig. 7.10. The Omnitron tube is placed next to a thick block of paraffin or polyethylene. A BF_3 thermal neutron detector is located behind the block.

The output of the BF₃ counter is displayed on an oscilloscope trace together with the 100-kv pulse of the source. Since there will be a significant time delay between the production of the burst and the detection of the neutron, the oscilloscope trace observed will look something like the diagram shown in Fig. 7.11. The time interval between the omnitron burst and the first neutron pulse is usually somewhere between 10 and 30 μsec and is very much longer than the time necessary for the fast, 14-mev neutron to reach the BF₃ tube. This time interval is the sum of the time required to slow down and

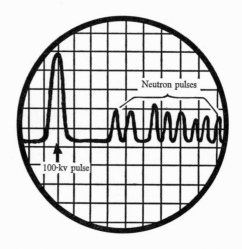

FIGURE 7.11

Oscilloscope trace illustrating the slowing-down time of neutrons produced by an Omnitron pulse.

the time to diffuse to the detector after slowing down. A thermal neutron has a velocity of approximately 10^5 cm/sec and thus moves about 1 cm/μsec. Therefore, if the BF₃ counter is placed approximately 10 cm away from the moderator, the time interval measured is reasonable if the neutrons have indeed been thermalized by the moderator. The large spread in the arrival time of the neutrons at the BF₃ counter is due to the different slowing-down and diffusion time of each neutron in the moderator.

REFERENCES

1. Rutherford, E., and F. Soddy: *Phil Mag.*, S. 6, **5**, 453, 1903; **4**, 582, 1902.
2. Curie, I., and F. Joliot: *Compt. Rend.*, **194**, 273, 1932.

3. Chadwick, J.: *Proc. Roy. Soc. (London)*, **136A**, 692, 1932.
4. Feld, B. T.: The Neutron, Part VII of "Experimental Nuclear Physics," vol. II, edited by E. Segré, John Wiley & Sons, Inc., New York, 1953.
5. Gow, J. D., and L. Ruby: *Rev. Sci. Instr.*, **30**, 315, 1959.
6. Hughes, D. J., and R. B. Schwartz: "Neutron Cross Sections," 2d ed., U.S. Government Printing Office, Washington 25, D.C., 1958.
7. Hanson, A. O., and J. L. McKibben: *Phys. Rev.*, **72**, 673, 1947.

GENERAL BIBLIOGRAPHY

1. Valente, F. A.: "A Manual of Experiments in Reactor Physics," The Macmillan Company, New York, 1963.
2. Fowler, J. L., and J. B. Marion: "Fast Neutron Physics," Parts I and II, Interscience Publishers, Inc., New York, 1960.
3. Hughes, D. J.: "Pile Neutron Research," Addison-Wesley Publishing Company, Inc., Reading, Mass., 1953.
4. Meghreblian, R. V., and D. K. Holmes: "Reactor Analysis," McGraw-Hill Book Company, New York, 1960.
5. Weinberg, A. M., and E. P. Wigner: "The Physical Theory of Neutron Chain Reactors," The University of Chicago Press, Chicago, 1958.
6. Glasstone, S., and M. C. Edlund: "The Elements of Nuclear Reactor Theory," D. Van Nostrand Company, Inc., Princeton, N.J., 1952.

Chapter 8

SOLID–STATE ELECTRONICS

8.1 INTRODUCTION

Perhaps one of the most exciting developments to result from the quantitative understanding of the structure of solids is the application of especially tailored materials for use as nonlinear electrical circuit elements. It has been possible, with the so-called solid-state electronic devices, to reduce the physical size (linear dimensions) of various important circuit elements by three or four orders of magnitude over the equivalent vacuum tube units. This enormous reduction in volume has resulted in the construction of computers with a capacity far beyond that which could be achieved with conventional tube-type circuitry. In addition, none of the very complex and compact electronic units used in the space vehicles flown since 1957 could have been constructed without solid-state components.

The electrical properties of various materials have been studied qualitatively for a long time. The ancient Greeks knew that certain substances, such as amber, could retain an electrical charge for an extended period of time. (The word electricity and its derivatives come

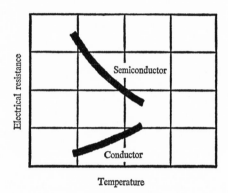

FIGURE 8.1

Temperature dependence of the electrical resistance of semiconductors and conductors.

from *electron*, the Greek word for amber.) It was also known that metals would not retain charges when touching the ground. The general electrical properties of materials now classed as insulators and conductors were well known in the early nineteenth century, even though no coherent theory of electricity existed. In addition to conductors and insulators, there is another class of materials with somewhat more complicated electrical properties. These substances are called semiconductors. Some of the first quantitative experiments with semiconductors were performed by Michael Faraday. He discovered that the electrical resistance of these materials decreased with increasing temperature, which is contrary to the behavior of conductors, whose resistance generally increases as a function of temperature[1] (see Fig. 8.1). Semiconductors were also found to have electrical resistances much larger than conductors but smaller than insulators, hence the name semiconductor. However, the temperature dependence of the resistance was usually taken as the defining criterion for semiconducting materials.

Several other interesting properties of semiconductors were discovered in the latter part of the nineteenth century. For example, it was shown that the junction between a semiconductor and a metal behaved like a rectifier, that is, the resistance of the junction was different for currents flowing through the junction in opposite directions. Perhaps the most familiar early application of the rectifying property of such a junction is the crystal radio detector. The "cat's whisker" of such a detector consists of a fine metal wire contacting a semiconducting material such as silicon or lead sulfide. The junction thus formed acted as a rectifier which filtered out the radio carrier wave but preserved the amplitude modulation of the signal.

Another development of semiconductors which began in the early 1930's was the use of copper oxide and, later, selenium cells for low-power a-c voltage rectification. None of these effects was well understood theoretically until after World War II. The principles of the theory of solids were developed in the 1930's, but the detailed applications have been worked out in the past fifteen years. As a result of this understanding, it has been possible to build circuit elements with very precisely controlled properties. Germanium diodes were among the first practical circuit elements to be sold commercially. Transistors, which were developed by Brattain, Bardeen, and Shockley[2] at the Bell Laboratories in the years between 1949 and 1955, are now commonly used in many different circuits. They have essentially replaced vacuum tubes in most electronic control circuits. Finally, there are even more recent advances, such as the so-called "tunnel" diode and the microminiature circuits. Both are excellent examples of what can be achieved with solid-state devices in electronics.

8.2 FREE ELECTRONS IN METALS

The fact that most metals readily conduct electricity means that electrons must be able to move in a relatively unhindered way inside a metal. Since all the metallic elements have lightly bound valence electrons, it was assumed that these electrons, called conduction electrons, could move more or less freely inside the material. The residual metallic ions thus form the lattice in which this electron gas, as it is called, exists. The quantitative behavior of metals based on this idea was worked out by Arnold Sommerfeld[3] and his collaborators. Two important features of the "electron gas" govern its properties and make it profoundly different from the ordinary gases usually encountered in thermodynamics. The first is that the gas is very dense. The density of "free" electrons in a metal is usually something of the order of 10^{22} to 10^{23}/cc, which would correspond to a "pressure" of somewhere between 10^3 and 10^4 atm. The second point is that electrons obey the exclusion principle. Hence classical Maxwell-Boltzmann statistics are not applicable, and Fermi-Dirac statistics must be employed to describe the situation.

With these ideas in mind, a number of statements can be made about the energy distribution of the electrons in the metal. The exclusion principle limits the population of each available energy level to two

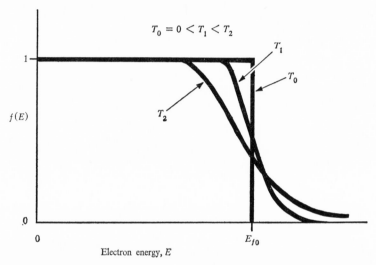

FIGURE 8.2

Fermi electron distribution function.

electrons having opposite spin orientations. Therefore, at very low temperatures (i.e., absolute zero), the distribution of electrons in the available energy levels is as shown in Fig. 8.2. The ordinate shows the probability that an energy state E is occupied by an electron, and the abscissa is the energy of the electron. In the lowest energy state of the metal, which is another way of saying at absolute zero temperature, all the energy levels are filled up to a certain maximum energy, E_{f0}. Above this energy, all the states are empty. This energy distribution contrasts sharply with the Maxwell-Boltzmann distribution function for which the exclusion principle does not apply. In the Maxwell-Boltzmann case, at $T = 0$, all the particles are in the lowest energy state, $E = 0$, and all other levels are empty.

At temperatures greater than zero, electrons close to E_{f0} (within a few kT) acquire enough energy to occupy levels above E_{f0}. This results in a "rounding off" of the absolute zero distribution function. It is important to note that only those electrons within a few kT of E_{f0} can move to higher energy levels because, if they acquire energy of the order of kT, they will move to an unoccupied energy level. On the other hand, those electrons occupying energy levels much lower than E_{f0} would be raised to other occupied levels, which means they cannot make the transition, hence the resulting rounding off of the distribution function near E_{f0} as the temperature increases.

The Fermi-Dirac distribution function, shown qualitatively in Fig. 8.2, is given analytically (see Appendix II) by

$$f(E) = \frac{1}{e^{(E-E_f)/kT} + 1} \tag{8.1}$$

where $f(E)$ is the probability that the energy level E is occupied and E_f is a quantity called the Fermi energy. At absolute zero E_f is just E_{f0}, but as the temperature increases, E_f decreases slightly.

As will be shown below, E_{f0} is determined only by the number of electrons in the metal. For temperatures greater than zero, the Fermi energy is determined from the condition:

$$N = \int_0^\infty f(E)n(E) \, dE \tag{8.2}$$

where N is the total number of electrons in the metal and $n(E) \, dE$ is the number of available energy states between E and $E + dE$. However, the Fermi energy calculated from Eq. (8.2) is nearly equal to E_{f0}, so that a good approximation is

$$E_f \cong E_{f0} \tag{8.3}$$

It is also interesting to note that when $E_f \ll kT$ and when $E \gg E_f$, the Fermi distribution of Eq. (8.1) turns into the Boltzmann distribution:

$$f(E) \approx e^{-E/kT} \tag{8.4}$$

This happens because the exclusion principle is not a strong limiting factor if the average particle energy is high enough so that the number of states available is much larger than the number of particles.

It is now of interest to determine whether the conditions leading to Eq. (8.4) are fulfilled in the case of an electron gas in a metal or whether it is necessary to use the more precise form of the distribution function given in Eq. (8.1). If it can be shown that, at room temperature, for example, the Fermi energy is much larger than kT, the energy distribution of the electrons in the metal will closely approximate the distribution function shown in Fig. 8.2. The Fermi energy E_f must therefore be determined from Eq. (8.2) in terms of the number of electrons in the metal.

Assume that the electrons are confined to move in a cube of the metal whose edges have length L. Assume also that the electrons move in the metal as if they were free. The electron wave functions are then plane waves obeying appropriate boundary conditions at the sides of the cube. These boundary conditions are that the wave functions vanish at the boundary of the metal (see Fig. 8.3). The energy levels

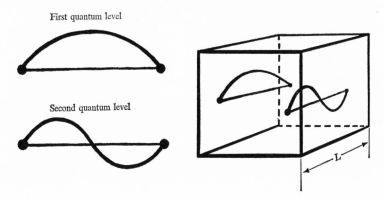

FIGURE 8.3

Possible electron wave functions in a cube of side L.

are thus the same as those of the "particle-in-a-box" problem

$$E = \frac{\hbar^2}{2m} \frac{\pi^2}{L^2} (n_x{}^2 + n_y{}^2 + n_z{}^2) \qquad (8.5)$$

where the quantum numbers n_x, n_y, and n_z describe the state of the electron. The number of states available to the electrons in the energy range from E to $E + dE$ can now be determined. To determine the number, a new coordinate space in which the quantum numbers n_x, n_y, and n_z are the coordinates is employed. The radial position in this space is given by R, where R^2 is defined as

$$R^2 = n_x{}^2 + n_y{}^2 + n_z{}^2 = \frac{2mL^2}{\hbar^2\pi^2} E \qquad (8.6)$$

The energy E then corresponds to a shell of radius R in this space. The volume of a spherical shell of radius R and thickness dR corresponds to the number of different sets of integers n_x, n_y, and n_z between R and $R + dR$. This quantity is $\frac{1}{8} \times 4\pi R^2\, dR$, where the factor $\frac{1}{8}$ comes from the fact that n_x, n_y, and n_z are all positive integers (i.e., the octant of the sphere corresponding to positive n's). Now, since each set of integers corresponds to a possible electron state, the number of states available between E and $E + dE$ is

$$n(E)\ dE = 2 \times \tfrac{1}{8} 4\pi R^2\ dR \tag{8.7}$$

where the factor of 2 in Eq. (8.7) accounts for the fact that there are two electron spin states possible in each volume element. Thus, in terms of the energy E, the number of states between E and $E + dE$ is

$$n(E)\ dE = \frac{2\pi L^3 (2m)^{3/2}}{h^3} E^{1/2}\ dE \tag{8.8}$$

If the metal is at zero temperature (i.e., if all levels are full up to the Fermi energy), then the total number of electrons in the sample is

$$N = \int_0^{E_{f0}} n(E)\ dE = \frac{2\pi L^3 (2m)^{3/2}}{h^3} \int_0^{E_{f0}} E^{1/2}\ dE$$

or

$$N = \frac{2\pi L^3 (2m)^{3/2}}{h^3} 2 E_{f0}^{3/2} \tag{8.9}$$

Thus the Fermi energy expressed in terms of the number of electrons in the metal cube is

$$E_{f0} = \frac{h^2}{2m} \left(\frac{3N}{8\pi L^3} \right)^{2/3} = \frac{h^2}{2m} \left(\frac{3n}{8\pi} \right)^{2/3} \tag{8.10}$$

where n is the number of electrons per unit volume.

In a metal, the density of electrons is approximately $10^{23}/\mathrm{cc}$. Hence the zero temperature Fermi energy in a metal is approximately

$$E_{f0} \simeq 6\ \mathrm{ev} \approx 70{,}000°\mathrm{K} \tag{8.11}$$

This is very much higher than room temperature; consequently, the condition for the distribution function shown in Fig. 8.1 is essentially fulfilled. A Fermi gas in which very nearly all electron states below the Fermi energy are filled is called a "degenerate" Fermi gas. The general conclusion therefore is that the electrons in a metal behave as a degenerate Fermi gas and therefore the Fermi energy defines the highest energy of the free electrons inside the metal.

8.3 MOTION OF ELECTRONS IN SOLIDS

The Fermi gas approximation developed in the previous section is the simplest model which can be constructed for a metal. It is sufficient to explain the specific heat of a metal in a reasonably quantitative manner. The paramagnetic susceptibility of the conduction electrons can also be computed qualitatively using the Fermi gas model. Finally, the Fermi gas model can also be used to understand thermionic and field emission (see Chapter 10). However, a number of very important properties of metals cannot be explained on the basis of free electron motion alone. The behavior of the electrical resistance as a function of temperature cannot be explained unless the interaction between the electrons and the crystal lattice is taken into account. A more important point is that the motion of electrons in insulators and semiconductors cannot be understood at all in terms of a free electron model. As a result, it is necessary to look at the motion of electrons in a solid in somewhat greater detail.

An electron moving in a metal experiences forces which will differ depending on whether the electron is near a lattice atom or whether it is between two lattice atoms. This problem is usually treated by assuming that the electron moves in a periodic potential.[4] Then the appropriate Schrödinger equation for such a potential function is solved. This procedure is quite complicated, and it will not be pursued here. Instead, a simpler argument will be used to outline the ideas involved. The wavelength of an electron according to the de Broglie relation is

$$\lambda = \frac{h}{p}$$

or
$$p = \hbar k \qquad (8.12)$$

In this equation p is the momentum of the electron and k is the wave number, which is equal to $2\pi/\lambda$. The energy of the electron is

$$E = \frac{p^2}{2m} = \frac{\hbar^2 k^2}{2m} \qquad (8.13)$$

which says that the energy is a quadratic function of the wave number as long as the electron moves freely (see Fig. 8.4). When the electron moves in a lattice, the situation is complicated by the fact that the electron waves can interfere destructively under certain circumstances, thus preventing electrons of certain wave numbers (and therefore of certain energies) from moving inside the solid. This situation is quite similar to the reflection of X rays by crystals, where the Bragg condition defines the directions in which electromagnetic radiations can and cannot travel (see Chapter 6). To see show this process works, consider the one-dimensional lattice shown in Fig. 8.5. For an electron incident from the left, the Bragg condition is

$$n\lambda = a \qquad (8.14)$$

If the electron wavelength satisfies Eq. (8.14), the electron wave is reflected and cannot travel through the lattice. Since the wave number

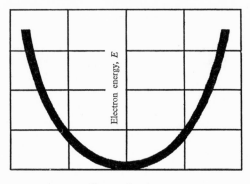

FIGURE 8.4

Electron energy versus electron wave number according to Eq. (8.4).

is defined as $k = 2\pi/\lambda$, there are no allowable electron energy levels in the lattice corresponding to the wave numbers

$$k = n\frac{2\pi}{a} \tag{8.15}$$

The energy levels available to electrons have discontinuities at these wave numbers. These discontinuities are illustrated in Fig. 8.6. It can be seen that they cause the existence of gaps in the energy levels where no electrons can exist. These gaps are usually called forbidden energy regions, since electrons with these energies cannot move in the crystal.

The existence of allowed and forbidden energy regions is the major consequence of the electron motion in the periodic lattice. This fact, together with the existence of a Fermi distribution of the electrons and a well-defined Fermi energy, can be used to find a qualitative explanation of the energy levels of a solid material.

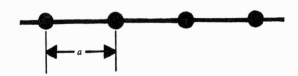

FIGURE 8.5

One-dimensional lattice capable of Bragg reflection of an electron wave.

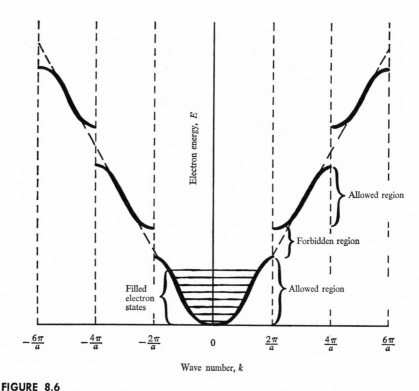

FIGURE 8.6

Forbidden and allowed electron energy levels as a result of Bragg reflection of electron waves.

8.4 METALS, SEMICONDUCTORS, AND INSULATORS

The energy band structures of the various types of solids are shown in Fig. 8.7. In both an insulator and a semiconductor, the valence band is filled with electrons while the next allowed (conduction) band is empty. In an insulator, the forbidden gap is quite wide, between 5 and 7 ev, whereas in a semiconductor the energy gap of the forbidden region is approximately one-tenth as large, about 0.5 ev. In a metal, the Fermi level of the electrons reaches into the first conduction band. This means that there are electrons available in the conduction band which are free to move readily and thus conduct electricity.

The behavior of insulators and semiconductors can now be qualitatively explained. An insulator cannot conduct electricity, for there are no electrons in the allowed regions. If very large electric fields are applied, however, then some of the electrons from the valence band

Metals, semiconductors, and insulators **159**

may be pulled out. In this situation the insulator is said to break down. In the case of a semiconductor it is relatively easier to pull electrons from the valence band into the empty allowed region. The substance thus conducts no electricity if the applied voltage is less than the critical value necessary to remove electrons from the valence band into the conduction region. Above this critical voltage, electrons are forced into the allowed region and the material thus conducts electricity. It is for this reason that "intrinsic" semiconductor materials can be employed as diodes. The decrease in resistance as a function of temperature for semiconductors also follows from the band model shown in Fig. 8.7. Since the energy gap is narrow, electrons may be

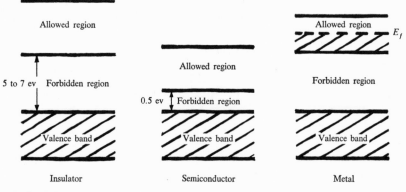

FIGURE 8.7

Filled electron levels and widths of forbidden gaps in insulators, semiconductors, and metals.

thermally excited into the conduction band. Thus the higher the temperature, the greater the number of electrons in the conduction band and the lower the resistance.

8.5 EFFECTS OF IMPURITIES IN SEMICONDUCTORS

The semiconductors described in the previous section are called "intrinsic" semiconductors because the properties of the materials are determined only by their own energy levels. Another interesting class of materials can be created by introducing impurities in a controlled manner into the lattice of a semiconductor. The major effect of an impurity in a regular semiconductor crystal lattice is that it introduces a low density of allowable energy levels into the normally forbidden region.

Two major classes of impurities can affect the properties of certain semiconductors—those which create filled electron levels at energies just below the conduction band and those which create unfilled levels at energies just above the valence band. The former are called donor levels, for these can supply electrons to the allowed band, where they are then free to move. The latter are the acceptor levels because they can trap electrons from the valence band, creating "holes" or vacancies in the valence band which are also relatively free to move. The situation is illustrated in Fig. 8.8. The material with the donor levels is called an n-type material and that with the acceptor levels is called a p-type material.

Semiconductors are usually made from single crystals of materials which lie between two closed shells in the periodic table, the Group IV

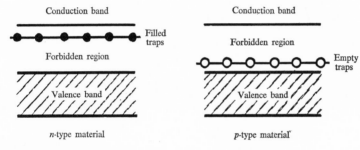

FIGURE 8.8

The two types of impurity semiconductors: n-type with donors near the conduction band and p-type with acceptors near the valence band.

elements for example. The most commonly used semiconductor materials for the manufacture of transistors are silicon and germanium. Materials which produce n-type impurities are the alkali metals, such as lithium, and other elements which have one to three electrons beyond a closed shell. The p-type materials are made by introducing impurities with one to three electrons short of a closed shell, such as phosphorus.

Several other important properties of the n-type and p-type materials are apparent from Fig. 8.8. The electrons in the n-type material form an effective Fermi energy level very close to the conduction band. Electrons are easily moved into the conduction band, where they are free to move around and conduct electric currents. These impurity semiconductors then behave the same as normal metals in that they have free electrons in the conduction band. The charge carriers in the material are thus negative.

The effective Fermi level in the p-type material is slightly above the top of the valence band but short of the acceptor levels. Thus some electrons from the valence band can be excited into the acceptor levels, leaving a hole in the valence band. The electron (negative charge) is trapped in the forbidden band, but the hole can move in the valence band and acts as a positive charge carrier (i.e., a hole in a "sea" of electrons). Both n-type and p-type materials can therefore conduct electricity, although their resistance is higher than the resistance of a metal. The n-type material carries current with negative charge carriers, and the p-type material has what appear to be positive charge carriers. This has been confirmed by measurements of the Hall effect in p-type and n-type materials. The n-type semiconductors have a Hall coefficient with the same sign as a metal, whereas p-type materials have a Hall coefficient of the opposite sign.

The term "effective Fermi level" needs further definition. It is used here to denote the highest energy level in the material filled with electrons at absolute zero temperature. The Fermi distribution function $f(E)$, defined in Eq. (8.1), may still be used to determine the probability that an electron has a certain energy E. However, this function must now be modified to account for the circumstance that the spectrum of energy levels available to the electrons is determined by the structure of the solid and the nature of the impurity atoms. For example, even though $f(E)$ might be quite large for energies corresponding to the forbidden band, no electrons can exist in that energy region. The electrons can only occupy available levels, and the Fermi function $f(E)$ may then be used to determine the probability that these levels are actually occupied.

8.6 PROPERTIES OF p-n JUNCTIONS, DIODES, AND TRANSISTORS

To make useful electronic elements, it is necessary to combine p- and n-type materials in one of a number of different ways. To understand their behavior in detail, the first step is to describe what happens when a p-type and an n-type material are placed in contact with each other. Such a boundary layer is called a p-n junction. Figure 8.9 shows the energy level diagram of the materials before and after the junction is made. When the materials are placed in contact with each other, the electrons from the donor levels move to the acceptor levels, thus "equalizing" the energy level of the impurity states. The impurity levels form an effective Fermi level which is the same in both p- and n-types of semiconductors. All electrons are below the Fermi level, and, to a first approximation, no electrons exist above the Fermi level. The left side of the junction has a layer of excess positive charge and the right side has an excess negative charge. This space charge creates a potential across the junction which just compensates for the original difference in the Fermi levels of the two materials.

The p-n junction shown in Fig. 8.9 may be employed as a rectifying element under certain circumstances. The magnitude of the potential step V across the junction may be varied by external biasing. For example, if the left side of the junction (n-type material) is biased negative $(-V_b)$ with respect to the right side, more electrons will be available on the left side, raising the effective Fermi level. The potential step, $V - V_b$, will thus be decreased. Conversely, if the left side is biased positive $(+V_b)$, the potential step, $V + V_b$, will increase. (The

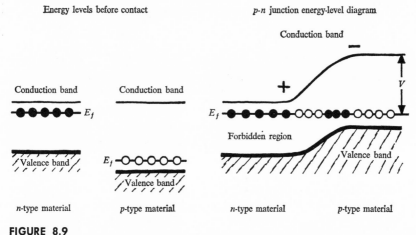

FIGURE 8.9

Fermi levels of n- and p-type semiconductors before and after contact.

negative biasing of the left side is called "forward bias" and the positive biasing is called "reverse bias" for reasons which will soon be obvious.) The energy diagrams are shown in Fig. 8.10. The ease with which electrons (or holes) can pass over the potential step depends on its magnitude. Electrons exist in the conduction band (and holes exist in the valence band) because of thermal excitation. To a first approximation, the conduction electrons (and also the holes) are distributed in energy according to a Boltzmann distribution in their respective bands. This happens because the number of states available is much larger than the number of electrons. It can be shown by pursuing this argument in detail that the observed current across the junction as a function of bias voltage, V_b, is

$$I = I_s(e^{-eV_b/kT} - 1) \qquad (8.16)$$

Properties of p-n junctions, diodes, and transistors **163**

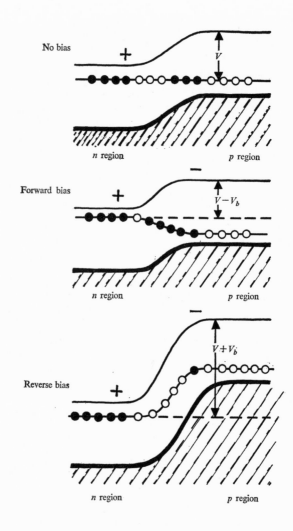

FIGURE 8.10

Effect of an external bias voltage on the Fermi levels across an n-p semiconductor junction.

For forward biasing $(-V_b)$, the exponent is positive and increases rapidly as the magnitude of V_b is increased. If no bias voltage is applied, the current is zero. In the case of reverse biasing, the current flows in the opposite direction (I is negative) and approaches a small saturation value I_s. Finally, as the reverse biasing voltage is increased, the junction breaks down. The current-voltage characteristic of the junction is shown in Fig. 8.11. This characteristic is quite similar to

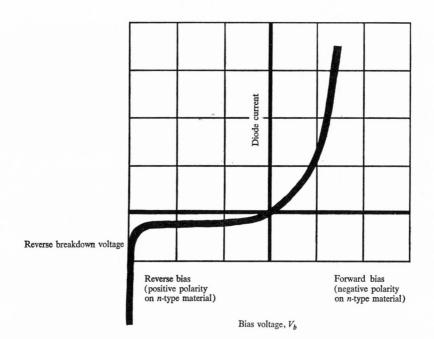

FIGURE 8.11

The i-v characteristic of an n-p semiconductor junction diode.

the usual diode current-voltage curve, since the junction behaves approximately as an insulator for reverse bias voltages and as a conductor for forward bias voltages.

In a circuit diagram, junction diodes are denoted by the symbol shown in Fig. 8.12. The arrow indicates the cathode (or the n-type material) and the line represents the plate.

Transistors are a further development of the p-n junction described in the previous paragraphs. Transistors[5] are electronic elements which consist of two successive junctions of the type shown in Fig. 8.9. For example, suppose that a third n-type material is now placed next to the p-type semiconductor. The energy level scheme of such an n-p-n

FIGURE 8.12

Schematic representation of a diode.

Properties of p-n junctions, diodes, and transistors **165**

junction is shown in the left panel of Fig. 8.13. The effective Fermi level is also shown in the drawing. Electrons may be easily moved in the n-type material by applying a small negative potential to the left side of the transistor. When the electrons approach the barrier as shown, they are stopped because the energy of the electrons corresponds to motion in the forbidden region of the p-type material. It is of some interest to describe what happens when the junctions are biased with respect to each other. The result is shown in the right panel of Fig. 8.13. The n-type material on the right side of the junction is

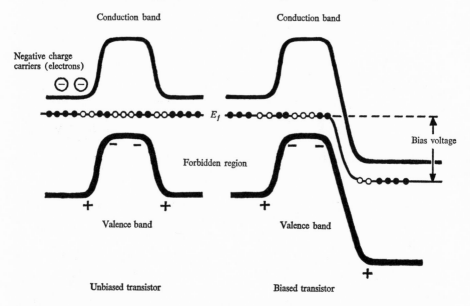

FIGURE 8.13

An n-p-n transistor junction showing effect of emitter-collector bias voltage.

biased positively with respect to the p-type material. In this case then, electrons will be drawn to the positive terminal, lowering the Fermi level on that side of the junction. The bias also lowers the top of the forbidden region, so that, if electrons could penetrate the p-type material from the left side, they would then easily move toward the positive terminal. The p-type material can also be biased with respect to the n-type material on the left side. If the p-type material is biased positively with respect to the n-type material on the left, electrons will be drawn out of the p-type material, lowering its Fermi level and making the p-type material energy levels more nearly equal to the energy levels of the n-type material on the left side. If the positive bias is sufficiently large, then electrons can pass from the left, n-type material, through the p-type material and on into the right, n-type material. The two-junction system, or transistor as it is called, therefore behaves precisely like a triode vacuum tube. If the center junction (or base) is biased positively with respect to the left n-type material (or emitter), electrons can pass through to the right side (or collector). The base, emitter, and collector correspond to the grid, cathode, and plate of a vacuum tube. As in the case of the vacuum tube, the collector (plate) is positive with respect to the emitter (cathode). Also, if the base

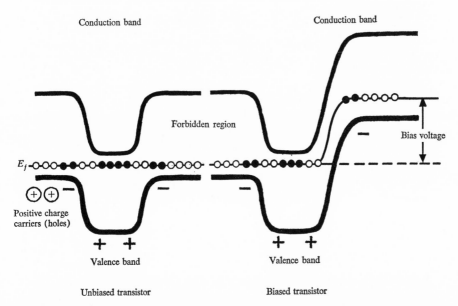

FIGURE 8.14

A p-n-p transistor junction showing effect of emitter-collector bias voltage.

(grid) is made positive, the transistor (tube) conducts current. A transistor of the type shown in Fig. 8.13 is called an n-p-n transistor.

Figure 8.14 shows an important variation of the n-p-n transistor discussed in the previous paragraph. This transistor is called the p-n-p junction. In this case the holes moving in the p-type material conduct the current. Here the bias voltages necessary to make the transistor work are precisely the opposite to those used in the case of the n-p-n transistor. The collector is biased negative with respect to the emitter, and a negative base bias causes the transistor to conduct. Thus all the voltages in a given circuit can be reversed in polarity without affecting the performance of the circuit if all the n-p-n transistors are changed

Properties of p-n junctions, diodes, and transistors **167**

to *p-n-p* transistors. This circumstance is one of the important advantages of transistor circuitry in contrast to vacuum tube electronics, since no equivalent *p-n-p* vacuum tubes exist.

In circuit diagrams, transistors are designated as shown in Fig. 8.15. The terminals are usually marked so that the little tab on the transistor case shown in Fig. 8.15 is next to the emitter. The direction of the arrow indicates the direction of positive current flow. Note that the current flow is, according to the usual convention, opposite to the actual flow of electrons.

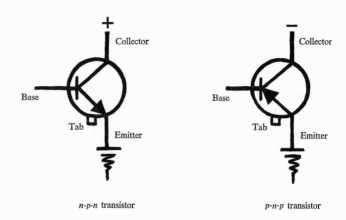

n-p-n transistor   *p-n-p* transistor

FIGURE 8.15

Schematic representation of n-p-n and p-n-p type transistors.

8.7 EXPERIMENTAL DETERMINATION OF TRANSISTOR AND DIODE CHARACTERISTICS

Before any circuits employing solid-state circuit elements can be built, it is important to determine their behavior. In the case of the junction diodes, for example, this means verifying Eq. (8.16) and reproducing the current-voltage characteristic shown in Fig. 8.12. Solid-state breadboard circuits are usually constructed by attaching the components to a perforated board made of an insulating material. These boards are available commercially. A typical breadboard circuit is shown in Fig. 8.16. Fittings and sockets which can be used to secure diodes and transistors to the circuit board are also available. The power source for transistor circuits is a multicell battery which should have terminals to provide voltages up to 20 volts or a 0 to 20 volt d-c power supply. A vacuum-tube voltmeter and a good laboratory oscilloscope should also be available to make appropriate measurements on circuit components.

Several important points should be kept in mind when working with transistor circuits:

1. Most solid-state circuit elements are temperature sensitive. They will cease to operate when overheated. In soldering connections it is therefore important not to hold hot soldering irons near the active elements themselves. It is also important not to overheat the lead wires. This is best accomplished by holding the lead wire with a needle-nosed pliers between the circuit element and the soldering iron. The pliers act as a heat sink and will prevent the circuit element from overheating.

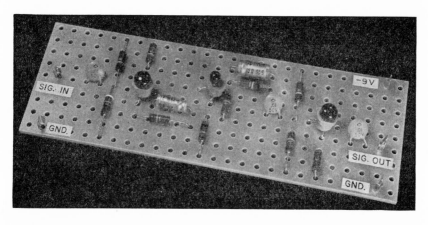

FIGURE 8.16

"Breadboard" prototype circuit construction of the linear pulse amplifier of Fig. 8.23.

2. In a breadboard circuit the leads should be kept as short as possible. This is especially important in pulse-circuit applications. Long leads increase the distributed capacities and inductances and thus make it difficult to predict quantitatively the behavior of the circuit.

3. Great care must be taken not to apply any voltages to solid-state circuit elements which exceed their breakdown potentials. This may be done inadvertently when using battery-powered measuring devices. Before using any diode or transistor in a circuit, the appropriate manufacturer's manual should be consulted[6] to determine the proper operating range of the circuit element. When using battery-powered measuring devices, it is important to determine all voltages which are likely to be applied to the circuit.

Transistor and diode characteristics **169**

4. All solid-state circuit elements are essentially low-impedance devices, that is, their internal resistances are low and they will not handle much power. It is therefore very important to make sure that the output impedance of the circuit is properly matched with the input impedance of the measuring device. If this is not done, the measuring device may load the circuit and change its operating characteristics.

Diode characteristics. As described in Sec. 8.6, *p-n* junctions display the diode characteristic of conducting current in one direction but not in the reverse direction. This property can be measured using the circuit shown in Fig. 8.17.

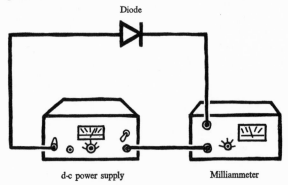

FIGURE 8.17

Circuit used for measuring i-v characteristics of a diode.

The voltage in the forward bias direction can be increased to the current limit of the diode. For reverse biasing measurements the breakdown voltage should be approached with caution. The diode will recover from operation in the breakdown region, but it should not be operated there for too long or at too high a reverse current.

The measured *i-v* characteristic should be checked for the exponential rise predicted by Eq. (8.16). This can be accomplished by making a semilog plot of *i* versus *v*. The temperature dependence of the current can also be checked by placing the diode in various temperature baths, such as liquid nitrogen, dry ice and alcohol, ice water, and hot water. Care must be taken not to exceed the upper temperature limit of the diode, which is usually 50 to 60°C. These *i-v* characteristics for the various temperatures should give straight lines on semilog plots, where the slopes increase with increasing temperature.

Transistor characteristics. As in the case of vacuum tubes, so-called "characteristic" curves can be obtained for transistors. These curves show the current passing through the transistor as a function of base voltage. This should be one of the first experiments to be performed. The circuit is shown in Fig. 8.18. The current through the transistor is measured by determining the voltage drop across the load resistor. Typical characteristics for various base bias voltages are shown in Fig. 8.19. These curves are very similar to those obtained for a vacuum tube under similar circumstances. Characteristics for several different base voltages should be measured. Great care must be taken to make certain that the collector voltage is not larger than the rated value for

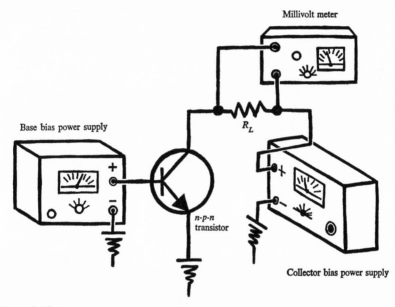

FIGURE 8.18

Circuit for measuring transistor characteristics.

the transistor; otherwise the junction can be burned out. Also, the base bias must always be such that the current in the transistor also stays below the rated value. These experiments should be performed with both *p-n-p* and *n-p-n* transistors.

From Fig. 8.19 it can be seen that the transistor is a controllable nonlinear element. In a certain region of emitter-collector voltages, the current is proportional to the voltage across the transistor. Beyond this maximum voltage, V_0, the current passing through the transistor depends only on the base voltage. Each curve is taken for a different base bias. Obviously, if the base voltage is altered rapidly, the current passed by the transistor changes. In the linear region the transistor can

Transistor and diode characteristics　**171**

be operated in certain circuits, such as oscillators. In certain other circuits, such as flip-flop and trigger, the transistor is used as a switch and is thus operated in the saturated region.

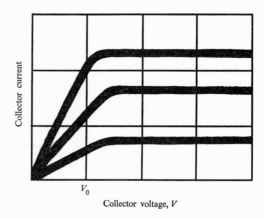

FIGURE 8.19

Typical collector current-collector voltage curves for various base voltages.

8.8 TRANSISTOR CIRCUITS

A great many electronic circuits employing transistor elements have been developed for a variety of uses.[7] A few of the simpler ones will be described here. These circuits can be easily constructed from readily available components. A pulse generator, a vacuum-tube voltmeter, and an oscilloscope should be available to test the properties of the circuits.

Flip-flop circuit. A very common circuit element is the so-called flip-flop circuit, which has many uses in scaling and computing circuits. The most important characteristic of a flip-flop circuit is that it has two stable states. The state of the circuit can be changed by feeding in an appropriate signal. A typical flip-flop circuit is shown in Fig. 8.20. This circuit uses p-n-p transistors and operates as follows. Suppose that in state A_1 the left transistor is conducting and right transistor is cut off. This means that the point A_1 will be at a more positive voltage than A_2. The base of the left transistor is thus at a voltage close to A_2 and the base of the right transistor is at a voltage near A_1. Thus the left transistor is indeed conducting because the base is more negative (or as negative) as the collector. The right transistor is cut off, since the base is quite positive with respect to the collector. (See the discussion in Sec. 8.6). The state of the circuit is then defined by the voltages A_1 and A_2. A negative trigger signal applied to the emitters of both transistors serves to change the state of the circuit, making A_1 more negative than A_2. This occurs because the emitter of the left transistor becomes negative, which results in a more positive emitter-base voltage, causing the transistor to conduct less current. Hence A_1 becomes more negative, which results in a negative signal on the

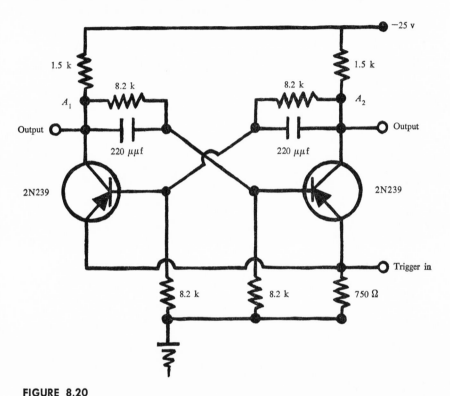

FIGURE 8.20

Transistor flip-flop circuit.

base of the right transistor. Thus the right transistor begins to conduct, making A_2 more positive, further cutting off the left transistor. The state of the circuit is thus changed, so that the point A_1 is now more negative than A_2.

The flip-flop circuit is often used as a scaling circuit. For this purpose the flip-flop circuit is connected as shown in Fig. 8.21. One arm of the circuit is connected to ground through a light, which is lit when that arm is at the battery voltage. The other arm is used as an input for the succeeding circuit. At the start, all circuits are in the state with the upper arm at the battery voltage. The first input signal turns on the light corresponding to one count. The next signal turns out the light and triggers the next flip-flop to turn on the two count light. The next pulse again turns on the one count light, resulting in a scaler reading of two plus one, or three counts. The next count triggers both No. 1 and No. 2 flip-flops, turning out the first two lights, and also triggers the third flip-flop, turning on the four count light. Further counts repeat the procedure, and it can be seen that the total number of counts corresponds to the sum of the labels on the lights.

Schmitt trigger circuit. An interesting variation of a circuit such as the flip-flop unit discussed in the previous section is the so-called trigger circuit. The function of this circuit is to produce an output pulse with a voltage independent of the size or shape of the input pulse.

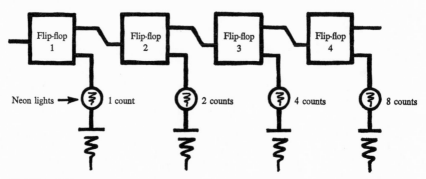

FIGURE 8.21

Binary counting circuit using successive flip-flops.

The circuit diagram is shown in Fig. 8.22. This circuit is similar to the flip-flop circuit in that it has two states. In this case, however, only one of the states of the circuit is stable. The circuit remains in the unstable state for a time comparable to the RC time constant of the network connecting the collector of the left transistor with the base of the right transistor. In the circuit's stable state, the right transistor is conducting and the left transistor is cut off. The point A_1 is thus more negative than A_2. A negative input signal causes the left transistor to conduct, which makes the voltage of point A_1 more positive, resulting in a positive signal at the base of the right transistor. This transistor stops conducting, making the voltage at the output A_2 more negative. The output stays negative as long as the input signal is applied. When the input voltage is removed, the circuit reverts to its original, stable state.

Linear pulse amplifier. A very important circuit element is the linear pulse amplifier shown in Fig. 8.23. The purpose of this unit is to increase the voltage of a transient signal applied to the base of the first transistor. The most important feature of the circuit is the resistive feedback loop between the first and second transistor. The presence of this feedback loop ensures that the gain of the amplifier is independent of the characteristics of the particular transistors used in the circuit. It

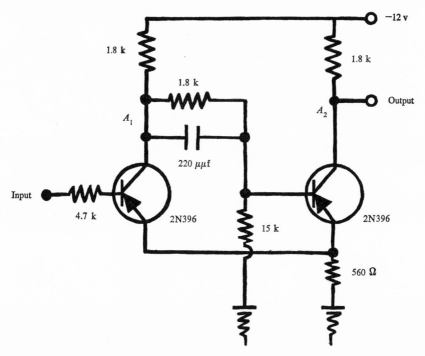

FIGURE 8.22

Schmitt trigger circuit which gives an output pulse independent of size and shape of input pulse.

can be shown that the gain of the circuit, defined as the ratio of the output voltage to the input voltage, is given by

$$G = \frac{V_{\text{out}}}{V_{\text{in}}} \approx \frac{R_1 + R_2}{R_1} \tag{8.17}$$

The feedback circuit serves to control the first transistor-emitter voltage so that it follows the second transistor-base voltage. The two voltages never differ by more than the amount specified by the voltage divider in the feedback loop. Thus the base-emitter voltage of the first transistor stays relatively small, so that the transistor is never driven to saturation. Hence the amplifier is always linear. This is an example of negative feedback which serves to stabilize the circuit.

The last transistor in the circuit is called an emitter follower. Its function is to provide sufficient power to drive low-input impedance circuits which may follow the amplifier.

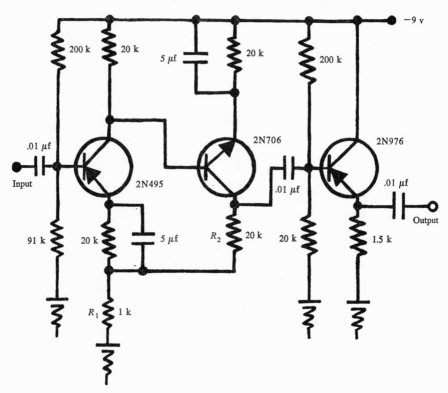

FIGURE 8.23

Circuit for a transistorized linear pulse amplifier.

An interesting experiment which should be performed is to determine the linearity of the amplifier. This is best done by displaying both the input and the output pulses on a dual trace oscilloscope and adjusting the gains of the two oscilloscope amplifiers so that the pulses appear equal on the scope face. The input pulse voltage is now varied and the pulses should increase and decrease together on the scope face with no relative change in size. If the input pulse voltage is increased beyond a certain value, no further change occurs in the output pulse. The reason is that the power output of the last stage of the amplifier must have

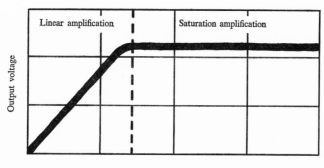

FIGURE 8.24

Amplifier performance curve indicating linear amplification and saturation regions.

some upper limit. At this point the amplifier is said to be saturated. The input versus output pulse voltage plot is shown in Fig. 8.24.

Coincidence and anticoincidence circuits. These circuits are somewhat more specialized than the ones discussed in the previous sections. The function of a coincidence circuit is to produce an output signal whenever two signals arrive simultaneously at the appropriate inputs. The circuit does not produce an output signal if a signal appears at only one of the inputs. In the terminology of computer technology, such a circuit is called an "and gate." An anticoincidence circuit passes

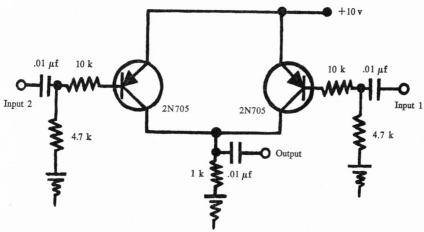

FIGURE 8.25

Transistor coincidence circuit.

pulses which are applied singly at either input, but it does not generate an output signal when two pulses appear simultaneously at the inputs. This circuit is often called an "or gate." Figure 8.25 shows a typical circuit which can be used as a coincidence (and gate) circuit. In its normal state, both transistors are on. A positive signal applied at either base will cause one of the transistors to cut off. Since the other transistor is still conducting, no voltage change will be observed at the output. If a positive signal is applied to both terminals simultaneously, the voltage at the output drops from somewhere near 10 volts to ground. Thus a negative signal is observed at the output when two positive signals appear simultaneously at the two inputs. Several other circuits will accomplish the function of the coincidence unit shown in Fig. 8.25, employing transistors in series. Similar reasoning is used in the design of anticoincidence units. For an important application of coincidence circuits, see Chapter 5.

REFERENCES

1. Faraday, M.: Experimental Researches in Electricity, Series IV (1833). Also, Beibl. *Ann. Phys.*, **31**, 25, 1834.

2. Brattain, W. H., and J. Bardeen: *Phys. Rev.*, **75**, 1208, 1949.

3. Sommerfeld, A.: *Z. Phys.*, **47**, 1, 1928.

4. Konig, R. de L., and W. G., Penney: *Proc. Roy. Soc. (London)*, **A130**, 499, 1931.

5. Schockley, W., M. Sparks and G. K. Teal: *Phys. Rev.*, **83**, 151 (1951).

6. RCA Transistor Manual, Radio Corporation of America, Somerville, N.J., 1962.

7. GE Transistor Manual, 6th ed., General Electric Company, Syracuse, New York, 1962.

GENERAL BIBLIOGRAPHY

1. Dekker, A. J.: "Solid State Physics," Prentice-Hall, Inc., Englewood Cliffs, N.J., 1957.

2. Shockley, W.: "Electrons and Holes in Semiconductors," D. Van Nostrand Company, Inc., Princeton, N.J., 1950.

3. Nussbaum, A.: "Semiconductor Device Physics," Prentice-Hall, Inc., Englewood Cliffs, N.J., 1962.

4. Van der Ziel, A.: "Solid State Physical Electronics," Prentice-Hall, Inc., Englewood Cliffs, N.J., 1959.

5. Kittel, C.: "Introduction to Solid State Physics," 2d ed., John Wiley & Sons, Inc., New York, 1956.

Chapter 9	# NUCLEAR MAGNETIC RESONANCE

9.1 INTRODUCTION

One of the very important postwar achievements in physics is the study of nuclear magnetism. This work grew out of the intensive development of radar during the war. The first actual nuclear magnetic resonance experiments were performed during 1946–1948 by Felix Bloch[1] of Stanford University and E. M. Purcell[2] of Harvard University. Both experimenters observed transitions between different orientation states of protons in an external magnetic field. Rapid strides in technique were made shortly after the first experiments were performed, and within a few years a large number of nuclear magnetic moments had been measured by many different workers. In addition to the measurements of nuclear magnetic moments, nuclear magnetic resonance experiments also contributed to the understanding of internal magnetic fields in crystals, and many important experiments have been performed in solid-state and molecular physics.

9.2 LARMOR PRECESSION

Nuclear magnetic resonance is closely related to the Zeeman effect in atomic spectroscopy. Both are caused by the precession in an external magnetic field of magnetic moments modified by quantum mechanical rules which define the behavior of atomic and nuclear systems. The quantum description of precessing magnetic moments was first derived for atoms and was then extended to nuclei when it was discovered that nuclei also possess magnetic moments. This same sequence will be followed here.

An electron moving in an orbit around a nucleus has an angular momentum and, also, a magnetic moment associated with the current produced by the charge moving in the orbit. The magnetic and mechanical moment vectors point in opposite directions because of the negative sign of the electronic charge. If the orbit is circular and has a radius r, the mechanical moment is

$$p = m_e v r = m_e r^2 \omega \tag{9.1}$$

and the magnetic moment is

$$\mu = -iA = -i\pi r^2 \tag{9.2}$$

where ω is the angular velocity of the charge, i is the current due to the electron moving in the orbit. The electron current is determined by the following expression:

$$i = e\nu = \frac{e\omega}{2\pi} \tag{9.3}$$

Assume the atom is now placed in an external magnetic field as shown in Fig. 9.1. The magnetic field $\mathbf{H}$ exerts a torque on the magnetic moment which tries to line up the moment with the field. The torque, which is the vector product of the magnetic field $\mathbf{H}$ and the magnetic moment $\mathbf{\mu}$, is given by

$$\mathbf{T} = \mathbf{\mu} \times \mu_0 \mathbf{H} \qquad \text{or} \qquad T = \mu\mu_0 H \sin \theta \qquad (9.4)$$

The quantity μ_0 is the permeability of free space and equals $4\pi \times 10^{-7} \simeq 12.57 \times 10^{-7}$ webers/amp-m.) This torque, which points out of the plane of the paper, is equal to the time rate of change of angular momentum. Thus

$$\frac{d\mathbf{p}}{dt} = \mathbf{T} \qquad \text{or} \qquad \frac{dp}{dt} = \mu\mu_0 H \sin \theta \qquad (9.5)$$

The rate of change of angular momentum is perpendicular to the angular momentum vector $\mathbf{p}$, so that the vector precesses around the

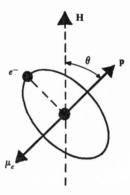

FIGURE 9.1

Orientation (relative to an external magnetic field) of the orbital angular momentum and resulting magnetic moment vectors of orbiting electron.

direction of the field. The frequency of precession can be computed with the help of Fig. 9.2. The change in the angular momentum in terms of the angle $d\alpha$ is

$$dp = p \sin \theta \, d\alpha \qquad (9.6)$$

Substituting Eq. (9.6) into Eq. (9.5) gives

$$\mu\mu_0 H \sin \theta = p \sin \theta \frac{d\alpha}{dt} \qquad (9.7)$$

The frequency of precession ν is equal to $(1/2\pi)(d\alpha/dt)$, so that

$$2\pi\nu = \frac{\mu}{p} \mu_0 H \qquad (9.8)$$

Using Eqs. (9.1), (9.2), and (9.3) for the mechanical moment, the magnetic moment, and the current, respectively, gives

$$\nu_L = \frac{\mu_0}{2\pi} \frac{eH}{2m_e} \qquad (9.9)$$

The frequency given in Eq. (9.9) is called the Larmor frequency. Note that the Larmor frequency is independent of the angle between the mechanical moment and the magnetic field. The Larmor frequency is the characteristic precessional frequency of an atomic orbital electron in an external magnetic field.

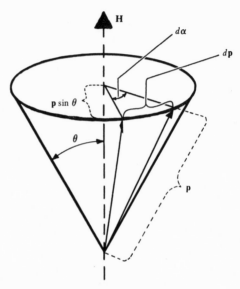

FIGURE 9.2

Angular momentum vector displacement caused by interaction force between the magnetic moment and the external field.

The magnetic field in Fig. 9.2 does not change the orientation of the magnetic moment with respect to the field direction, that is, the angle θ is a constant. It can easily be seen that a magnetic field component perpendicular to **H** is necessary to cause θ to change. Furthermore, this perpendicular component cannot be simply a static field, since this would only add vectorially to **H** and thus change the axis around which the moment precesses. The perpendicular component should rotate with the same angular frequency as the angular momentum vector **p**. Such a rotating field can be applied, but in practice it is generally easier to use a linearly oscillating field which is perpendicular to **H**. A sinusoidally oscillating field can always be split into two circularly polarized components. In this case one of the two rotating field vectors precesses around the fixed field at the same rate as the magnetic moment. The other circularly polarized component rotates in the opposite direction with an apparent frequency (with respect to the precessing moment) equal to twice the Larmor frequency.

The effect of applying the oscillating field ($H_0 \sin 2\pi\nu_L t$) can be readily understood if the precessing vectors are viewed from a coordinate system which rotates around the fixed field with an angular velocity $2\pi\nu_L$. The magnetic moment and one of the rotating components will be in phase with each other and will thus appear as "constant" vectors in the new coordinate system. The magnetic moment vector will precess around the in-phase component, thus changing the angle θ. Since the fixed field H is very much larger than the maximum value of the oscillating field, the angle θ changes only slightly during each cycle of the Larmor precession. The oscillating magnetic field is thus usually regarded as a small perturbation on the strong constant field. The out-of-phase component of the oscillating field will not change θ. It can be shown that it causes the magnetic moment vector to perform small oscillations around some equilibrium value of θ, but no net change in θ occurs. If the oscillating field is applied with any frequency other than the Larmor frequency, neither of the rotating field components will be in phase with the moment and thus will cause no net change in θ.

9.3 ENERGY LEVELS AND TRANSITIONS

The potential energy of a magnetic moment vector $\mathbf{\mu}$ in a magnetic field H is a function of the angle between the vectors. The torque defined in Eq. (9.4) tries to line up the vectors $\mathbf{\mu}$ and H so that they are parallel. This state of the system has the lowest potential energy, whereas the state in which $\mathbf{\mu}$ and H point in opposite directions has the highest potential energy. The work done to rotate the magnetic moment from the lowest energy position ($\theta = 0$) to a position where the angle θ has a finite value is

$$E = \int_0^\theta T \, d\theta' = \mu\mu_0 H \int_0^\theta \sin \theta' \, d\theta' = \mu\mu_0 H(1 - \cos \theta) \quad (9.10)$$

To change the orientation of the magnetic moment, energy must either be emitted or absorbed. It has already been shown that this energy can be supplied by an oscillating magnetic field applied to the sample at the proper "resonant" (Larmor) frequency, hence the name magnetic resonance.

To understand how energy is transferred to the system in a real situation, some elementary knowledge of quantum mechanics is necessary. An angular momentum vector **p** has only a certain number of discrete orientations with respect to an external axis. This result is based on the well-known Stern-Gerlach experiment[3] in which the various discrete components of a magnetic-mechanical moment system are separated using a nonhomogeneous magnetic field. It was shown

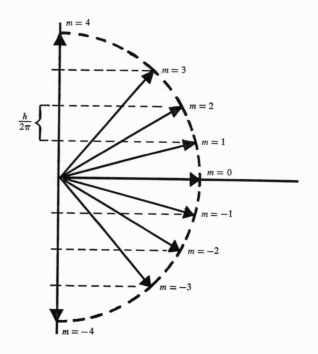

FIGURE 9.3

Possible orientations relative to an external field direction of an angular momentum vector of quantum number l = 4.

that the component of the angular momentum with respect to the field axis z is

$$p_z = \frac{mh}{2\pi} \tag{9.11}$$

where m is an integer and h is Planck's constant. The values of m range between $-l$ and $+l$, where l is the orbital angular momentum quantum number. The situation is illustrated in Fig. 9.3 for the case when the maximum component of the angular momentum along the magnetic field is 4. The change in energy between successive orientations of the moment system can be calculated using Eq. (9.10). The energy change is

$$\Delta E = \mu\mu_0 H \sin \theta \, \Delta\theta = \Delta(\mu\mu_0 H \cos \theta) \qquad (9.12)$$

This expression can be rewritten in terms of the Larmor frequency, using Eq. (9.8),

$$\Delta E = \Delta(p \cos \theta) \, 2\pi\nu_L \qquad (9.13)$$

The quantity in parenthesis in Eq. (9.13) is the z component of the angular momentum vector $\mathbf{p}$. From Eq. (9.11) it is obvious that any change in this component must be equal to at least $h/2\pi$. Thus

$$\Delta E = h\nu_L \qquad (9.14)$$

which is the spacing between the energy levels of a magnetic-mechanical moment system in a magnetic field. It is interesting to note that Eq. (9.14) is also the statement governing the emission and absorption of radiant energy derived in Appendix II. The major problem in magnetic resonance experiments is to detect the energy associated with the transitions corresponding to the different orientations of the magnetic moments in the external field.

The introduction of quantized angular momenta in Eq. (9.11) leads to the more usual manner in which the relationships between transition energies and magnetic moments are written. Starting again with Eq. (9.8), the quantized mechanical moment is given by

$$p = \frac{h}{2\pi} I \qquad (9.15)$$

where I may be of either integer or, as will be seen later, half-integer value. Substituting (9.15) into (9.8) gives

$$\nu_L = \frac{\mu}{hI} \mu_0 H \qquad (9.16)$$

and since $\Delta E = h\nu_L$

$$\Delta E = \frac{\mu}{I} \mu_0 H \qquad (9.17)$$

It is customary to write Eq. (9.14) in terms of a quantity called the "Bohr magneton," μ_B, which is defined as

$$\mu_B = \frac{e\hbar}{2m_e} \qquad (9.18)$$

so that in the case of quantized angular momenta, Eq. (9.17) can be rewritten as

$$\Delta E = (\mu/\mu_B I)\mu_B\mu_0 H \qquad (9.19)$$

Energy levels and transitions **185**

by multiplying the numerator and denominator by μ_B. The factor $(\mu/\mu_B I)$ is called the Lande g factor so that

$$\Delta E = g\mu_B\mu_0 H \qquad (9.20)$$

and

$$g = (\mu/\mu_B I) \qquad (9.21)$$

For the case of an electron moving in a circular orbit, it can be shown that $g = 1$ so that substituting Eq. (9.18) into (9.20) and using (9.14) leads to the correct expression for the Larmor frequency (9.9). It can be shown that $g = 1$ for all classically rotating objects having uniform charge-to-mass ratios throughout their volumes. The same is not true, however, in the case of the intrinsic angular momentum, or spin, of the electron. It is known that the value of the electron spin is $I = \frac{1}{2}$, while the magnetic moment associated with this spin is equal to one Bohr magneton, μ_B. Therefore, the g factor defined in Eq. (9.21) is equal to 2 for the electron spin. This result is a consequence of the complete relativistic theory of the electron. In general, a group of magnetic and mechanical moments may be coupled together in such a way that g can take on noninteger values.

9.4 NUCLEAR MAGNETISM

Nuclei also possess magnetic moments. These were first discovered when atomic spectra, particularly for hydrogen and deuterium, were investigated with spectrographs having ultrahigh resolution. It was found that many spectral lines were split into multiplets with very small separations. This phenomenon is called hyperfine structure and was explained by W. Pauli[4] as being caused by the interaction between the atomic and nuclear magnetic moments. The unit used to express nuclear magnetic moments is the "nuclear magneton," μ_N, which is identical to the "Bohr magneton" defined in Eq. (9.18) except that electron mass, m_e, is replaced by proton mass, m_p. Nuclear moments are thus about 1830 times smaller than atomic magnetic moments.

The magnetic moment of the proton has been measured by determining the Larmor frequency of protons in a magnetic field, H. The associated energy splitting was found to be

$$\Delta E = 2.8\mu_N\mu_0 H \qquad (9.22)$$

Thus, it can be said that the proton possesses a magnetic moment of 2.8 nuclear magnetons. The value of the g factor of the proton is 5.56, which can be obtained by substituting μ_N for μ_B in Eq. (9.21) and remembering that the intrinsic spin of the proton is $I = \frac{1}{2}$. The reason for the large g factor of the proton is not understood, and all attempts at making an accurate quantitative prediction of the proton magnetic moment have failed.

The frequencies necessary to observe transitions between various nuclear orientation states can be easily estimated. For protons, the g factor is 5.56, so that

$$\nu_L = 5.56 \frac{\mu_0}{2\pi} \frac{eH}{2m_p} \tag{9.23}$$

To evaluate this expression, a word about the units used to measure magnetic fields is in order. The magnetic field H is measured in units of ampere-turns/meter, and H is determined by the configuration of the field coils and the magnitude of the current in them. The magnetic induction B resulting from the field H is defined as $B = \mu_0 H$ in free space and is measured in units of webers/square meter. The magnetic induction is determined by the properties of a material, and for the same field H, different values of B occur in different materials. In this case $B = \mu H$, and μ is the permeability of the material.

In practice, the important quantity is B, for it defines the field strength the nuclear magnetic moment resides in. It will be assumed for the remainder of the chapter that the materials investigated have a permeability equal to that of free space (i.e., $\mu = \mu_0$ and so the symbol μ will be reserved to stand only for magnetic moments). Thus, for an assumed induction of one-tenth of a weber/square meter, the proton Larmor frequency is

$$\nu_L = \frac{5.56}{2\pi} \frac{eB}{2m_p} \simeq 4 \times 10^6 \text{ cycles/sec} \tag{9.24}$$

(To relate this quantity of B to the corresponding units in the Gaussian system, it is convenient to remember that 1 weber/m^2 = 10^4 gauss.) This frequency corresponds to short-wave radio frequencies used in communications. Power must be supplied to the sample with a radio-frequency oscillator operating at this frequency. The energy of the nuclear reorientation transitions considered here is

$$E = h\nu_L = 6 \times 10^{-27} \times 10^6 = 6 \times 10^{-21} \text{ ergs}$$
$$= 4 \times 10^{-9} \text{ ev} \tag{9.25}$$

This energy is very small indeed. It serves to define the energy scale of the phenomena investigated in nuclear magnetic resonance experiments. A typical sample in a proton resonance experiment might consist of a tenth of a cubic centimeter volume of water or roughly 10^{22} protons. If the spin orientations of all the protons in the sample are flipped simultaneously, the total energy involved is roughly

$$E_T = 4 \times 10^{-9} \times 10^{22} \approx 4 \times 10^{13} \text{ ev}$$
$$\approx 20 \text{ ergs} \tag{9.26}$$

This energy is also very small, corresponding to a few microwatts if it were delivered continuously at the rate of 20 ergs/sec. Actually, not all the protons in a given sample are flipped when radio-frequency power of the correct frequency is applied. The actual power which can be absorbed by the sample under a given set of conditions is determined by the temperature, the applied magnetic field, and the interaction between the nuclear spins and the lattice. It can be calculated quite easily from certain simple assumptions.

When a magnetic field is applied to a sample containing an assembly of protons, there exists a difference in the number of protons with their spins parallel ($m = \frac{1}{2}$) and those with their spins antiparallel ($m = -\frac{1}{2}$) to the field. This difference is determined by the Boltzmann factors. If there are N_0 protons in the sample, the number of protons having $m = \frac{1}{2}$ is given by the relation

$$N_{\frac{1}{2}} = \frac{N_0}{2} e^{\mu B/kT} \tag{9.27}$$

and for $m = -\frac{1}{2}$ it is

$$N_{-\frac{1}{2}} = \frac{N_0}{2} e^{-\mu B/kT} \tag{9.28}$$

In practice μB is always much smaller than kT, so that the exponentials can be expanded. Thus the difference between the two populations is

$$\Delta N = N_{\frac{1}{2}} - N_{-\frac{1}{2}} = \frac{N_0}{2}\left(1 + \frac{\mu B}{kT}\right) - \frac{N_0}{2}\left(1 - \frac{\mu B}{kT}\right)$$
$$= N_0 \frac{\mu B}{kT} \tag{9.29}$$

At room temperature, and for a magnetic induction of one-tenth of a weber per square meter, the quantity $\mu B/kT$ of Eq. (9.24) is approximately 10^{-7}. Thus, in a sample of 10^{22} protons, the excess population in the lower energy state is only 10^{15} protons.

When the oscillating magnetic field is applied, it can induce transitions in both directions. That is, the protons may gain energy from the radio-frequency field or they may give energy to the radio-frequency field. (For a complete discussion of absorption and stimulated emission of electromagnetic energy, see Chapter 11.) The rate at which energy is absorbed from the oscillating field by a group of protons is very close to the rate at which the protons give energy to the radio-frequency field. This is because the spontaneous emission term in this case is negligible (i.e., for $n_r + 1$, the $n_\nu \gg 1$). Therefore any net energy absorbed by the sample from the radio-frequency field depends only on the population difference between the two orientation states. If the states are equally populated, no net energy is absorbed or emitted.

In the case of the proton sample considered, the excess population in the lower energy state ($m = \frac{1}{2}$) is 10^{15} protons. When the applied radio-frequency field has changed half of these protons (5×10^{14}) to the higher energy state, equilibrium is reached, and no further change in population occurs. At this point the sample is said to be saturated. This situation exists only if there is no other mechanism for reorienting the protons. In all practical cases, the interaction between the proton magnetic moment and the fields of other magnetic moments (usually large atomic moments) in the sample material provides a means by which the proton spins can be reoriented independent of the radio-frequency field. Thus, if a sample is saturated by the radio-frequency field (i.e., the populations are made equal) and the radio-frequency field is then turned off, the proton moments will return to the thermal equilibrium of Eqs. (9.27) and (9.28). The characteristic decay time for reaching equilibrium is called the "relaxation time."

From the arguments outlined in the foregoing paragraphs it is obvious that the radio-frequency power absorbed by the sample will depend on a competition between the tendencies of the applied radio-frequency field to saturate the sample and the relaxation mechanism to return the spin distribution to thermal equilibrium. To observe resonance absorption, a significant fraction of the population difference must be available so that transitions can occur. It is clear that the energy absorbed will generally be very much smaller than the amount calculated in Eq. (9.26).

To observe resonance signals from protons, a small glass tube filled with water is used as a sample. Since the relaxation time of pure water is quite long ($\sim$3.6 sec), it is necessary to add some paramagnetic ions to obtain easily observable proton resonance signals. These ions have large permanent magnetic moments, and they help to randomize the proton spins more rapidly, thus reducing the relaxation times to values smaller than 10^{-3} sec. Therefore a large excess proton population is always available in the lower energy level to absorb radio-frequency energy when the magnetic field and resonance frequency are properly adjusted.

9.5 EXPERIMENTAL METHODS

Nuclear resonance experiments are usually conducted using an apparatus of the kind shown in Fig. 9.4. The permanent magnet or electromagnet supplies the constant magnetic field in which the nuclei precess. The modulating field is provided by the two coils shown. The function of the modulating coil is to vary the value of the magnetic field while the frequency of the radio-frequency field is held constant, so that, at least for some values of the magnetic field, H, the condition of Eq. (9.23) is satisfied. This is easier than holding the magnetic field constant and varying the oscillator frequency to sweep through the resonant condition of Eq. (9.23). The oscillating radio-frequency magnetic field is

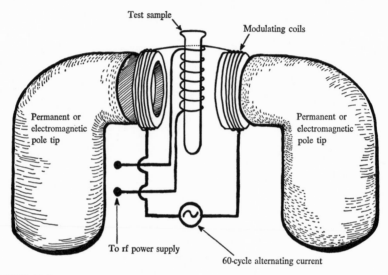

FIGURE 9.4

Experimental configuration showing magnet poles, modulating coils, and the resonance sample, using the marginal oscillator or bridge methods of resonance detection.

perpendicular to the external field. The modulated field is shown in Fig. 9.5. The magnetic induction B_0 has a value of approximately 0.10 weber/m² in most cases, so that the appropriate Larmor frequencies for nuclear systems are of the order of a few megacycles. The modulating field usually has a peak value of the order of 2.5×10^{-4} webers/m² gauss, so that the external field is given by an expression of the form

$$B(t) = B_0 + B_1 \sin \omega t \qquad (9.30)$$

where typically
$$B_0 = 0.10 \text{ weber/m}^2$$
$$B_1 = 2.5 \times 10^{-4} \text{ webers/m}^2$$

The resonance condition can be observed in a number of different ways. One common method is to observe a change in the power emitted by the oscillator which supplies the radio-frequency perturbing field. The coil in which the sample resides is part of the LC-tuned circuit in the oscillator. When the resonance condition [Eq. (9.23)] is fulfilled, the impedance of L changes, since a small amount of energy is absorbed by the sample. This change can be detected as a change in the bias voltage on the collector of a transistor. The oscillator is usually adjusted in such a way that the feedback signal from the LC circuit to the oscillator

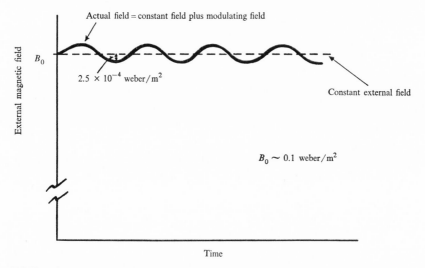

FIGURE 9.5

External field resulting from the superposition of the constant and oscillating fields.

transistor is just barely positive, that is, the oscillations are just sustained. In this condition even a small change in the load may stop the oscillator completely, thus causing a large, observable effect. A schematic diagram of the system used to observe the nuclear resonance signal is shown in Fig. 9.6 and the oscillator circuit[5] is shown in Fig. 9.7. The horizontal sweep of the oscilloscope is driven by the 60-cycle modulating coil signal. The vertical sweep is connected to the output of the oscillator. If the oscillator frequency is not correct [i.e., does not fulfill the resonance condition of Eq. (9.23)], then the oscilloscope pattern observed is that shown in the left panel of Fig. 9.8; if the resonance condition is properly satisfied, the pattern shown in the right-hand panel is observed.

Experimental methods **191**

The radio-frequency coil of the oscillator circuit in Fig. 9.7 should consist of 10 to 20 turns (depending on the frequency range desired) wound on a $\frac{1}{4}$-in. diameter core. The wire used should be about No. 20 lacquered copper wire. The radio-frequency coil and the modulating coils can be combined into an integral head for convenient use. A piece of brass ($1\frac{1}{2}$ in. OD $\times$ 1 in. high) can be used as a form on which the

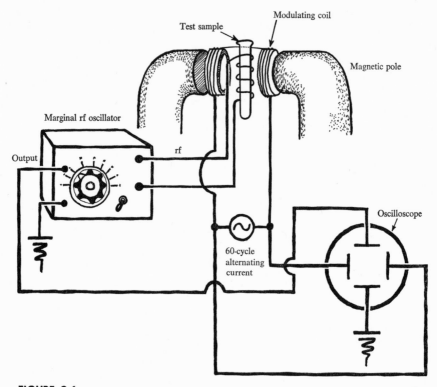

FIGURE 9.6

Experimental configuration for using the marginal oscillator for nuclear magnetic resonance measurements.

modulating coils are wound. The radio-frequency coil is wound on the inside with a hole cut in the brass form to facilitate inserting various samples. The radio-frequency power can be fed down an extra brass tube which acts as a coaxial lead and thus shields the radio-frequency circuit. This head is shown in Fig. 9.9.

Another method commonly used to observe the resonance signal is to pick up directly the radio-frequency energy emitted when the nuclei

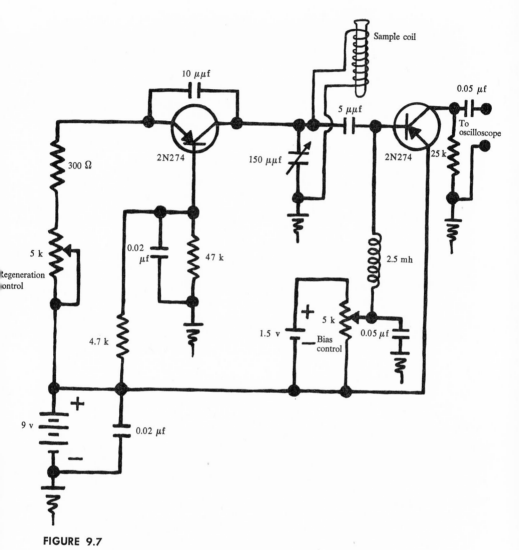

FIGURE 9.7

Schematic diagram of a transistorized marginal oscillator circuit.

in the sample change their orientations. The system is similar to the one shown in Fig. 9.4 except that another pickup coil must be used. This system is shown in Fig. 9.10. The pickup coils are located as shown, with their axis perpendicular to the radio-frequency exciting coil and also to the external field. The principal difficulty with this method is that it is hard to make certain that the pickup coils do not

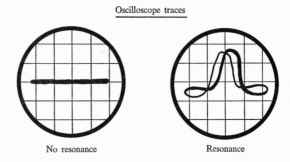

No resonance   Resonance

FIGURE 9.8

Oscilloscope traces of the marginal oscillator output for nonresonance and resonance cases.

see the signal from the excitation coil. The pickup coils can only detect an H field along their own axes; hence they should not see the radio-frequency energy radiated by the oscillator coil provided that they are carefully aligned. The radio-frequency signal from the reorienting magnetic moments within the sample has a component of an H vector parallel to the axis of the pickup coils. This component will be detected by the pickup coils. The output from the pickup coils is fed to a conventional radio-frequency receiver and the output signal from the receiver may be displayed in a manner similar to that used in the marginal oscillator method. The oscilloscope's horizontal sweep is con-

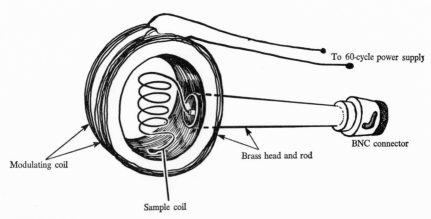

To 60-cycle power supply

BNC connector

Brass head and rod

Modulating coil

Sample coil

FIGURE 9.9

Marginal oscillator resonance head containing modulating and resonance coils with shielded radio frequency feed.

194 *Nuclear magnetic resonance*

trolled by the modulator signal and the vertical sweep is actuated by the radio-frequency receiver output signal. The oscilloscope trace is similar to that shown in Fig. 9.8.

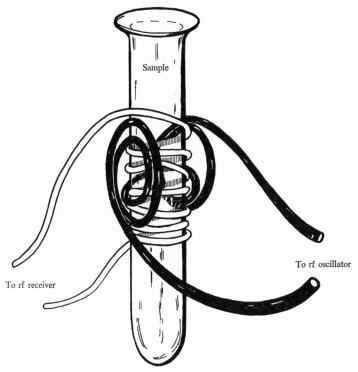

FIGURE 9.10

Crossed-coil arrangement for detecting energy radiated when magnetic moments flip under the resonance condition.

9.6 EXPERIMENTS

Measurement of the proton magnetic moment. A very precise measurement of the proton magnetic moment is possible by employing a technique where it is necessary only to determine frequencies. The Larmor frequency associated with the precession of the proton spins is

$$\nu_L = \frac{g}{2\pi} \frac{eB}{2m_p} \tag{9.31}$$

All the factors in Eq. (9.31) are known with great accuracy except B. One way to eliminate the measurement of B is to use the orbital motion of protons in the same magnetic field. In Chapter 11 the "omegatron" has been described. The omegatron determines the cyclotron frequency of the orbital motion of protons in a magnetic field. The cyclotron frequency is given by

$$v_c = \frac{1}{2\pi} \frac{eB}{2m_p} \qquad (9.32)$$

If the measurements of v_L and v_c are made in the same magnetic field, then the g factor is given by the ratio of the frequencies. From Eqs. (9.31) and (9.32),

$$\frac{v_L}{v_c} = g \qquad (9.33)$$

Since frequencies can be measured with great accuracy, this method yields a very precise measurement of g for the proton. The proton magnetic moment can also be determined in terms of the Bohr magneton by using the electron rather than the proton cyclotron frequency.

Determination of nuclear magnetic moments. The magnetic moments of other nuclear species can be measured by using the equipment described in the previous sections. For example, if saturated aqueous solutions of either lithium or fluorine compounds are placed in the sample tube, the magnetic moments of Li^7 and F^{19} can be measured. Li^7 is the most abundant isotope of lithium (92.5 percent). It has a ground state spin of $\frac{3}{2}$ so that the nucleus has four possible orientations with respect to the external field instead of two, as was the case for the proton (see Fig. 9.11). However, spin values cannot be determined using nuclear magnetic resonance techniques because only the energy *change* for $\Delta m = \pm 1$ is measured by this method. This energy change is independent of the value of m and thus gives no information about the spin of the nucleus. Fluorine is monoisotopic (F^{19}) and has a ground state spin of $\frac{1}{2}$. Thus F^{19} behaves very much like the proton. The approximate g factors for Li^7 and F^{19} can be computed from the observed resonance frequencies and from certain simple assumptions about nuclear structure. The results are shown in Table 9.1.

With the equipment described in Sec. 9.5, the signal-to-noise ratio for the proton resonance signal shown in Fig. 9.8 is roughly 10 to 1. In order to observe resonance signals from various other species dissolved in the water, the concentration of ions must be of the order of 10 percent of the hydrogen (i.e., proton) concentration in the water. Compounds must therefore be found which are very soluble in water.

It is interesting to note that F^{19} has a magnetic moment quite close to that of the free proton, whereas the moment of Li^7 is somewhat larger. Nuclear magnetic moments are not yet well understood from a

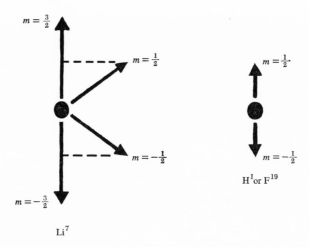

FIGURE 9.11

Possible spin states of Li^7 and F^{19}.

theoretical point of view. It is possible to make some general predictions about the expected trends, but no reliable quantitative statements can be made. Assume that F^{19} consists of a proton plus an O^{18} core (i.e., eight protons and ten neutrons) in which all the spins and moments cancel. If the proton is in a state having no orbital angular

TABLE 9.1

Magnetic moments and g factors for H^1, Li^7 and F^{19}

Isotope	Spin	g	Magnetic moments in nuclear magnetons
H^1	$\frac{1}{2}$	5.56	2.8
Li^7	$\frac{3}{2}$	2.16	3.2
F^{19}	$\frac{1}{2}$	5.24	2.7

momentum with respect to the core, the magnetic moment of F^{19} should be roughly equal to that of the free proton. This is what is observed, and it is therefore generally accepted that the structure of F^{19} is as assumed, that is, the proton is in an $S_{\frac{1}{2}}$ state with respect to the O^{18} core. In the case of Li^7 the situation is somewhat different. The magnetic moment (3.2 μ_N) is larger than the moment of the free proton. This means that the magnetic moment of Li^7 cannot be ascribed solely to the spin moment of the proton as was the case in F^{19}.

A possible explanation is that the Li⁷ nucleus consists of a He⁶ core with cancelled spins and moments and a proton moving around the core with an orbital angular momentum $l = 1$ (i.e., a P state). If the spin moment and the orbital moment are parallel, a magnetic moment larger than the one of the free proton would result. The proton is thus probably in a $P_{3/2}$ state (see Fig. 9.12).

Arguments such as those made in the last paragraph illustrate one of the important ideas in modern nuclear physics, which is that the nucleus has a shell structure quite similar to that of an atom. In an odd A nucleus, A-1 nucleons pair off to form an even Z, even N core. The last nucleon then moves in a potential produced by this core, and

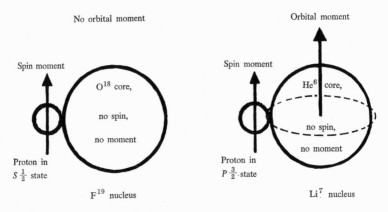

FIGURE 9.12

Possible models which would account for the observed magnetic moment of F^{19} and Li^7.

its motion is described by quantum numbers very similar to those used to describe the motion of an electron in an atom. This idea has been a very powerful aid in the description of several important nuclear phenomena.

Chemical shift. An important application of nuclear magnetic resonance is the study of the magnetic properties of materials. A proton in a material is always surrounded by atomic electrons. This electronic structure around each proton is always slightly diamagnetic, so that the precession of the electrons creates a new field H_D which opposes the externally applied field. The observed resonance frequency is therefore not quite the same as that observed if the protons were free but is that corresponding to free protons in a field $H_0 - H_D$. This effect is called the "chemical shift," for it is due to the electrons which determine the

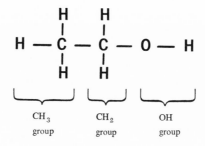

FIGURE 9.13

Molecular structure of ethyl alcohol.

chemical nature of the sample, and it shifts the resonance frequency from the value which would be observed for free protons.

An interesting example of the chemical shift is that of ethyl alcohol.[6] The chemical structure of ethyl alcohol is shown in Fig. 9.13. The protons in this material are distributed in such a way that they belong to three distinctly different chemical groupings, CH_3, CH_2, and OH. The electrons in each of these groupings have slightly different diamagnetic properties, so that the usual proton resonance signal is split into three different components as shown in Fig. 9.14. The intensity ratio of the three components is $1:2:3$, which corresponds to the fact that the OH group has a single proton, the CH_2 group has two protons,

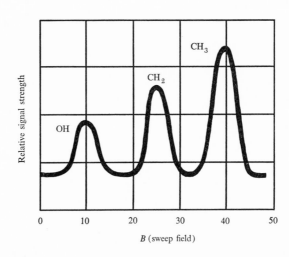

FIGURE 9.14

Proton resonance shifts for the three molecular groups of ethyl alcohol.

and the CH_3 group has three protons. The external field used in this experiment is roughly 0.9 weber/m^2. It is also interesting to note that the least affected frequency is that of the OH group and the one shifted most is the CH_3 group signal. This corresponds to the fact that the electrons in the OH structure are more tightly bound and hence less diamagnetic than those in the CH_2 and CH_3 structures. Also, it is important to notice that the chemical shift is quite small, about five parts per million. High-resolution instruments are therefore required to observe this effect.

It is obvious from the foregoing discussion that nuclear magnetic resonance is a powerful tool for determining the electronic environment of the nuclei which are being studied. Consequently, much can be learned about the detailed chemical structure of many complex molecules, particularly protein molecules encountered in biochemistry.

REFERENCES

1. Block, F., W. Hansen, and M. Packard: *Phys. Rev.*, **69**, 127, 946.
2. Purcell, E., H. Torrey, and R. Pound: *Phys. Rev.*, **69**, 37, 1946.
3. Stern, O.: *Z. Phys.*, **7**, 249, 1921; W. Gerlach and O. Stern, *Ann. Phys.*, *Leipzig*, **74**, 673, 1924.
4. Pauli, W.: *Naturwissenschaften*, **12**, 741, 1924.
5. Singer, J. R., and S. D. Johnson: *Rev. Sci. Instr.*, **30**, 92, 1959.
6. Roberts, J. D.: "Nuclear Magnetic Resonance," McGraw-Hill Book Company, New York, 1959.

GENERAL BIBLIOGRAPHY

1. Andrew, E. R.: "Nuclear Magnetic Resonance," Cambridge University Press, London, 1955.
2. Ramsey, N. F.: Nuclear Moments and Statistics, Part III of "Experimental Nuclear Physics," edited by E. Segré, John Wiley and Sons, Inc., New York, 1953.
3. Slichter, C. P.: "Principles of Magnetic Resonance," Harper and Row, Publishers, Incorporated, New York, 1963.
4. Pople, J. A., W. G. Schneider, and H. J. Bernstein: "High-resolution Nuclear Magnetic Resonance," McGraw-Hill Book Company, New York, 1959.
5. NMR and EPR Spectroscopy, NMR-EPR Staff of Varian Associates, Pergamon Press, New York, 1960.

Chapter 10

THE THERMIONIC EMISSION
OF ELECTRONS
FROM METAL SURFACES

10.1 INTRODUCTION

The fact that heated metals emit electrons was discovered by Thomas A. Edison in 1883. (The effect is often called the Edison effect.) However, a quantitative explanation of the phenomenon could not be given until quantum mechanics was thoroughly understood. In spite of this, many practical applications of the Edison effect were found before the theory of thermionic emission was developed. The major use was, and still is, in the filaments or cathodes of various vacuum tubes. The design of efficient cathodes using thermionic emission is still one of the most important fields in electronics. More recently, serious attempts to convert thermal energy directly into electricity have been made using thermionic emission. The idea is quite simple: A metal plate is heated by some energy source causing electrons to be emitted. The electrons are collected on another plate (the anode), and the resulting current is employed for whatever purpose is desired. Such a device (a diode) would be particularly desirable for the direct conversion of nuclear energy to electrical power. In this case the hot metal plate could be a fuel element of a nuclear reactor. To accomplish this objective in practice is quite difficult. Much of the recent quantitative work in the field of thermionic emission has been inspired by this goal, and some of the results of this work will be discussed in more detail in the following sections.

10.2 THE BEHAVIOR OF ELECTRONS IN METALS

In Chapter 8 an elementary theory of the structure of metals was presented. This theory was developed by A. Sommerfeld and his collaborators, and it is based on the assumption that some electrons can move freely inside a metal. A derivation of the statistical distribution function of the electrons (or electron "gas") is given in Appendix II, and it successfully explains many electrical and thermal properties of metals. The important point to stress is that the density of free electrons is sufficiently large that a quantum mechanical distribution function must be used. The properties of the Fermi distribution function have already been discussed (see Chapter 8), but a short description here will be necessary to introduce the principles of thermionic emission.

The Fermi energy distribution is shown in Fig. 8.2 of Chapter 8, for a number of different temperatures. The energy level diagram of the metal has also been discussed and is shown in Fig. 8.7 of Chapter 8. The electrons move essentially as if they were free. Therefore, for the purpose of calculating the thermionic emission of electrons, the metal surface has an energy level structure as shown in Fig. 10.1. The metal can be considered as a potential well in which the electrons move freely. While at the surface of the metal, there is a potential energy step E_s. This energy can be considered as the sum of two energies, the Fermi energy E_f and an energy ϕ, which is usually called the "work function" of the metal:

$$E_s = E_f + \phi \tag{10.1}$$

Strictly speaking, the potential step shown in Fig. 10.1 is not quite accurate because the electron, once it leaves the metal surface, also experiences an attractive force due to an "image charge" inside the metal. This effect will be discussed in a subsequent section of this chapter.

The work function is defined as the minimum energy which must be supplied to an electron to remove it from the metal at 0°K. A less cumbersome definition is simply Eq. (10.1). The work function is the difference between the Fermi energy and the potential well depth. The smaller the work function, the easier it is to liberate an electron from

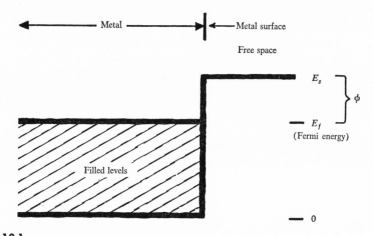

FIGURE 10.1

Electron potential energy level diagram at a metal surface.

the metal surface. This, however, is not the only criterion for choosing a good thermionic emitter; the physical properties of the materials are also important.

10.3 ELECTRON EMISSION CURRENT FROM METALS

It is a straightforward matter to derive the expression for the emission current by calculating the number of electrons in the metal which strike the surface per unit time with energies greater than E_s. Suppose that the x direction is taken as being perpendicular to the surface of the metal. The number of electrons per unit volume having momentum components between p_x and $p_x + dp_x$ is $n(p_x)\, dp_x$. The function $n(p_x)$ is the Fermi distribution function if the present model is applied, or it may be some other distribution function more appropriate to the case.

Thus the number of electrons striking the surface of the metal per square centimeter per second is $v_x n(p_x)\, dp_x$. The contribution to the emission current for electrons in this momentum range is $e v_x n(p_x)\, dp_x$. The total emission current is therefore

$$J = \frac{e}{m} \int_{p_s}^{\infty} p_x n(p_x)\, dp_x \qquad (10.2)$$

The lower limit of the integral p_s is the momentum corresponding to E_s, where E_s is the minimum energy an electron must have if it is to escape from the metal.

The emission current is calculated by evaluating the integral of Eq. (10.2) using the Fermi distribution for $n(p_x)$. The number of states available to an electron in the momentum interval $dp_x\, dp_y\, dp_z$ is

$$\frac{2}{h^3} dp_x\, dp_y\, dp_z \qquad (10.3)$$

This expression has the dimensions of reciprocal volume so that it defines the number of energy states available per unit volume. Using the Fermi energy distribution, Eq. (II.27) Appendix II, and multiplying it by expression (10.3) gives the number of electrons per unit volume in the momentum interval $dp_x\, dp_y\, dp_z$. Thus

$$n(p_x p_y p_z)\, dp_x\, dp_y\, dp_z = \frac{2}{h^3} \frac{dp_x\, dp_y\, dp_z}{e^{(E-E_f)/kT} + 1} \qquad (10.4)$$

where

$$E = \frac{1}{2m}\,(p_x^2 + p_y^2 + p_z^2) \qquad (10.5)$$

The only contribution to the emission current is from those electrons for which $E_x > E_s$. Thus the y and z components of the momentum distribution in Eq. (10.4) do not contribute to the current and must be integrated out in the final result. This gives for the x component distribution

$$n(p_x)dp_x = \frac{2}{h^3} dp_x \int_{-\infty}^{\infty} \int_{-\infty}^{\infty} \frac{dp_y\, dp_z}{e^{(E-E_f)/kT} + 1} \qquad (10.6)$$

In order to evaluate the integral in Eq. (10.6), it is necessary to make a simple approximation. Since $E_s > E_f$ and since for the present case $E - E_f \gg kT$, only the exponential term in the Fermi distribution need be considered. Using this approximation

$$n(p_x)\, dp_x = \frac{2}{h^3} e^{E_f/kT}\, e^{-p_x^2/2mkT}\, dp_x \int_{-\infty}^{\infty} \int_{-\infty}^{\infty} e^{-(p_y^2 + p_z^2)/2mkT}\, dp_y\, dp_z$$

$$= \frac{4\pi mkT}{h^3} e^{E_f/kT} e^{-p_x^2/2mkT}\, dp_x \qquad (10.7)$$

By substituting the result obtained in Eq. (10.7) into Eq. (10.2), the emission current is

$$J = \frac{e}{m} \frac{4\pi mkT}{h^3} e^{E_f/kT} \int_{P_s}^{\infty} p_x e^{-p_x^2/2mkT} \, dp_x$$

$$= \frac{e}{m} \frac{4\pi mkT}{h^3} mkT \, e^{(E_f - E_s)/kT} \tag{10.8}$$

This equation is usually written in the following form

$$J = A_0 T^2 e^{-\phi/kT} \tag{10.9}$$

where the definition, Eq. (10.1), of the work function ϕ has been used. The constant A_0 is

$$A_0 = \frac{4\pi emk^2}{h^3} = 120 \text{ amps cm}^{-2} \text{ deg}^{-2} \tag{10.10}$$

Equation (10.9) is called the Richardson-Dushman[1] law, and it predicts the thermionic emission-current density as a function of temperature and work function.

10.4 VACUUM DIODES AND SPACE-CHARGE LIMITATION

The electron emission characteristics of materials are measured using a vacuum diode. This device has two electrodes, a cathode which is made of the material to be investigated and which can be heated to high temperatures, and an anode designed to collect the electrons. Two commonly used geometrical arrangements of vacuum diode electrodes are shown in Fig. 10.2. The flat-plate geometry has the advantage that the electric field between the plates is uniform, but it has the drawback that the cathode must necessarily be rather large. This means that considerable power must be used to heat the cathode to appropriate temperatures. The upper limit of the temperature is determined primarily by the fact that the vacuum envelope must survive.

In the cylindrical geometry, the cathode is much smaller, so that higher temperatures can be attained. However, the electric field is no longer uniform, so that calculations are not as simple as in the flat-plate case. End effects may also cause field distortions which can be eliminated by installing grounded guard rings as shown in Fig. 10.2. When vacuum diodes such as these are used to determine emission characteristics, great care must be taken to see that the residual gases adsorbed on the electrodes and the vacuum envelope are eliminated by baking out the diode at high vacuum. If this is not done, ionized residual gas atoms may produce currents which will be confused with electron emission currents.

To verify the Richardson-Dushman equation [Eq. (10.9)], the electron current must be measured as a function of cathode temperature. The current is determined using the circuit shown in Fig. 10.3. The cathode temperature is usually obtained by observing the cathode through the glass envelope (or a glass viewing port) with a calibrated optical

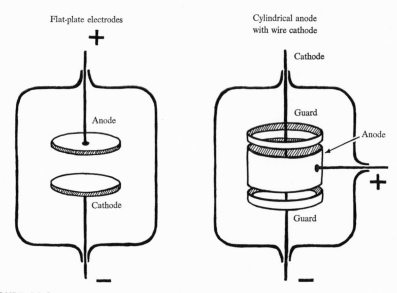

FIGURE 10.2

Two cathode–anode configurations for thermionic diodes.

pyrometer. For these purposes Eq. (10.9) is usually rewritten in the following form:

$$\ln \frac{J}{T^2} = \ln A_0 - \frac{\phi}{kT} \tag{10.11}$$

Therefore, if $\ln J/T^2$ is plotted against $1/T$, a straight-line plot should result with an intercept depending on the constant A_0 [see Eq. (10.10)], and a slope determined by the work function ϕ of the material.

In practice, the measurement of ϕ by the method outlined above is valid only if the emission currents are kept very small. If too many electrons are emitted by the cathode, they form a cloud of negative charge around the cathode which tends to inhibit the emission of additional electrons. This phenomenon is called space-charge limitation, and to include it properly in the analysis of experimental results requires a modification of the Richardson-Dushman equation [Eq. (10.9)]. It is thus often desirable to perform the experiments in such a way that the anode can be biased positively with respect to the cathode in order to draw electrons from the cathode. Experiments of this kind can be performed using the circuit shown in Fig. 10.3, in which an anode-bias power supply is included.

The Richardson-Dushman equation will be considered in two steps. The first accounts for the different work functions and the biasing potentials which may exist between the anode and the cathode. The

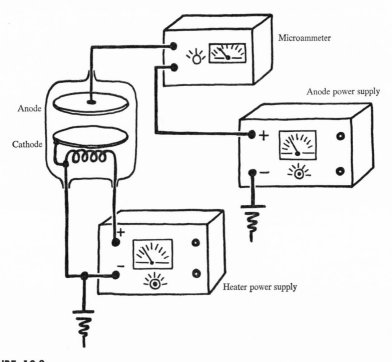

FIGURE 10.3

Instrumentation for measuring i-v characteristics of a thermionic diode.

second accounts for the distortion of the electric field between the anode and cathode caused by the presence of the electrons between them. The energy level diagram of both the anode and cathode when the anode potential is zero ($V_A = 0$) is shown in Fig. 10.4. Their Fermi levels are the same, for the cathode and anode are both grounded externally. In the case illustrated, the anode work function ϕ_A is smaller than the cathode work function ϕ_C. If the two materials are connected by an external conductor, and if the cathode is hot, electrons can flow between the electrodes. The "contact" potential,

$\Delta = \phi_C - \phi_A$, which exists between the electrodes, does not create any additional potential for the electrons to overcome, so that they will flow unimpeded from the cathode to the anode.

The opposite occurs if the anode is operated at a negative potential with respect to the cathode, since the applied anode potential simply changes the difference between the Fermi levels of the cathode and anode. The net effect of applying an anode potential will be to change the minimum energy an electron must have to move from the cathode

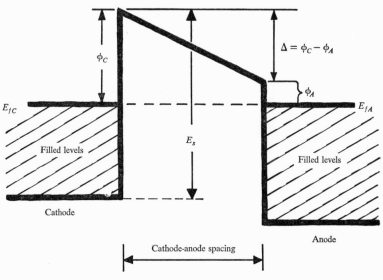

FIGURE 10.4

Electron potential energy level diagram for the region between a cathode and anode, both of which are grounded.

to the anode. In the experiment illustrated in Fig. 10.3, the current in the circuit is determined not by the electrons leaving the cathode but by those which reach the anode. If the anode potential V_A is negative, the energy level diagram shown in Fig. 10.4 must be modified to the one given in Fig. 10.5. The lower limit of the integral in Eq. (10.8) is now equal to either E_s or E'_s, whichever is larger. If $E'_s < E_s$, the electrons do not have to overcome any potential greater than E_s to reach the anode so that the emission current is unaffected. However, if $E'_s > E_s$ as shown in Fig. 10.5, the electrons must surmount an increased potential to reach the anode with the result that the observed current will therefore be reduced. The magnitude of this new potential barrier shown in Fig. 10.5 is

$$E'_s = E_{fC} + V_A + \phi_A \qquad (10.12)$$

In the case that E'_s is greater than E_s (i.e., $V_A \geq \Delta$ or $V_A \geq \phi_C - \phi_A$),

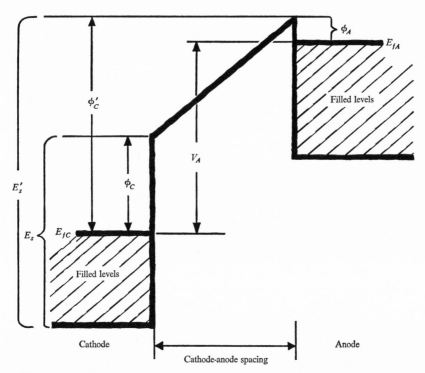

FIGURE 10.5

Electron potential energy-level diagram with the anode biased negative by the amount V_A.

E_s in Eq. (10.8) must be replaced by E'_s, so that the electron current is

$$J = A_0 T^2 e^{-(E_{fC} + V_A + \phi_A - E_{fC})/kT}$$
$$= A_0 T^2 e^{-(V_A + \phi_A)/kT} \qquad (10.13)$$

Adding and subtracting ϕ_C from the numerator of the exponent make it possible to rewrite Eq. (10.13) as

$$J = (A_0 T^2 e^{-\phi_C/kT}) e^{-[V_A + (\phi_C - \phi_A)]/kT} \qquad (10.14)$$

Equation (10.14) defines the current-voltage characteristic of the diode. For a constant temperature, the first term in Eq. (10.14) is a

Vacuum diodes and space-charge limitation **209**

constant, J_0, since it depends only on the properties of the cathode material. It can be seen that the current J_0, usually called the saturation current, will be observed when the bias potential is equal to or greater than the contact potential (i.e., Eq. 10.14 simply becomes Eq. 10.9). If, however, the bias potential V_A is more negative that the contact potential $\phi_C - \phi_A$, then $E'_s > E_s$ and the quantity E'_s must be used as the lower limit of integration. Thus Eq. (10.14) must be used to compute the emission current and the second exponential will attenuate the saturation current in the brackets.

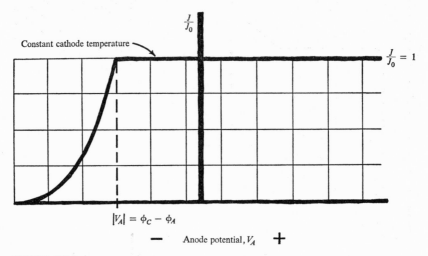

FIGURE 10.6

Current-voltage characteristic for a diode with a constant cathode temperature.

The diode i-v characteristics for various anode potentials V_A are shown in Fig. 10.6. In this derivation it has been assumed that $\phi_C > \phi_A$. If $\phi_A > \phi_C$, the result is still the same except that the saturation current will be reached for positive values of the anode potential instead of negative anode potentials. The current-voltage relation shown in Fig. 10.6 [and given by Eq. (10.14)] is valid only in the absence of space-charge effects.

In order to account properly for the existence of free charges between the plates, the electric field existing between the plates must be modified. Qualitatively, the situation is illustrated in Fig. 10.7. For no space charge, the electric field is constant and the potential between the anode and the cathode is V_1. As the space charge increases, the electrons act to neutralize the field so that the potential near the cathode will be less than the value which would exist if there were no electrons. As the space charge increases further, the gradient of the potential at the surface, dV/dx, eventually vanishes. There will then be no electric field at the boundary, so that no further electron current can be drawn from the cathode. Increasing the potential difference does not increase the emission current. The current is therefore said to be emission limited. When this occurs, the effective potential between the plates will be V_3. If the cathode temperature is raised, more electrons will

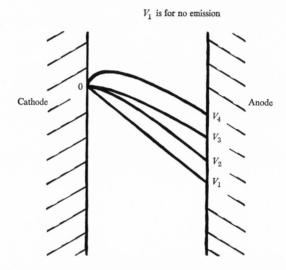

V_1 is for no emission

Cathode 0 Anode V_4 V_3 V_2 V_1

FIGURE 10.7

Electron space-charge neutralization for increased emission currents.

be driven off, and the resulting charge cloud near the cathode will reverse the direction of the electrostatic force at the cathode. In this case the emission is space-charge limited, and the potential function is the curve 0 to V_4 shown in Fig. 10.7.

To compute the diode characteristic when space-charge effects are important, Poisson's equation must be applied. This equation relates the charge density in a region to the electrostatic potential in the region and is a generalization of Coulomb's law:

$$\nabla^2 V = 4\pi\rho \qquad (10.15)$$

The charge density ρ is equal to the number of electrons per unit volume residing between the diode plates. The charge density can be related to the current density using the equation

$$J = v\rho \qquad (10.16)$$

where v is the average velocity of the charges. Therefore, in terms of the current J defined before, Poisson's equation becomes

$$\nabla^2 V = 4\pi \frac{J}{v} \qquad (10.17)$$

This equation is difficult to solve because J and v are generally functions of position in some complicated manner. In the case of the flat-plate diode (see Fig. 10.7), it is possible to make some simplifying assumptions. The electrostatic potential now depends only on the x direction, so that

$$\nabla^2 V = \frac{d^2 V}{dx^2} \qquad (10.18)$$

The kinetic energy of the electron can be related to the potential at the point x by the equation (see Fig. 10.8)

$$\tfrac{1}{2} mv^2 = eV(x) \qquad (10.19)$$

This relation is valid if the electron leaves the cathode with a velocity which is small compared to the velocity it has at the point x. Also, the velocity of the electron must be sufficiently small so that the classical expression for the kinetic energy is valid. The velocity of the electron at the point x is thus

$$v = \left(\frac{2eV(x)}{m} \right)^{1/2} \qquad (10.20)$$

so that Poisson's equation becomes

$$\frac{d^2 V}{dx^2} = 4\pi J \left(\frac{m}{2e} \right)^{1/2} (V(x))^{-1/2} \qquad (10.21)$$

It can readily be shown that the solution of this equation for two plates separated by a distance d is

$$V = 9\pi J d^2 \frac{m^{2/3}}{2e} \qquad (10.22)$$

Thus the current density J in the space-charge limited case considered here is

$$J = \frac{1}{9\pi} \frac{V^{3/2}}{d^2} \frac{2e}{m} \qquad (10.23)$$

This relation was first derived by C. D. Child[2] in 1911 and is usually referred to as Child's law. Thus, instead of the exponential relation between the current and the voltage shown in Fig. 10.6, at high emission currents the relation changes to a much slower ($\frac{3}{2}$ power) dependence. The current will continue to increase according to Eq. (10.23) until the saturation current is reached.

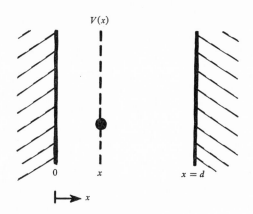

$$V(x)$$

$$0 \qquad x \qquad\qquad x = d$$

$$\longmapsto x$$

FIGURE 10.8

Geometrical considerations in deriving Child's law.

10.5 THE SCHOTTKY EFFECT

In Sec. 10.1 it was assumed that the electrons in a metal move in the potential field shown in Fig. 10.1. It was also pointed out that this picture is not quite accurate because of the image potential which exists between the electron and a conducting surface. A more accurate surface potential is illustrated in Fig. 10.9. If the distance between the electron and the surface of the metal is x, the force on the electron is

$$F = \frac{e^2}{(2x)^2} \tag{10.24}$$

so that in addition to the well potential there is the following image potential:

$$V = \frac{e^2}{4x} \tag{10.25}$$

This potential caused by the image charge must be added to the potential between the plates. If the external field is small, the potential gradient is weak and the image potential goes to zero before it can cause any effect. (This result is illustrated in Fig. 10.9.) If the external field between the plates is strong, the image potential tends to lower the barrier which the electron must surmount in order to leave the

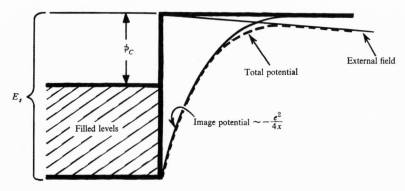

FIGURE 10.9

Electron surface potential considering image charges and in the presence of a weak external field.

metal surface. (This result is illustrated in Fig. 10.10.) The total potential is now

$$V(x) = -\frac{e^2}{4x} - eEx = -\frac{e^2}{4x} - e\frac{V}{d}x \qquad (10.26)$$

The maximum, pictured in Fig. 10.10, occurs at the point

$$x_m = \frac{1}{2}\left(\frac{e}{E}\right)^{\frac{1}{2}} \qquad (10.27)$$

The change in the work function $\Delta\phi$ is equal to the potential [Eq. (10.26)] evaluated at x_m:

$$\Delta\phi = V(x_m) = -e(eE)^{\frac{1}{2}} = -e^{\frac{3}{2}}\left(\frac{V}{d}\right)^{\frac{1}{2}} \qquad (10.28)$$

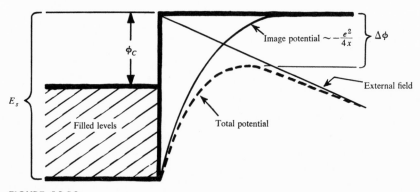

FIGURE 10.10

Work-function decrease as a result of a strong external field.

214 *Thermionic emission of electrons from metal surfaces*

The current at saturation is now given by Eq. (10.14) with an extra term due to $\Delta\phi$ of Eq. (10.28):

$$J = A_0 T^2 e^{(-\phi_c + \Delta\phi)/kT}$$

or

$$\frac{J}{J_0} = e^{\Delta\phi/kT} \tag{10.29}$$

The saturation current is thus increased above the Richardson-Dushman value as a result of the lowering of the potential barrier. This phenomenon is usually called the Schottky[3] effect; it was discovered in 1914 by W. Schottky.

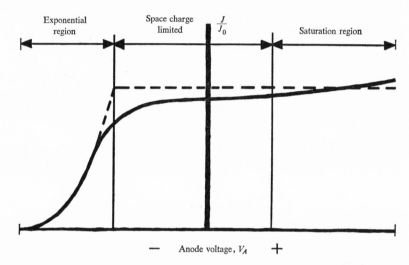

FIGURE 10.11

Current-voltage characteristics of a diode at high electron emission densities.

Qualitatively, the current-voltage relation of a diode at high current densities, considering all effects, is shown in Fig. 10.11. At low fields the dependence is exponential; then at higher voltages the space-charge limited dependence is observed, and finally the saturation current is reached.

In view of the complicated manner in which the current depends on the applied voltage, it is not always easy to determine the quantities ϕ and A_0. (These constants fix the behavior of the diode and are thus the important quantities which must be determined.) The usual procedure is to measure the current at several anode voltages and a number of different cathode temperatures. If for a given temperature $\ln J$ is plotted against $E^{1/2}$, a straight line should result [see Eqs.

The Schottky effect **215**

(10.28) and (10.29)]. When this line is extrapolated to $E = 0$, the saturation current for that temperature should be obtained. By using these values of J_0, a plot of $\ln J_0/T^2$ versus $1/T$ should yield the correct values of A_0 and ϕ.

10.6 DESCRIPTION OF THE EXPERIMENT

Two experimental arrangements suitable for measuring diode i-v characteristics are illustrated in Figs. 10.12 and 10.13. The difference

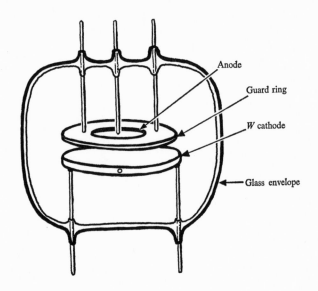

FIGURE 10.12

Resistance heated cathode-glass envelope diode.

between the two is that the diode of Fig. 10.12 is enclosed in a glass vessel, creating a static vacuum condition, whereas the diode of Fig. 10.13 can be enclosed in a conventional vacuum vessel, which can be pumped during the experiment. The advantage of the glass diode is that no vacuum equipment is required once the diode has been constructed, whereas in the live-vacuum diode, modifications can be made by simply opening the vacuum vessel. In either case the measurements should be made at a pressure of 10^{-7} torr or less.

The two diodes are essentially the same except for the live and static vacuums. The cathode should be a refractory metal (usually tungsten) which can be heated to sufficiently high temperatures for electron emission (1000 to 2300°C) without melting. The anode can be made of any material that is not affected by the thermal radiation from the cathode. Copper is a very suitable anode material. The anode, as indicated in Figs. 10.12 and 10.13, should have an annular guard ring around it so that a fringe field between the cathode and anode does not affect the electron emission.

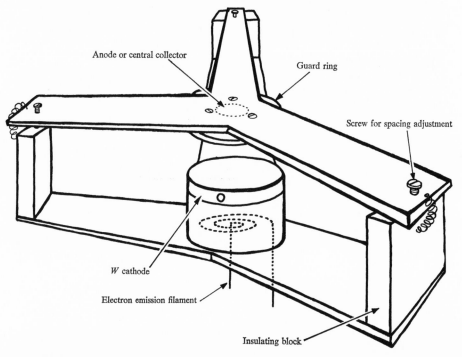

FIGURE 10.13

Thermionic diode with an electron bombardment heated cathode for use in a live vacuum.

The cathode can be either resistance heated, as illustrated in Fig. 10.12, or heated by electron bombardment, as illustrated in Fig. 10.13. Resistance heating has the undesirable feature that the potential drop across the cathode creates a nonuniform field between the cathode and anode. Therefore, instead of direct current to heat the cathode, half-wave rectified alternating current is used, and the i-v characteristics are measured during the off half-cycle.

If electron-bombardment heating is used, no potential gradients exist across the cathode face, and hence i-v characteristics can be measured continuously. However, without elaborate feedback controls

Description of the experiment **217**

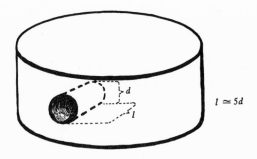

$l \simeq 5d$

FIGURE 10.14

Black-body hole proportions for measuring cathode temperatures.

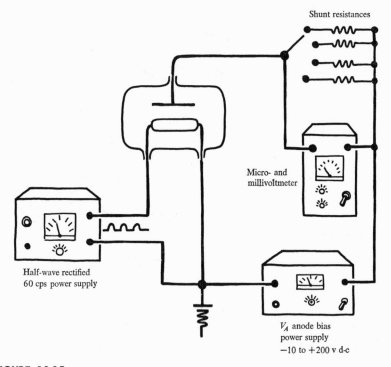

Shunt resistances

Micro- and
millivoltmeter

Half-wave rectified
60 cps power supply

V_A anode bias
power supply
-10 to $+200$ v d-c

FIGURE 10.15

Instrumentation required to measure diode i-v characteristics for resistance-heated cathode.

electron bombardment is not suitable above 2000°C because it is not stable. At higher cathode temperatures the thermal radiation from the cathode heats the electron-emitting filament, causing more electron emission, which in turn causes a further rise in the cathode temperature. This positive feedback situation will run away, causing the filament to burn out.

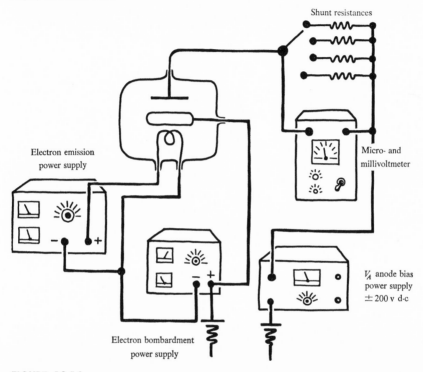

FIGURE 10.16

Instrumentation required to measure diode i-v characteristic for electron bombardment heated cathode.

For either diode, the cathode temperature should be measured using an optical pyrometer. Optical pyrometers are calibrated to measure the radiation emitted by a black body, so that if the temperature of the cathode is measured by viewing its surface, a correction must be made for the cathode thermal emissivity. This problem can be circumvented by drilling a small black-body hole (length ≃ 5 times the diameter) in the side of the cathode as illustrated in Fig. 10.14. The radiation spectrum emitted from such a hole closely approximates the Planck distribution.

Description of the experiment **219**

The viewing window in the diode body should be quartz so that the thermal spectrum is not distorted. The quartz window is easy to incorporate in the case of a metal body diode. However, if a glass diode is used, a temperature correction should be made by inserting an addi-

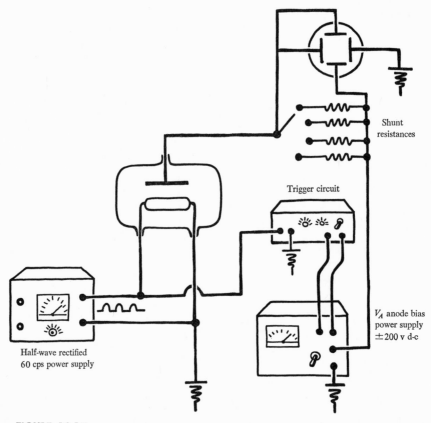

FIGURE 10.17

Instrumentation required to measure diode i-v characteristics on an oscilloscope.

tional piece of glass (the same material and thickness as the diode wall) between the diode and pyrometer and observing the temperature shift. The diode wall can be assumed to cause a similar shift.

The diode of Fig. 10.13 has incorporated an anode which is mounted on adjusting screws so that the cathode-anode spacing can be varied. This device is useful for measuring the Schottky effect, which can be observed at a field of 10^4 volts/cm (i.e., a 1 mm spacing and a cathode-anode voltage of 100 volts).

The circuits necessary for measuring the *i-v* characteristics of both the resistance-heated cathode and the electron-bombardment-heated cathode are shown in Figs. 10.15 and 10.16, respectively. Shunt resistances are used to measure the cathode-anode current by measuring the voltage drop across the known resistances. The value of the shunt resistance must be small compared with the internal impedance of the diode (i.e., contact potential/emission current) so that the potential drop across the resistance is small compared with the contact potential. Thus, at a low emission current of 1 μa, the shunt resistance can be

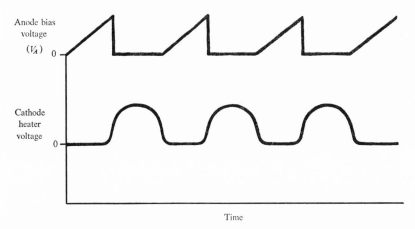

FIGURE 10.18

Relative sequence of cathode-heater voltage and anode-bias voltage.

1000 ohms (i.e., $\Delta V = 1 \times 10^{-6}$ amp $\times 10^3$ ohms $= 10^{-3}$ volt, which is small compared with a Δ of $\sim$1 volt), while at an emission current of 100 ma the shunt resistance should be 0.1 ohm (i.e., $\Omega = 10^{-2}$ volt/ $10^{-1}\,a = 10^{-1}$ ohm).

As was stated previously, the *i-v* characteristics of the diode in the resistance-heated case must be measured in the off portion of the half-wave restified voltage. For this reason it is desirable to employ a dynamic rather than a static method to measure the diode characteristics. The circuit used for this purpose is shown in Fig. 10.17. If the heat capacity (or "thermal inertia") of the cathode is sufficiently large, the cathode temperature does not change substantially during the "off" part of the rectified cycle. The anode power supply generates the saw-toothed signal shown in Fig. 10.18. The saw-tooth generator is on during the "off" part of the heater cycle so that the field at the cathode is not distorted by the heater voltage drop. If the inputs of an oscilloscope are connected to the circuit as shown in Fig. 10.17, the voltage across the vertical axis will be proportional to the current between the cathode and the anode of the diode. The horizontal axis is connected so that the cathode-anode potential difference appears directly as a horizontal deflection. Thus, as the bias potential is varied, the i-v characteristic of the diode will appear on the face of the oscilloscope. This circuit is particularly useful, for example, in determining diode characteristics as a function of cathode temperature. It also has other important applications in determining diode characteristics of tubes which may contain some gas in the glass envelope. The behavior of diodes under these circumstances will be discussed in the next section.

10.7 SPACE-CHARGE NEUTRALIZATION

Recently much work has been done on high-current diodes. These investigations have been stimulated by the need for finding more efficient ways to convert the power produced in nuclear reactors directly to electrical power. In principle, a diode can be used for this purpose. The cathode of such a power-conversion diode is heated by the reactor. The current drawn from the cathode can then be used directly. Since only small voltages are developed across the diode plates, a conversion system is necessary to transform the high-current low-voltage power obtained from the diode to electrical power of more conventional voltages.

The most important difficulty which must be overcome before such a process can work in practice is the space-charge limitation discussed in Sec. 10.5. The electron cloud in the vicinity of the cathode severely restricts the current (and hence the power) which can be produced. In order to use the diode as a power converter, the electron space charge is usually neutralized by placing a positive ion cloud in the neighborhood of the cathode. The positive ions are most easily made by filling the diode with a gas which has an ionization potential that is smaller than the work function of the cathode material. A commonly used material is cesium, which has an ionization potential of 3.9 volts compared to the work function of the cathode material (usually 4.5 volts for tungsten). When cesium vapor comes in contact with the cathode, the difference in work functions causes the cesium to be ionized. The positive cesium ions produced in this manner serve to neutralize the electron limitation of the space-charge limited region.

Qualitatively, the most important effect of neutralizing the space charge is that the Richardson equation again governs the emission current rather than the Child equation. This statement is true only under certain conditions of cathode temperature and cesium pressure. If the cesium pressure is high or if the current density is large, then layers of positive ions or electrons (sheaths) tend to form. These cause complicated potential distributions to appear between the anode and the cathode. Under these conditions it is generally not possible to predict the diode characteristics with any precision.

The neutralizing effect of cesium vapor may be observed experimentally using a diode and a circuit similar to the one employed in the vacuum diode experiments. The static-vacuum diode is used by putting

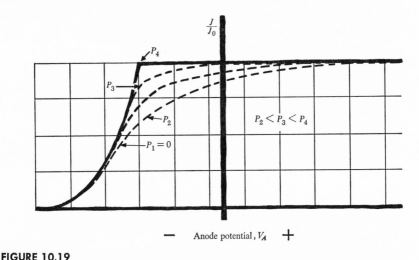

FIGURE 10.19

Space charge neutralized i-v characteristics.

a few grams of cesium in it before it is sealed off. The vapor pressure of the cesium is then varied by immersing the diode body in a variable temperature bath. The current-voltage characteristics obtained for various cesium pressures are shown in Fig. 10.19. Initially, as the cesium pressure is increased, more current is drawn from the cathode until at some upper limit of cesium pressure, the current no longer increases. At this point enough cesium ions exist between the electrodes to neutralize all the electrons, and adding more ions will not change the current. The curve in Fig. 10.19 illustrates how neutralization of the space charge causes the diode characteristics to approach the shape predicted by the Richardson equation. Much work is being done on cesium plasma diodes of the type described here to try to achieve direct power conversion.

Space-charge neutralization **223**

REFERENCES

1. Richardson, O. W.: *Proc. Cambridge Phil. Soc.*, **11**, 286, 1901; Dushman, S.: *Phys. Rev.*, **21**, 623, 1923.
2. Child, C. D.: *Phys. Rev.*, **32**, 498, 1911.
3. Schottky, W.: *Z. Physic.*, **15**, 872, 1914.

GENERAL BIBLIOGRAPHY

1. Beck, A. H. W.: "Thermionic Values," Cambridge University Press, New York, 1953.
2. Kaye, J., and J. A. Welsh: "Direct Conversion of Heat to Electricity," John Wiley & Sons, Inc., New York, 1960.
3. Dekker A. J.: "Solid-State Physics," Prentice-Hall, Inc., Englewood Cliffs, N.J., 1957.

Chapter 11	# LASERS AND THE STIMULATED EMISSION OF RADIATION

11.1 INTRODUCTION

In recent years a number of devices have been developed which produce and amplify beams of electromagnetic radiation using stimulated emission. The first of these operated at microwave frequencies and was developed in 1954 by C. H. Townes and his collaborators at Columbia University.[1] This device was called the *maser*, which is an acronym for Microwave Amplification by the Stimulated Emission of Radiation. Devices of this kind also have been built to operate at other frequencies of the electromagnetic spectrum. The instrument of interest for the present purpose operates in the visible frequency range and is called the *laser* (i.e., light instead of microwave). The most significant property possessed by these instruments is that they are able to produce very intense and well-collimated beams of radiation. In order to understand in detail how this is done, the phenomenon of stimulated emission must be thoroughly explained.

11.2 STIMULATED EMISSION OF RADIATION

The stimulated emission of electromagnetic radiation is a consequence of the principle of detailed balance and of the quantum theory of radia-

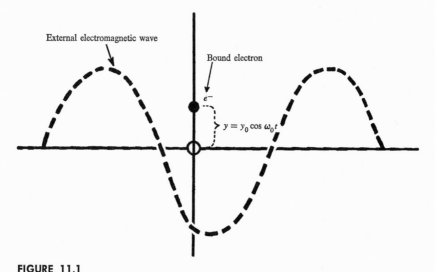

FIGURE 11.1

External electromagnetic wave passing a bound atomic electron.

tion. The existence of stimulated emission was recognized nearly sixty years ago by Einstein.[2] He showed that stimulated emission was necessary to explain the behavior of radiation in thermodynamic equilibrium with matter. However, the effect was not observed directly at optical frequencies until 1960 (T. H. Maiman[3]), for very special circumstances are necessary to induce and observe stimulated emission successfully.

In terms of classical arguments, the existence of stimulated emission is very easy to demonstrate. Consider a bound electron oscillating with a frequency ω_0 as shown in Fig. 11.1. An electromagnetic wave of the same frequency and relative phase ϕ passes over the oscillating electron. The rate at which energy is transferred from the wave to the electron is

$$\frac{dw}{dt} = e|\mathbf{E}|\left(\frac{dy}{dt}\right) \tag{11.1}$$

where $\mathbf{E}$ is the electric field vector and dy/dt is the electron velocity. Now,

$$y = y_0 \cos \omega_0 t \tag{11.2}$$

and $$\mathbf{E} = \mathbf{E}_0 \cos (\omega_0 t + \phi) \tag{11.3}$$

Substituting Eqs. (11.2) and (11.3) into Eq. (11.1), and averaging over one cycle, determines the energy transfer per cycle. The result of the substitution is

$$w = \tfrac{1}{2} y_0 \mathbf{E}_0 \sin \phi \tag{11.4}$$

The quantity w can be positive or negative depending on the value of the phase angle ϕ. If it is positive, the wave transfers energy to the electron; if it is negative, the oscillating electron gives some of its energy to the wave. Thus energy from the wave is either absorbed or the wave can "stimulate" the electron to "emit" some radiant energy.

The existence of stimulated emission can also be deduced from the quantum statistics of the radiation field. The cavity shown in Fig. 11.2 contains radiant energy such that there are n_ν photons in the frequency interval between ν and $\nu + d\nu$. Assume that the walls are made of oscillators which can emit and absorb radiation in the frequency interval ν to $\nu + d\nu$. Oscillators in the energy level n can absorb a photon and make a transition to level m with an absorption probability A_{nm}. Similarly, the oscillators in the energy level m can emit a photon and return to the level n with a probability B_{mn}. If the system is in an equilibrium state, these quantities are related as follows:

$$A_{nm} e^{-E_n/kT} = B_{mn} e^{-E_m/kT} \tag{11.5}$$

That is, the number of transitions $n \to m$ must be equal to the number of transitions $m \to n$. The exponential factors determine the fraction of the oscillators which are in the states m and n, respectively. (These factors are usually called the "Boltzmann" factors.) The ratio of the absorption to the emission probability is then

$$\frac{A_{nm}}{B_{mn}} = e^{(E_n - E_m)/kT} \tag{11.6}$$

This ratio can now be expressed in terms of the number of light quanta (or photons) which exist in the radiation field having frequencies between ν and $\nu + d\nu$. The number of photons n_ν in that frequency interval is given by the Planck distribution law:

$$n_\nu \, d\nu = \frac{d\nu}{e^{h\nu/kT} - 1} \tag{11.7}$$

In Eq. (11.7) h is the Planck constant and k is the Boltzmann constant. In addition to the distribution function given in Eq. (11.7), the energy of the photons in the field is related to the oscillator energy levels by

$$E_m - E_n = h\nu \tag{11.8}$$

which is usually called Planck's condition. By using Eqs. (11.7) and

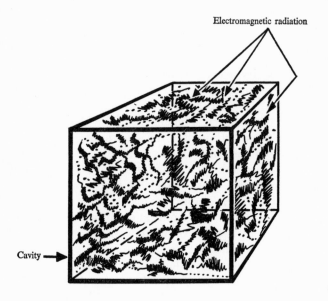

FIGURE 11.2

Electromagnetic radiation "bouncing around" inside a cavity.

(11.8), the ratio of the absorption probability to the emission probability can be expressed in terms of the number of photons in the field as follows:

$$\frac{A_{nm}}{B_{mn}} = e^{E_n - E_m/kT} = e^{-h\nu/kT} = \frac{n_\nu}{n_\nu + 1} \tag{11.9}$$

Therefore it follows that the absorption probability is proportional to the number of photons in the field able to cause transitions between the levels n and m,

$$A_{nm} \sim n_\nu \tag{11.10}$$

228 *Lasers and the stimulated emission of radiation*

and the emission probability is proportional to $n_\nu + 1$, that is,

$$B_{mn} \sim n_\nu + 1 \tag{11.11}$$

A short physical interpretation of the results given in Eqs. (11.10) and (11.11) is appropriate at this point. The meaning of Eq. (11.10) is quite clear, that is, there can be no absorption unless the radiation field contains some photons which can be absorbed by the oscillator. The second condition, Eq. (11.11), is slightly more complicated. There are two terms, one is constant and the other again depends on the number of photons in the field which can cause transitions $m \rightarrow n$. The constant term corresponds to the processes of "spontaneous" emission in which the oscillator emits a photon into the field with an energy given by Eq. (11.8). The term depending on n_ν is called "stimulated" emission. Photons in the field can, if they have the proper frequency, cause the oscillator to make transitions $m \rightarrow n$ and emit photons.

The foregoing arguments show that stimulated emission exists, but they do not touch on some very fundamental features of a radiation field produced entirely by stimulated emission. Using some of the elementary ideas of quantum field theory, it can be shown that all of the photons in such a radiation field have the same propagation vector, that is, they are all in the same "quantum state."[4] In the correspondence limit, this leads to an electromagnetic wave which is moving only in one direction and thus behaves like a highly collimated beam. Moreover, the beam is a coherent beam, so that its intensity is proportional to the square of the number of field sources rather than simply the number of sources. These properties of stimulated emission have led to the important modern applications of the phenomenon. The high degree of collimation of the beam makes it possible to concentrate large amounts of energy in small volumes. The coherence of the beam leads to the important applications of masers, and possibly lasers, as communication devices.

11.3 INTERACTION OF RADIATION WITH MATTER

In the previous section no attempt was made to determine under what conditions it might be possible to observe stimulated emission. The oscillators mentioned are, of course, the atoms of the cavity wall material, and these can emit and absorb radiation in quanta of energy $h\nu$ provided that they have energy levels so that the condition (11.8) is fulfilled. These energy level schemes are, in general, very complicated, so that the particular levels dealt with will not be specified until a particular case is considered.

When a beam of radiation passes through matter, it is attenuated. If the attenuation process is such that the same fraction of the incident beam is scattered in each thickness element dx, then the intensity of the beam at the point x in the material is

$$I = I_0 e^{-\mu_\nu x} \qquad (11.12)$$

where I_0 is the intensity of the incident beam. In the attenuation process it is assumed that *only* absorption occurs, so that the intensity of the beam is always reduced by the presence of the material. Under

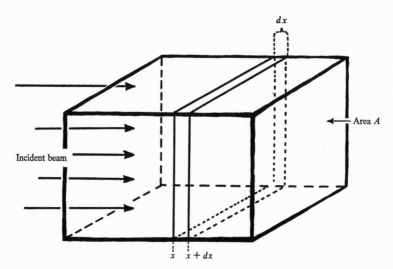

FIGURE 11.3

Attenuation of a beam of photons incident upon a volume of material.

certain circumstances, however, it will be shown that the intensity of a radiation beam can actually be increased when it passes through matter.

Consider a beam of light passing through matter as shown in Fig. 11.3. Assume that there are N_1 atoms per unit volume capable of absorbing photons in the frequency range $\nu + d\nu$ and N_2 atoms per unit volume capable of emitting in the same frequency range. The intensity change in a light beam passing through the volume element $A \, dx$ will thus be

$$-dI_\nu = I_\nu (A_{12} N_1 - B_{21} N_2) A \, dx \qquad (11.13)$$

If it is now assumed that there are many photons in the incident beam (i.e., $n_\nu \gg 1$), then it follows from Eq. (11.9) that

$$A_{12} \approx B_{21} \tag{11.14}$$

Therefore the absorption coefficient μ_ν depends only on N_1 and N_2, the number of atoms in each of the two levels

$$\mu_\nu = K(N_1 - N_2) \tag{11.15}$$

If $N_1 > N_2$, then μ_ν is positive and the light beam is absorbed. However, if $N_2 > N_1$, then μ_ν is negative and the intensity of the beam builds up exponentially as it passes through the material. This amplification is commonly referred to as the laser process.

The next problem is to investigate how the condition for laser action $(N_2 > N_1)$ can be induced and how the effect can best be observed. Assume that the energy of the state 2 is E_2 and the energy of the state 1 is E_1. By the definition of the levels, $E_2 > E_1$. If the radiators are classical oscillators, they obey a Maxwell-Boltzmann distribution. The relative numbers of atoms in each of the levels is then

$$\frac{N_2}{N_1} = \frac{e^{-E_2/kT}}{e^{-E_1/kT}} \tag{11.16}$$

For transitions in which visible light is emitted, the energy difference $(E_2 - E_1)$ is of the order of an electron volt, whereas at room temperature the value of kT is 0.025 ev. Thus the population of the state 2 is very small, relative to that of the state 1. That is,

$$\frac{N_2}{N_1} \approx e^{-40} \approx 10^{-17} \tag{11.17}$$

Under normal circumstances, therefore, μ_ν is always positive, for N_2 is very much smaller than N_1. The material in which stimulated emission is to be observed must thus be subjected to special treatment before any effect can be obtained. Somehow the population of state 2 must be increased so that it becomes sufficiently large to give a measurable change in the absorption coefficient μ_ν as defined in Eq. (11.15). It may sometimes be possible to induce situations where $N_2 > N_1$, that is, where the population of the higher energy state exceeds that of the lower energy state. Such a population inversion gives rise to the exponential growth in intensity discussed before. Systems which contain such a population inversion are often said to possess negative temperatures, owing to the fact that the sign of the temperature in the Boltzmann distribution must be changed if the exponent is to behave in the conventional manner. Actually, temperature is probably not a useful concept when dealing with stimulated emission, for it applies only to a system at or near equilibrium. In many cases where stimulated emission is observed, the systems are far from the equilibrium state.

11.4 THE RUBY LASER

The first practical laser in which some of the principles discussed in the foregoing sections were applied was operated by T. H. Maiman in 1960. A schematic diagram of the instrument is shown in Fig. 11.4. Pink ruby, which is a crystallized form of aluminum oxide (Al_2O_3), is used as the laser element. For reasons which will be discussed shortly, the ruby must contain 0.05 percent chromium impurity. The ruby is in the

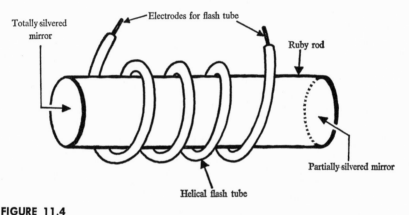

FIGURE 11.4

Schematic illustration of a ruby rod laser.

shape of a cylinder, usually about 1 cm in diameter and 10 cm long. The ends of the cylinder are plane and parallel to each other within a fraction of a wavelength. One of the ends is covered with a totally reflecting material and the other with a material that is partially reflecting. The ruby is placed inside a helical xenon flash tube (or perhaps surrounded by an array of straight tubes). When in operation, the laser beam emerges from the partially reflecting end of the ruby rod.

In order to understand the operating sequence of the laser shown in Fig. 11.4, it is necessary to know something about the energy level structure of the chromium-doped ruby crystal used in the device. A simplified version of the electron energy level scheme is shown in Fig. 11.5. As indicated, ruby has a broad band of energy levels, approximately 2.5 ev above the ground state. Electrons can be raised from the ground state to the band of levels in the ruby by the absorption of the xenon light. The light absorbed by the ruby is in the blue and the green region with a wavelength between 4000 and 5000 Å units. The metastable levels shown in Fig. 11.5 correspond to an excited state in trivalent chromium which is used to dope the ruby. Electrons in these metastable levels can make transitions back to the ground state, emitting red light with a wavelength of 6943 Å units in the process. The metastable levels do not decay instantaneously but have a relatively long half-life compared to usual atomic transitions. Normal atomic processes have characteristic lifetimes ranging from 10^{-9} to 10^{-15} sec, whereas the lifetime of the 6943 Å line is between 2 and

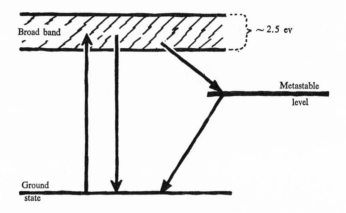

FIGURE 11.5

Electron energy level diagram of chromium doped ruby showing metastable excited chromium level.

3 msec at room temperature. The long lifetime of these levels is absolutely essential to the operation of the laser, for it would not otherwise be possible to obtain the required level inversion.

By applying the principles discussed in the previous paragraph, the operation of the laser can now be described. The light from the flash tube is absorbed and electrons are raised to the broad band of levels. Some of these electrons make radiative transitions back to the ground state immediately, while others populate the metastable levels. These transitions to the metastable states occur without the emission of radiation. The flash tube is on for approximately half a millisecond, which is sufficient time to fill the metastable levels to some equilibrium concentration. The metastable states start to decay and most of the light emitted escapes out the walls of the tube. A small fraction of the light is emitted within a small cone along the axis of the ruby rod. These radiations are reflected by the mirrors at the end of the cylinder. The wave passes back and forth through the ruby rod hundreds of thousands of times, and the probability that the photons corresponding to this wave stimulate other transitions from the metastable levels is quite large. Since the photons produced by stimulated emission are always emitted in the same direction as the incident wave, the stimulated photons serve to reinforce the wave moving parallel to the laser axis. The laser light can be observed, for it passes through the half-silvered end of the laser rod. The process is illustrated in Fig. 11.6. It is in this way that very intense, collimated, and coherent beams of light are produced.

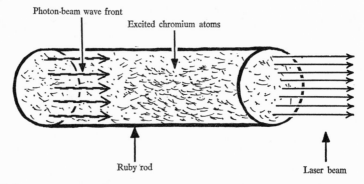

FIGURE 11.6

Schematic illustration of photon-beam amplification from stimulated decay of excited chromium atoms.

The light pulses appear with a definite time history which serves to confirm the process described. A typical time sequence for laser action is shown in Fig. 11.7. The relative durations of the various processes are also illustrated. The spikes of approximately 1 msec in duration represent the rapid buildup of stimulated emission. The pulses decrease again because the metastable levels are actually emptied by the large number of photons produced by the stimulated emission process. The microsecond "laser" pulses reappear as long as the flash-lamp pulse lasts to fill the metastable levels. These signals can be observed by a fast-acting photomultiplier pointed toward the end of the ruby rod.

It is important to recognize that the laser action observed in ruby rods is a threshold effect. If the xenon flash-lamp light pulse is not intense enough to depopulate the ground state sufficiently to cause level inversion, no laser beam is observed. The threshold intensity can

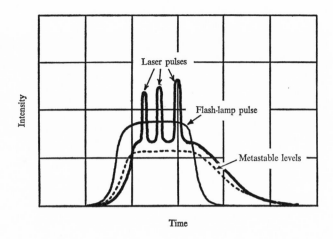

FIGURE 11.7

Time sequence of flash lamp pulse, metastable level build-up, and laser pulses.

be determined qualitatively by measuring the energy stored in the capacitors, which are discharged through the xenon flash lamp.

11.5 OTHER LASER PROCESSES AND MATERIALS

A number of other interesting processes and variations can be found in the ruby laser described in the previous section. One of the difficulties with the so-called "three-level" ruby laser is that laser action does not begin until the ground state is more than half emptied by the flash lamp. (Remember that the condition $N_2 > N_1$ must be fulfilled before light amplification can occur.) This circumstance means that very intense light flashes are necessary to start the laser and, also, that laser action stops relatively rapidly because the ground state is again filled by the stimulated emission process. This problem can be overcome by using different laser materials. An interesting example is the so-called "four-level" laser. The energy level diagram of a four-level laser is shown in Fig. 11.8. These materials have another energy level near the ground state which is normally empty. If most of the transitions from the metastable level go to this level just above the ground state, then laser action can begin immediately because the condition $N_2 > N_1$ is always fulfilled. Four-level lasers of this kind have been produced by embedding uranium, samarium, neodymium, and various other rare earth elements in calcium fluoride crystals. Four-level lasers have the important property that they can be operated continuously.

Other laser processes and materials **235**

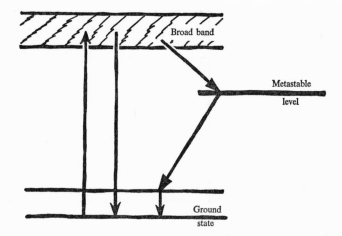

FIGURE 11.8

Typical electron energy level diagram for a "four-level" laser.

A good example of a continuously operating "multilevel" laser is the helium-neon gas laser. A schematic drawing of this device is shown in Fig. 11.9. An appropriate mixture of helium and neon is placed in a tube which is fitted with parallel mirrors on each end in a manner similar to the ruby rod. A radio-frequency induction heater coil is placed around the tube. In the case of this gas laser, the metastable level is the 2^3S excited level in the helium at 19.81 ev. This level is populated as a

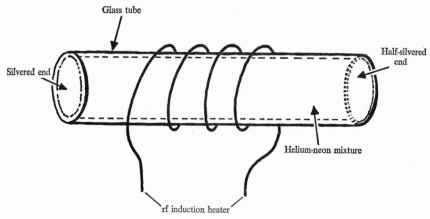

FIGURE 11.9

Helium-neon continuously operating gas laser.

236 *Lasers and the stimulated emission of radiation*

result of collisions between helium atoms and high-energy electrons produced in the radio-frequency discharge. The helium atoms can transfer their excitation energy to a neon atom during a collision, for the neon atoms have an energy level at 19.77 ev, slightly below that of the helium. Thus there will be an equilibrium concentration of neon atoms in the 19.77-ev level in the discharge tube. This level is not metastable, and it can decay to the level at approximately 18.6 ev in neon. Since the 18.6-ev level is generally not occupied, laser action can begin immediately. The 18.6-ev level then decays to the ground state of neon in the

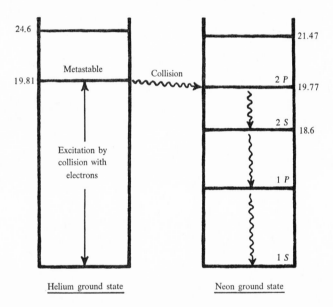

FIGURE 11.10

Multiple electron energy levels in a helium-neon laser.

usual manner. An energy level diagram of the helium-neon multiple level laser is shown in Fig. 11.10. For the purpose of operating a laser continuously, the primary advantage of the gas system is that it is simple to obtain a proper gas mixture, whereas it is sometimes difficult to produce the rather exotic crystals necessary for solid-state laser devices.

Another important modification of the laser geometry described in Sec. 11.3 is the use of a Kerr cell rather than a half-silvered mirror at one end of the laser rod. In this manner the small laser pulses observed in a normal ruby laser (see Fig. 11.7) can be controlled. It will be recalled that the small pulses arise because the laser starts to be

Other laser processes and materials   **237**

regenerative (i.e., $N_2 > N_1$) whenever the number of electrons in state 2 exceeds that in state 1. The precise time at which this condition occurs is very difficult to control, and hence the laser pulses are distributed along the time axis. For practical applications it is exceedingly important that some means be available so that the laser can be

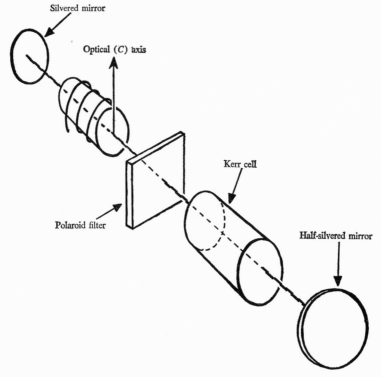

FIGURE 11.11

Experimental arrangement for controlled "dumping" of the laser energy into a single pulse.

"dumped" in a controlled manner. The elimination of the uncontrolled dumping of the laser would permit the concentration of the entire energy of the laser in a single pulse.

Control of laser oscillations was first achieved by McClung and Hellwarth,[5] who used the fact that the fluorescent light emitted by a ruby laser is partially polarized if the C axis (optic axis) of the ruby crystal is perpendicular to the cylinder axis. A schematic diagram of the system is shown in Fig. 11.11. The Kerr cell is an electro-optical device which rotates the plane of polarization of the light passing through the cell. The system thus operates as follows: The Kerr cell is set so that the plane of polarization of the light passing through the cell is rotated through 45 degrees. A Polaroid filter is placed between the ruby rod and the Kerr cell and oriented so that it passes the polarized light leaving the end of the laser rod. This light passes through the Kerr cell, is partially reflected by the half-silvered mirror, and passes through the Kerr cell again. Traversing the Kerr cell twice rotates the axis of

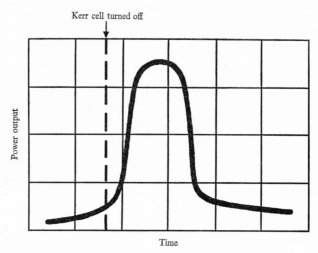

FIGURE 11.12

Time sequence of a controlled laser pulse.

polarization of the light by 90 degrees. The Polaroid filter therefore prevents the reflected light from re-entering the laser rod. The metastable levels can therefore become highly populated, for there is no mechanism for "dumping" the levels other than the relatively slow ($\sim$2.0 msec) process of spontaneous emission. The Kerr cell can then be turned off very rapidly (in less than 0.05 microsecond) so that the light can pass through the Polaroid filter and back into the laser rod, causing stimulated emission. All the electrons in state 2 are now rapidly dumped, and a so-called giant laser pulse results, as shown in Fig. 11.12. A peak power in the pulse of several hundred megawatts is not uncommon. There are other versions of this system, but the principle of allowing only photons, which cannot stimulate emission, to pass through the rod repeatedly is always used.

Other laser processes and materials **239**

11.6 EXPERIMENTS

Time dependence of laser pulses. The first experiment is to demonstrate laser action by measuring the time dependence of the light emitted by a ruby laser. The expected result is shown in Fig. 11.7. The laser pulses themselves are very narrow (10^{-6} sec or less). The

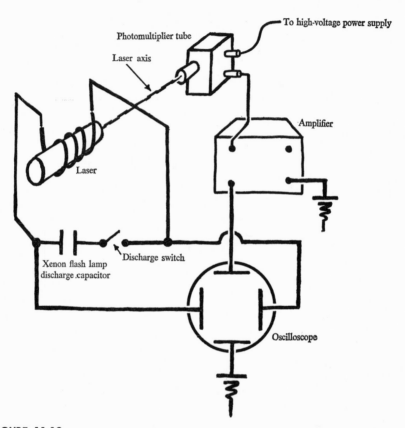

FIGURE 11.13

Experimental arrangement for verifying the laser time dependence illustrated in Fig. 11.7.

pulse width observed is at least partially due to the electronic circuits associated with the photomultiplier tubes. A schematic block diagram of the experiment is shown in Fig. 11.13.

The experiment iself should be conducted in the following way: The oscilloscope should be adjusted so that a Polaroid Land Camera can be mounted to view the oscilloscope tube. About 30 flash-lamp shots

240   *Lasers and the stimulated emission of radiation*

should be observed. The pictures should then be used to make two measurements. The average number of laser pulses per flash-lamp burst should be determined and the distribution of the laser pulses around the mean time between pulses should be established.

Spectrum of laser light. Another experiment which can be done relatively easily is to determine the spectral distribution of the laser light. A small prism or plastic replica grating can be used to analyze the light emitted by the laser. The spectrum should be recorded photographically. The spectrum of the flash lamp alone should be measured first. This should lie in the blue region of the visible spectrum. The ruby rod should then be inserted, and the spectrum should again be determined. This time, a continuous spectrum in the blue-green region should be detected due to light from the flash lamp scattered in the ruby rod. In addition, a very sharp line in the red portion of the spectrum at 6943 Å should be observed corresponding to the light emitted by stimulated emission.

Angular aperture of laser light. One of the more dramatic experiments which can be performed with a ruby laser is to determine the angular divergence of the laser beam. It will be remembered that one of the important features of stimulated emission is that the light quanta produced by stimulated emission have the same direction of propagation as the incident light wave. The arrangement for this experiment is shown in Fig. 11.14. A phototube is fitted with collimators consisting of two screens with small holes in them mounted as shown in Fig. 11.14. The two holes are drilled in such a way that the angular acceptance of the collimator is of the order of 1 degree. The phototube-collimator combination is mounted so that it can be pivoted away from the laser axis as shown. The angular distribution of the laser light can then be measured.

Below the threshold for laser action, the red fluorescence radiation of the ruby rod is emitted more or less in all directions. This fact can be easily established by measuring the intensity as a function of the angle θ. The signal observed is roughly independent of the angle θ, which is what is expected for spontaneous emission. The power of the flash lamp is now increased so that the laser-action threshold is exceeded and the angular distribution measurement is repeated. The observed distribution of the intense light burst is confined to a very narrow cone around the laser axis. The cone angle depends on the precision with which the ends of the laser rod have been made parallel to each other and also on the uniformity of the laser material. If the laser material does not have a very uniform density, fluctuations in the index of refraction may cause the light in the ruby to be bent, so that the resulting beam emerges with a cone angle larger than that due to the nonparallel ends. Even if the faces of the rod were perfectly parallel and the ruby crystal were perfectly uniform, there would still be another limit on the angular distribution of the radiation. The end of the laser may be likened to an aperture in a screen irradiated by a plane wave. The light passing through the end of the laser rod is thus diffracted in the usual manner. The angular distance between the first

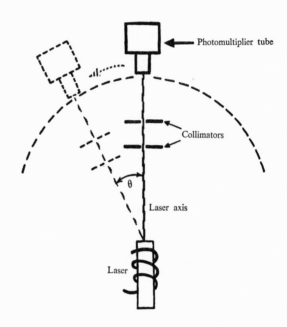

FIGURE 11.14

Experimental arrangement for measuring the divergence of the laser beam.

minimum of the pattern and the beam center is

$$\theta_0 = \frac{1.22\lambda}{d} \tag{11.18}$$

where d is the diameter of the laser rod and λ the wavelength of the laser light. The larger the diameter of the laser rod, the smaller the diffraction angle. In practice, laser beams with angular divergences of much less than 1 degree can be readily produced.

The most important potential practical applications of laser beams depend to some extent on the narrow angular aperture of the emitted light. As a communications device, a laser could be used as a highly directional "antenna" to send messages over large distances. However, suitable means to modulate the laser beams properly must first be developed. Potentially, lasers are excellent communication devices for another important reason. The very high frequency of visible light should make very wide bandwidth (and hence larger information-carrying capacity) transmission possible, provided that a good modulating system can be devised.

Important Note: In all experiments with lasers, great care should be taken not to look directly down the axis of the laser tube. Laser pulses are sufficiently intense that damage to the eye results if the light is viewed directly.

REFERENCES

1. Gordon, J. P., H. Z. Zeiger, and C. H. Townes: *Phys. Rev.*, **95**, 282, 1954; **99**, 1264, 1955.

2. Einstein, A.: *Phys. Zeits.*, **18**, 121, 1917.

3. Maiman, T. H.: *Nature*, **187**, 493, 1960.

4. Schiff, L. I.: "Quantum Mechanics," McGraw-Hill Book Company, New York, 1955.

5. McClung, F. J., and R. W. Hellwarth: *J. Appl. Phys.*, **33**, 828, 1962.

GENERAL BIBLIOGRAPHY

1. Heitler, W.: "Quantum Theory of Radiation," Oxford University Press, London, 1947.

2. Lengyel, B. A.: "Lasers," John Wiley & Sons, Inc., New York, 1962.

3. Vuylsteke, A. A.: "Elements of Maser Theory," D. Van Nostrand Company, Inc., Princeton, N.J., 1960.

4. Troup, G.: "Masers," John Wiley & Sons, Inc., New York, 1959.

5. Hogg, C. A., and L. G. Sucsy: "Masers and Lasers," Maser/Laser Associates, Cambridge, Mass., 1962.

Chapter 12 | ION ACCELERATORS

12.1 INTRODUCTION

The history of ion accelerators is one of the most spectacular chapters in modern science. From very modest beginnings roughly forty years ago, vast laboratories have grown up to exploit the possibilities of these machines. Many of the most important purely scientific discoveries in the last decades have been made using particle accelerators. These include the discovery of many of the mesons and other previously unobserved subnuclear particles. Most of the early measurements, which made the development of nuclear reactor technology possible, were made with ion accelerators of various types. These dealt primarily with the measurement of neutron interaction cross sections. The production of new isotopes and transuranic elements was also first achieved on a large scale with ion accelerators.

Two distinct lines of progress have been followed in the development of ion accelerators. One was started by John Cockcroft and E. T. S. Walton[1] and by R. J. Van de Graaff.[2] Their first machines were linear accelerators in which a large direct-current potential gradient is placed across an accelerating tube. The most modern versions of these machines have an upper energy limit of some tens of millions of electron volts. Their most important feature is that it is possible to control the beam energy with great precision. Particle beams in the energy range of 10 million volts can be controlled to about one part in 10^4, and many precision experiments in nuclear physics have been performed using them. The other school of accelerator design and construction was led by the late E. O. Lawrence,[3] who developed the cyclotron. Magnetic fields were employed to bend the charged particles into circular orbits. These charged particles are then accelerated by a radio-frequency field on successive orbits. Relatively small radio-frequency voltages can be employed to achieve very high energies by repeated accelerations. Particle energies up to 30 billion ev have been achieved using circular accelerating machines. Figures 12.1 and 12.2 show some examples that illustrate the development of both linear and circular accelerators. These pictures are intended only for information, for some of the accelerators to be discussed will be described in much greater detail.

There is another important division among accelerators: some are designed to accelerate electrons and others to accelerate positive ion beams. There are also positive ion machines with some interesting special features, such as the heavy ion accelerator (HILAC). These machines are capable of accelerating triply and quadruply ionized argon atoms, and work is in progress to accelerate even heavier ions.

In this chapter it is not possible to examine the properties of all the many types of accelerators. Two representative examples will be treated, an electrostatic accelerator of the moving belt (Van de Graaff) type and a small model of a cyclotron which illustrates the principles involved in circular-orbit accelerators. Since this book is designed primarily as a guide for a laboratory course, the examples selected for discussion are devices which can actually be constructed by students.

FIGURE 12.1

These photographs show the stages in the development of circular accelerating machines. The upper left photograph was taken in 1934. It shows the first large cyclotron built at the University of California in Berkeley. The two scientists responsible for building the machine, Professor M. S. Livingston (left) and the late Professor E. O. Lawrence, are standing next to the machine. The next development in Berkeley was the 60-inch cyclotron, shown lower left. Many important scientific discoveries were made with this machine during the quarter-century of its operation. Perhaps the most important was the production of the first transuranic elements, neptunium and plutonium. The picture directly above shows the bevatron, which is one of the world's large particle accelerators. The picture shows the circular arrangement of sector magnets used to keep the beam in orbit. The linear accelerator used to inject the beam into the circular beam is shown in the lower right hand corner of the picture. The bevatron produces proton beams with a particle energy up to six billion electron volts. In 1956, Professors E. Segré and O. Chamberlain used the beam from the bevatron to verify the existence of antiprotons. (Courtesy Mr. Daniel Wilkes, Lawrence Radiation Laboratory, Berkeley, California)

FIGURE 12.2

Some steps in the development of electrostatic particle accelerators. Upper left: a large air-insulated electrostatic machine built by Prof. R. J. Van de Graaff and his associates of M.I.T. The machine was used at the Round Hill Laboratory, then moved to M.I.T. after the war and converted to a particle accelerator. It was capable of delivering proton beams with energies up to 2 million electron volts. Lower left: the high voltage terminal and equipotential stack of a modern single-stage electrostatic machine, designed to operate inside a vessel containing a high dielectric-strength gas at a pressure of about ten atmospheres. It is capable of delivering particle beams with energies up to 5.5 million electron volts. Above: recent development in the technology of electrostatic accelerators. This machine is a pressurized tank accelerator which employs the voltage doubling or "tandem" principle. Negative ions are injected into the machine at the far end and are accelerated to the positively charged terminal at the center. The electrons are stripped off the ions in the terminal and the resulting positive ions are accelerated again. The beam emerges from the machine into the beam tubes (foreground). This machine is capable of delivering particle beams with energies up to 20 million electron volts. (Courtesy Mr. Henry S. Lodge, High Voltage Engineering Corporation, Burlington, Massachusetts)

The devices described are therefore dated, but the principles they illustrate are still being applied in the most modern machines.

12.2 PURPOSES OF ION ACCELERATORS

Before discussing the properties of various particle accelerators, it might be useful to outline some of the reasons which brought about the development of these machines. In 1921 Lord Rutherford and his co-workers discovered that various elements could be transmuted into others by bombardment with alpha particles. These transmutations occurred because the energetic alpha particles were capable of penetrating, and hence changing, atomic nuclei. In these early experiments the alpha particles were obtained from the alpha decay of radioactive sources. As a result of this work it became apparent that a great deal could be learned about nuclear structure if intense beams of high-energy particles could be produced without the use of radioactive sources. The principal difficulty with using radioactive isotopes was that only high-energy alpha particles were obtainable and radioisotopes have too low an intensity for most useful purposes.

It is not too difficult to estimate the particle energy which is required to induce a nuclear transformation. It has already been shown in Chapter 3 that the nucleus of the atom is a very small, massive body, carrying a positive charge, with a diameter of approximately 10^{-12} cm. If a nuclear reaction is to be initiated by a charged particle, it is necessary to overcome the coulomb repulsion between the two particles. As shown in Fig. 12.3, the electrical potential between the incident particle (proton) and the nucleus is

$$V = \frac{1}{4\pi\epsilon_0} \frac{e^2 Z}{r} \tag{12.1}$$

The energy necessary to bring the proton to the surface of the nucleus is

$$E = \frac{1}{4\pi\epsilon_0} \frac{e^2 Z}{R} \tag{12.2}$$

where R is the nuclear radius. For a nucleus in the region $Z = 20$ (calcium), the energy computed from Eq. (12.2) is approximately 4 million ev. It is this figure which roughly fixes the energy necessary to induce nuclear processes and which therefore determined the practical energy range of some of the early accelerators.

Although the coulomb barrier argument outlined above gave the original impetus for the construction of particle accelerators, it became apparent very quickly that there were several other reasons. Several species of unstable particles (called mesons) were discovered in cosmic rays.[4] These could be produced artificially if particle beams with a kinetic energy equal to the rest energy of the unstable mesons were available. The first "artificial" mesons were observed in 1948 by using particle beams from the University of California's 184-in. synchrocyclotron. Much of the research done with very high-energy accelerators is devoted to the search for new mesons. Ultrahigh-energy accelerators may also serve as "microscopes" for studying the ultimate structure of matter. The relation between the wavelength and the momentum of a particle is

$$p = \frac{h}{\lambda} \tag{12.3}$$

The shorter the wavelength of particles used for scattering experiments, the more sensitive it will be to the detailed structure of the target. At 30 billion ev, the wavelength of a proton is roughly 5×10^{-14} cm, or

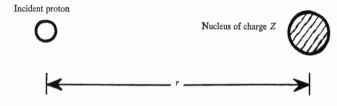

Incident proton

Nucleus of charge Z

r

FIGURE 12.3

Geometry used for Eqs. (12.1) and (12.2).

about one half the radius of a nucleon. With particle beams of this energy, it should therefore be possible to determine the charge and matter distribution in nucleons.

The preceding material outlines some of the important reasons for constructing high-energy particle accelerators. In the following sections two machines illustrating the important operating principles of electrostatic accelerators and cyclotrons will be discussed. Some nuclear physics experiments to be performed with the machines will also be discussed.

12.3 ELECTROSTATIC ACCELERATORS

Most of the early particle accelerators were machines in which a steady potential was created on a terminal insulated from ground. An evacuated column in which an ion beam could be accelerated was then placed between the terminal and ground. Several methods for charging the terminal were invented. The one which has been most successful is the moving-belt principle first suggested by R. J. Van de Graaff in 1930.[2] The idea is to employ a charged, moving belt which carries the charge from ground to the high-voltage terminal. Figure 12.4 shows how the charging system of a Van de Graaff machine operates. The moving belt is mounted on two low-friction pulleys which are driven by an electric

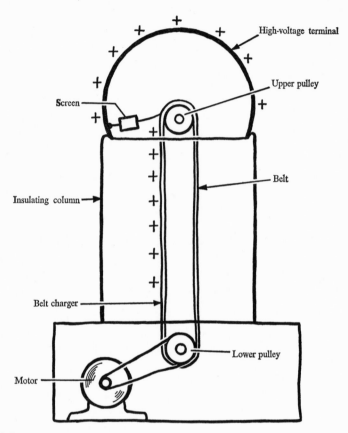

FIGURE 12.4

Method used to charge the high-voltage terminal of Van de Graff accelerators.

motor. One pulley is mounted in the high-voltage terminal which is attached to a long insulating column. The belts on the very early machines were usually made of silk, but today rubber-impregnated fabric belts are employed because silk is too fragile.

A very important feature of the design of an electrostatic accelerator is the method used to deposit the charge on the belt at the bottom of the machine and to remove it at the high-voltage terminal. Figure 12.5

illustrates how this is accomplished. At the bottom of the machine, a row of needles is mounted near the outside of the belt and a ground plane is mounted behind the belt. If the high-voltage terminal is to be positively charged, then the needles are biased positive with respect to the ground plane by a d-c power supply. This potential difference is usually on the order of 20 to 30 kv. At these potentials, corona discharges appear at the tips of the sharp needles, and electrons are

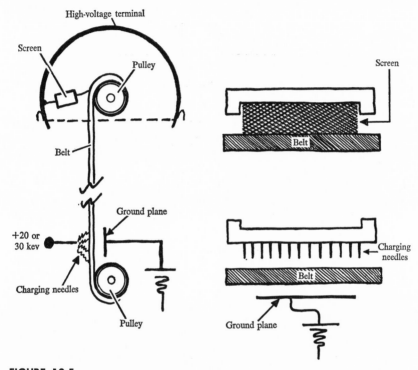

FIGURE 12.5

Belt charging and removal techniques.

drawn from the belt. At the high-voltage terminal, the belt is neutralized by electrons drawn from the terminal through a wire screen in contact with the belt, leaving the terminal positively charged. The wire screen itself is connected to the high-voltage terminal so that the remaining positive charge distributes itself uniformly on the conducting shell, which serves as the high-voltage terminal. This process works, for there are no electric fields inside the hollow-conducting terminal shell to oppose the electron flow from the terminal to the belt.

The equivalent circuit of an electrostatic accelerator is shown in

Fig. 12.6. The high-voltage terminal acts as a capacitor which is charged by a constant-current power supply. The capacitor has a resistor in parallel with it. This resistance is determined by both the resistance of the column and by leakage of charge from the high-voltage terminal due to corona discharge. Under normal operating conditions the latter can be kept very small, so that the leakage current from the high-voltage terminal is determined primarily by the resistance of the

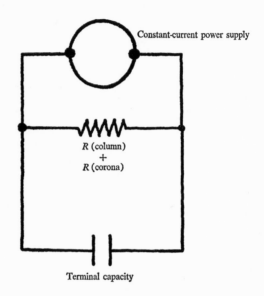

FIGURE 12.6

Equivalent circuit of an electrostatic accelerator.

insulating column. The potential of the high-voltage terminal can be computed from the equivalent circuit:

$$V = \frac{q}{C} - R\frac{dq}{dt} + K\frac{dq}{dt} \tag{12.4}$$

If the charge delivered by the belt precisely equals the leakage current, the potential of the conducting shell depends only on the equilibrium charge and the capacity of the shell with respect to ground. The factor limiting the terminal voltage is the breakdown potential of the air surrounding the high-voltage terminal. If a high enough field exists across an air gap, ionization eventually occurs and a spark results, discharging the terminal.

Very large air-insulated machines have been constructed with insulating columns up to 30 ft high and high-voltage terminal spheres with radii up to 6 ft. Potentials of the order of 2 million volts have been reached with these machines. Higher voltages can be obtained if the generator is placed in a container filled with a gas having a high dielectric constant. In many instances the gas (usually a mixture of nitrogen, carbon dioxide, and sulfur hexafluoride) is under high pressure, which further increases the breakdown potentials. Many pressurized electrostatic generators exist today, and potentials up to 6 or 7 million volts can be readily obtained.

Up to this point, no mention has been made of the methods which are employed to produce ions and accelerate them. The first ion accelerators utilizing Van de Graaff's moving-belt principle were constructed in 1934 by M. A. Tuve[6] and his collaborators at the Carnegie Institution in Washington, D.C. Two important changes had to be incorporated into the simple Van de Graaff machines to make them practical particle accelerators. A source of ions had to be put in the high-voltage terminal and an evacuated accelerating column had to be placed between the high-voltage terminal and ground. The design of ion sources has evolved in the past fifteen years from primitive arc discharge sources to the highly efficient sources used on modern electrostatic machines. A schematic diagram of one common type of radio-frequency ion source is shown in Fig. 12.7. (The source design shown here is a rather primitive radio-frequency source. It was chosen because it can be constructed from readily available parts in a student laboratory.) A radio-frequency oscillator is mounted in the high-voltage terminal—usually operating at a frequency between 5 and 10 megacycles—which supplies radio-frequency power to a coil. The coil is placed around a glass container as shown. If hydrogen ions are to be produced, the container is filled with hydrogen at a pressure of approximately 100 microns. The radio-frequency field within the coil causes ionization in the gas, creating a discharge containing many ions. The electrostatic probe is used to help establish the discharge and then to maximize the ion concentration in the ion-source gas. The extraction and focusing electrode below the gas bottle is used to extract ions from the plasma and to establish an electric field which helps to guide the ions through the small hole at the top of the electrode. Sometimes a variable "focusing" potential is supplied between the extraction electrode and the first accelerating electrode in the column.

The electrical power necessary for this radio-frequency oscillator and the focusing and extraction power supplies is provided by a small generator mounted in the high-voltage terminal. The generator is powered by being attached to a belt pulley on the roller in the high-voltage terminal.

Hydrogen gas is stored in a small pressurized container also located in the high-voltage terminal. The gas is bled into the ion-source discharge bottle at a controlled rate through a variable leak. Ion sources of this type are capable of delivering ion currents up to 100 μa at the exit port.

The ion accelerating column is shown in Fig. 12.8. The most important feature in the design is that provisions must be made to keep the

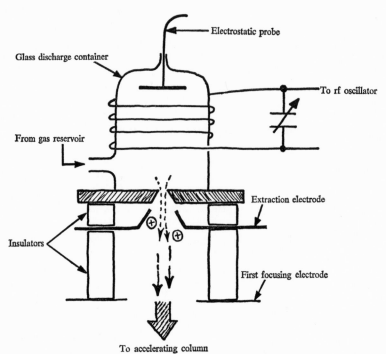

FIGURE 12.7

Schematic diagram of a radio-frequency ion source showing the extractor electrode and first focusing electrode.

beam focused. This is accomplished by placing iris-shaped electrodes at intervals in the accelerating column. These are connected to each other with resistors—usually about 10^3 megohms apiece—so that the potential difference between each of the iris electrodes is the same. The field lines between each of the sections of the column are shown in Fig. 12.8. The effect of this field pattern is to focus the particle beam, because the particles are always moving more slowly where the field lines are converging than where they diverge. Thus the net effect is to keep the beam together. The iris rings of the accelerating column are connected electrically to the equipotential rings, which are stacked as shown in Fig. 12.9 to form the main support for the terminal. The resistor chain between the successive irises and equipotential rings

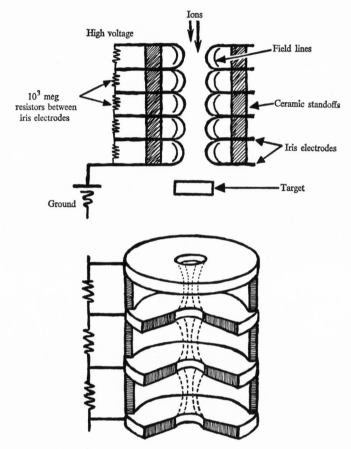

FIGURE 12.8

Van de Graff accelerating column showing voltage-dividing resistors, insulating vacuum column, iris electrodes, and focusing fields.

serves to ensure a uniform gradient along the accelerating column. The subdivision of the planes in this manner also makes it possible to avoid large voltage drops across only part of the length.

A schematic diagram of the entire electrostatic accelerator system to be used for this experiment is shown in Fig. 12.9. After the beam leaves the accelerator, it is passed through a magnetic field which bends the ions

Electrostatic accelerators **257**

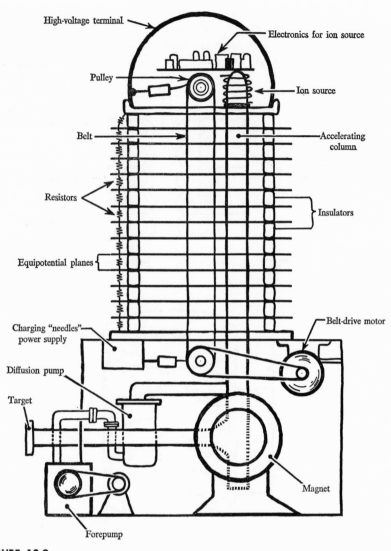

FIGURE 12.9

Schematic diagram of the entire Van de Graff electrostatic accelerator.

through 90 degrees. The primary reason for the magnet is to separate the various components of the ion beam. The ion source produces H^+, H_2^+, and H_3^+ ions. Each of these species arrives at the end of the accelerating column with the same kinetic energy but with differing momenta. The magnetic field, being a momentum selector, separates the particle beams, and the magnetic field should be adjusted so that the H⁺ beam comes out horizontally.

Important components of the accelerator system are the vacuum pumps used to evacuate the accelerator column. This vacuum system must have a good pumping speed to remove the residual hydrogen gas produced by the ion source. (See Chapter 4 for a discussion of vacuum pumping speeds.) In order to operate properly, the pressure in the accelerating column should be below 5×10^{-5} torr. If the pressure is higher, the beam will not be properly focused because of scattering by the gas molecules. High-energy ions thus strike the walls of the accelerating column producing secondary electrons. These electrons are in turn accelerated back toward the high-voltage terminal, which they strike, producing X rays. These X rays ionize the air around the high-voltage terminal and eventually cause a breakdown or discharge.

The Van de Graaff accelerator described here has an insulating column about 4 ft high, and the potential developed between the high-voltage terminal and ground is approximately a half-million volts. The beam energy is determined by setting the magnetic field in the deflecting magnet and then using the orbit equations for charged particles in a magnetic field to compute the beam energy. Since the particle is injected perpendicular to the field, the orbits will be circular and the centrifugal force must be equal to the Lorentz force:

$$\frac{mv^2}{R} = evB \tag{12.5}$$

Here R is the radius (~ 15 cm in this case), m is the mass of the proton, B is the magnetic induction, v is the velocity of the ion, and e is the charge. (For a more complete description of this orbit equation, see Chapter 2.) The energy of the beam is

$$\frac{\sqrt{2mE}}{R} = eB \tag{12.6}$$

or

$$E = \frac{e^2 B^2 R^2}{2m} \tag{12.7}$$

and is thus proportional to the square of the magnetic field intensity.

The beam current is measured by using a "Faraday cup." The arrangement is shown in Fig. 12.10. The particle beam strikes a cup which is insulated from the rest of the beam pipe by two insulators and a guard ring. The guard ring is kept at -300 volts in order to prevent secondary electrons, which would give false current readings, from leaving the target. Each ion striking the target may produce several secondary electrons. If the secondaries leak past the insulators, the current reading will be higher because every electron leaving the target is electrically indistinguishable from a positive ion striking the target. The negatively biased guard ring creates an electric field which prevents the electrons from leaving the target region. The machine is capable of producing particle beam currents as high as 10 μa. Since the charge on the proton is 1.6×10^{-19} coul, this current means that approximately 1.6×10^{14} protons/sec strike the target. (An ampere is

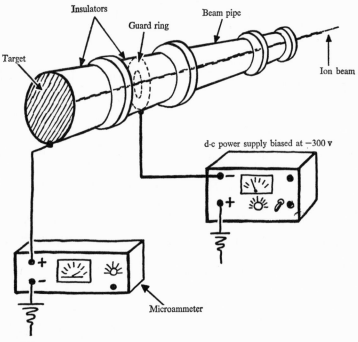

FIGURE 12.10

Faraday cup for secondary electron suppression while measuring positive ion beam currents.

one coulomb per second.) The power dissipated on the target is

$$P = i \times E = 10^{-5} \times 0.5 \times 10^6 \approx 5 \text{ watts} \qquad (12.8)$$

This power is not negligible, so that it is sometimes necessary to cool the target.

12.4 NUCLEAR REACTIONS

Two important types of nuclear reactions can be produced with particles in the energy range of a half-million electron volts. The first is the class of reactions which emit neutrons as one of the products and the second consists of those which produce gamma rays.

Neutron reactions. The neutron-producing reactions which are of interest here are induced by deuteron beams. Since deuterium is an isotope of hydrogen, the Van de Graaff machine can be employed to accelerate deuterium ions with no change in the ion source system. Thus deuterium ion beams can be easily obtained at energies up to 0.5 mev, provided that the magnetic analyzer is set properly to account for the higher deuteron mass [see Eq. (12.7)]. The two reactions most commonly employed for the production of neutrons are the following:

$$H^2 + H^2 \rightarrow He^3 + n \text{ or } H^2(d,n)He^3 \tag{12.9}$$
and
$$H^3 + H^2 \rightarrow He^4 + n \text{ or } H^3(d,n)He^4 \tag{12.10}$$

In the first reaction, Eq. (12.9), the process results in the formation of the light isotope of helium (He^3) and a neutron. In the second case, Eq. (12.10), which is the so-called D-T reaction, the products are He^4 and a neutron. In practice these reactions are carried out by bombarding specially prepared targets with fast deuterium ions. The targets are usually made in the following way. Certain metals, such as titanium or palladium, have the property of absorbing hydrogen if they are heated. The hydrogen behaves as if it were dissolving in the metal and, under good conditions, concentrations as high as one atom of hydrogen per one metal atom can be obtained. The target is made by evaporating a thin layer of titanium (5 mg/cm²) on a tantalum backing. This target is heated in a deuterium or tritium atmosphere until the titanium layer is saturated with gas. The target is then ready for use. Great care must be taken not to heat the target with the beam; otherwise the gas will diffuse out, for the target is used in the vacuum of the accelerating column.

It is important for many purposes to know something about the energies and the angular distributions of the neutrons emitted in the reactions of Eqs. (12.9) and (12.10). To do this, it is necessary to understand the kinematics and the energetics of the nuclear process. Three important rules govern nuclear processes of this kind:

1. The conservation of energy and momentum
2. The equivalence of mass and energy through the Einstein relation, $E = mc^2$
3. The assumption that the chemical state of the atom does not affect the nuclear process

If these rules are followed, the nuclear reaction may then be considered as a collision between two solid objects in which energy and mass are exchanged. The situation is illustrated in Fig. 12.11. Before the collision, a deuteron moving with a momentum corresponding to its energy of 500 kev approaches a stationary deuteron in the target. After the nuclear reaction occurs, the products move away from the site of the reaction with a total (i.e., vector sum) momentum equal to the initial deuteron momentum. The final energy is equal to the sum of the kinetic energy of the incident deuteron and whatever energy becomes available because of the mass changes occurring during the reaction. This energy is computed as follows:

$$Q = c^2 \Sigma M \text{ (initial particles)} - c^2 \Sigma M \text{ (product particles)} \quad (12.11)$$

If Q is positive, the emerging particles have more kinetic energy than the initial ones and the reaction is called exoergic. If Q is negative, the

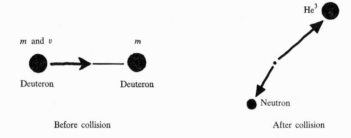

FIGURE 12.11

Kinematics of a deuteron-deuteron collision.

reaction is endoergic and no energy is liberated. The endoergic reaction implies that there is a minimum threshold energy required of the incident particle to cause the reaction to go. The reactions of Eqs. (12.9) and (12.10) are exoergic. The masses of the particles involved are:

PARTICLE	MASS (ATOMIC MASS UNITS*)
He⁴	4.00260
He³	3.01603
H³	3.01605
H²	2.01410
H¹	1.007593
Neutron	1.008661

*Where the mass of C^{12} is defined as exactly 12 atomic mass units.

The Q values computed for the neutron-producing reactions in Eqs. (12.9) and (12.10) are

$$Q(\text{H}^2,\text{H}^2) = 3.27 \text{ mev}$$
$$Q(\text{H}^2,\text{H}^3) = 17.6 \text{ mev}$$

(12.12)

The calculation of the energy of the emerging neutrons is simply a straightforward application of conservation of energy and momentum.

The computation is especially simple if only neutrons emitted in the forward direction are considered. In this case, as shown in Fig. 12.12, the neutron moves in the same direction as the deuteron which initiates the reaction. The momentum and energy equations are

$$m_1 v_1 = M_1 V_1 + M_2 V_2 \quad \text{or} \quad p_1 = P_1 + P_2 \quad (12.13)$$

and
$$\tfrac{1}{2} m_1 v_1{}^2 + Q = \tfrac{1}{2} M_1 V_1{}^2 + \tfrac{1}{2} M_2 V_2{}^2 \quad (12.14)$$

These equations can be solved for the final neutron energy $(\tfrac{1}{2} M_2 V_2{}^2)$ in

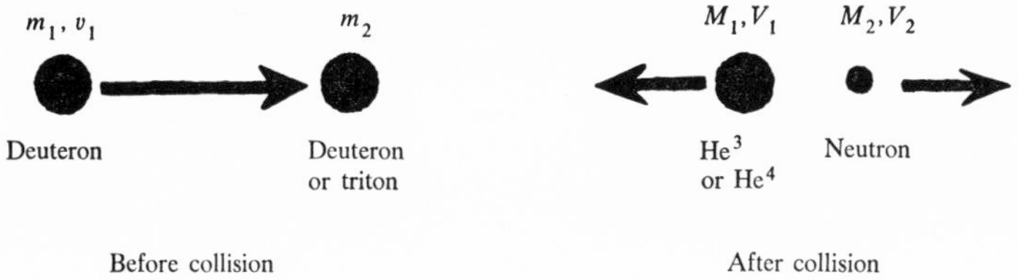

m_1, v_1 m_2 M_1, V_1 M_2, V_2

Deuteron   Deuteron   He^3 Neutron
or triton   or He^4

Before collision   After collision

FIGURE 12.12

Kinematics of a deuteron-deuteron or a deuteron-triton collision in which the neutron is emitted in the direction of the original deuteron.

terms of the known parameters m_1 (deuteron mass), m_2 (deuteron or triton mass), M_1 (He^3, H^3, or He^4 mass), the Q value, and the initial kinetic energy of the incident deuteron. The momentum of the neutron is given by

$$P_2 = \frac{\dfrac{p_1}{M_1} + \sqrt{\dfrac{p_1{}^2}{M_1{}^2} - 2\left(\dfrac{1}{M_1} + \dfrac{1}{M_2}\right)\left[p_1{}^2\left(\dfrac{1}{2M_1} - \dfrac{1}{2m_1}\right) - Q\right]}}{\left(\dfrac{1}{M_1} + \dfrac{1}{M_2}\right)}$$

(12.15)

or, if it is assumed that the energy of the incident deuteron is 500 kev, the final neutron energies for the two different reactions are

$$E_2[\text{H}^2(d,n)\text{He}^3] = 3.51 \text{ mev} \quad (12.16)$$

and
$$E_2[\text{H}^3(d,n)\text{He}^4] = 15.8 \text{ mev} \quad (12.17)$$

If neutrons emitted in other directions are also considered, two momentum conservation equations must be employed, one for the component along the initial deuteron direction and another for the momentum perpendicular to the incident direction. The neutron energy then depends on the angle of emission of the neutron. In this case the neutron momentum is

$$P_2 = \frac{\dfrac{p_1 \cos \theta}{M_1} + \sqrt{\dfrac{p_1{}^2 \cos^2 \theta}{M_1{}^2} - 2\left(\dfrac{1}{M_1} + \dfrac{1}{M_2}\right)\left[p_1{}^2\left(\dfrac{1}{2M_1} - \dfrac{1}{2m_1}\right) - Q\right]}}{\left(\dfrac{1}{M_1} + \dfrac{1}{M_2}\right)}$$

(12.18)

Again assuming that the energy of the incident deuteron is 500 kev, the energies of the final neutrons are

$$E_2[\text{H}^2(d,n)\text{He}^3] = \frac{\cos^2 \theta}{16} + \frac{3\sqrt{2}}{16} \cos \theta \sqrt{\frac{2 \cos^2 \theta}{9} + 9.16}$$
$$+ \frac{9}{32}\left(\frac{2 \cos^2 \theta}{9} + 9.16\right) \text{mev} \quad (12.19)$$

and

$$E_2[\text{H}^3(d,n)\text{He}^4] = \frac{\cos^2 \theta}{25} + \frac{4\sqrt{2}}{25} \cos \theta \sqrt{\frac{\cos^2 \theta}{8} + 22.31}$$
$$+ \frac{8}{25}\left(\frac{\cos^2 \theta}{8} + 22.31\right) \text{mev} \quad (12.20)$$

The details of the derivation are not given because they are too lengthy. However, for practical purposes the neutron energies obtained from the D-D and D-T reactions are essentially independent of angle because Q is generally much larger than the initial deuteron energy. In this case Eqs. (12.18), (12.19), and (12.20) reduce to the expression of Eqs. (12.15), (12.16), and (12.17).

The detection of neutrons has already been discussed in Chapter 7. In this experiment a neutron recoil scintillation detector is employed to count the neutrons emitted from the target. A plastic scintillator mounted on a phototube which is connected to the associated scaling and counting equipment should be placed near the target (see Chapter 7). The neutrons from the target are scattered by the protons in the plastic, and these so-called "recoil" protons cause pulses in the scintillator. Since neutrons and protons have roughly equal masses, the most energetic protons observed should have an energy equal to that of the incident neutron. This occurs for a "head-on" collision between the particles. Smaller pulses are observed for less than head-on collisions, in which the neutron still retains some of its energy. There are also smaller pulses observed due to various background effects. The pulse-height spectra observed from the D-D and D-T reactions are shown in Fig. 12.13. These spectra show conclusively that the D-T reaction yields neutrons much higher in energy than D-D reactions.

Several other interesting experiments can be performed with the neutrons produced in the reactions described in the foregoing paragraphs. One is to use the D-D reaction to verify Eq. (12.19). In this experiment, the observed end-point energy of the spectrum is meas-

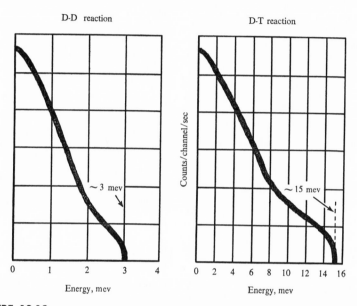

FIGURE 12.13

Proton recoil spectra (indicating maximum neutron energy corresponding to head-on collisions) for neutrons produced in D-D and D-T reactions.

ured as a function of the angle between the counter and the deuteron beam. The end-point energy should decrease as the angle is increased. In the D-D reaction this effect should be quite noticeable because the initial deuteron energy is sizable compared to Q. The same is not true in the case of the D-T reaction where Q is much larger compared to the initial deuteron energy, so that it is relatively harder to observe the effect. The experimental geometry for verifying Eq. (12.19) is shown in Fig. 12.14.

Another important effect which can be easily observed with the D-T neutrons is the inelastic scattering of fast neutrons. All nuclei have excited energy levels. It is possible for an energetic neutron to be scattered from a nucleus, leaving the nucleus in an excited level. The excited nucleus decays subsequent to the scattering event by the emission of gamma rays which can be detected. The first few energy levels of Fe^{56} are shown in Fig. 12.15. The first excited level has a particularly large cross section for neutron excitation and is thus easy to observe. A gamma-ray counter is located in the position shown in Fig. 12.16. The 14-mev neutrons strike the iron target. The excitation gamma rays emitted by the iron are observed by a sodium iodide (NaI) scintillation detector shielded from the direct neutron beam. When

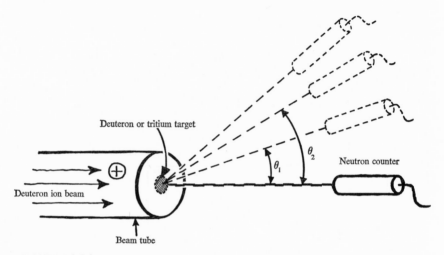

FIGURE 12.14

The experimental arrangement used to verify the end-point energy as predicted by Eq. (12.19).

the neutrons strike the iron, a strong signal from the iron gamma rays can then be observed. Several other materials should be tried, and the gamma-ray lines observed should be related to the various nuclear energy-level schemes.

Gamma-ray-producing reactions. Gamma rays are electromagnetic radiations emitted by nuclei during various nuclear processes. Several gamma-ray-producing reactions can be initiated using the protons produced with the Van de Graaff accelerator. One important gamma-ray-yielding reaction is the proton capture process. The particular one of interest in this case is the proton capture in Li^7:

$$p + Li^7 \rightarrow Be^8 + \text{gamma rays or } Li^7(p,\gamma)Be^8 \qquad (12.21)$$

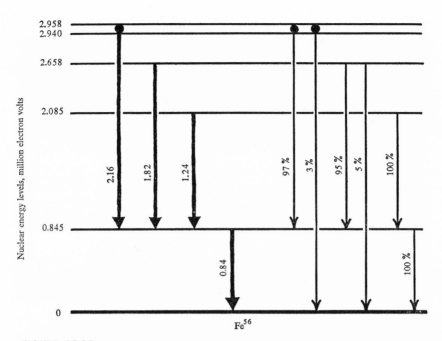

FIGURE 12.15

Nuclear energy levels and relative decay modes of Fe^{56}.

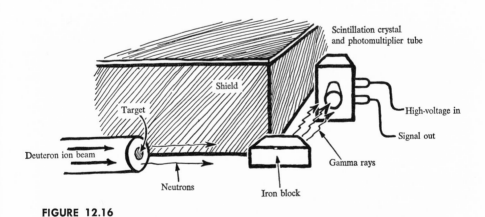

FIGURE 12.16

Excitation gamma rays produced by neutrons inelastically scattered from Fe^{56} nuclei.

The gamma rays emitted in the reaction (12.21) are very energetic. Two gamma rays are emitted, one with an energy of 17.6 mev and the other with an energy of 14.8 mev if the bombarding proton energy is 0.440 mev. The gamma-ray energy comes from the binding energy of the proton in the Be^8 nucleus. The process may be illustrated symbolically as in Fig. 12.17. The ground state of Li^7 lies 17.2 mev above the ground

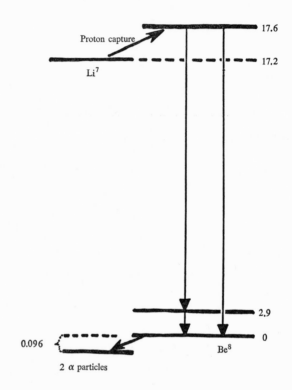

FIGURE 12.17

Proton capture by Li^7 and the subsequent decay of the excited Be^8 nucleus.

state of the Be^8 nucleus. The proton comes in with an energy of 0.440 mev and is captured, creating a highly excited level of Be^8, which decays by emitting gamma rays. The lower energy gamma rays come about when the capture state decays to an excited level in Be^8. The gamma rays emitted in this process are detected by a large (5-in. by 5-in.) NaI crystal used in a normal scintillation counting system. The counter is placed next to the target. The large crystal is necessary to absorb all the energy of the gamma rays.

In contrast with the neutron-producing reactions discussed in the previous section, gamma rays carry little momentum compared to energetic nucleons (the relation between the energy and momentum of the gamma rays is $p = E/c$). To compute accurately the energy of the gamma ray emitted in the reaction, it is also necessary to use both the conservation of energy and momentum equations. However, the small momentum carried off by the gamma ray makes it unnecessary to take it into account in most practical cases. The energy of the gamma ray emitted in the reaction is therefore very closely equal to the proton binding energy.

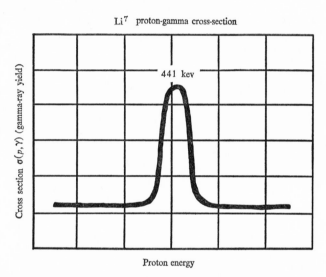

FIGURE 12.18

Proton capture cross-section resonance of Li⁷.

The targets used in these experiments are made by evaporating lithium metal on an inert metal-backing disk, such as tantalum, which is a good heat conductor. If the lithium targets are very thin ($\sim$0.1 mg/cm²), a very interesting feature of nuclear reactions can be illustrated. Varying the proton beam energy produces a sharp change in the cross section, as illustrated in Fig. 12.18. The peaks observed in the cross section are called nuclear resonances. They occur in most nuclear reactions and are caused by the existence of energy levels in the nucleus that is formed when the proton is captured by the target nucleus. These levels are usually called compound levels. In the case of the Li⁷(p,γ) reaction, the resonance is quite narrow (a few kev), indicating that the level in the compound nucleus is quite long-lived.

Since these levels have small widths, resonances in the cross section are often employed to calibrate the energy of nuclear particle beams. The energy of the $Li^7(p,\gamma)$ reaction resonance at 441 kev has been determined with particular precision, so that it is often employed as an energy standard for nuclear accelerators in this energy region.

Besides the proton-capture reactions discussed in the foregoing paragraph, there are also other reactions in which both nuclear particles

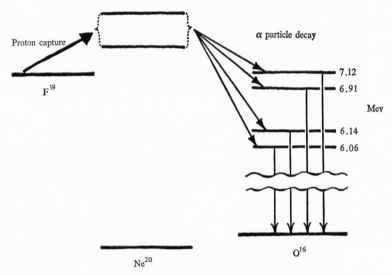

FIGURE 12.19

F^{19} proton capture with α-decay of resultant Ne^{20} to excited levels of O^{16}.

and gamma rays are emitted. A reaction which is particularly easy to study with the Van de Graaff machine is

$$F^{19} + p \rightarrow O^{16} + He^4 + \text{gamma rays or } F^{19}(p,\alpha,\gamma)O^{16} \quad (12.22)$$

In this reaction the gamma rays come from excited levels in the O^{16} nucleus as shown in Fig. 12.19. The targets for this reaction are made by evaporating thin layers of a fluorine containing salt (i.e., NaF or KF) on some inert target backings. The gamma rays observed in the reaction are characteristic of the energy levels in O^{16}. This reaction also exhibits "resonances" at certain proton energies corresponding to energy levels in the compound nucleus, Ne^{20}. If the scintillation counter is set to observe the O^{16} gamma rays, the yield curve shown in Fig. 12.20 is obtained. These "resonances" are also often used as beam-energy calibration points.

270 *Ion accelerators*

Several other experiments of general interest can be performed with the Van de Graaff machine. For example, the experiments investigating the passage of charged particles through matter could be repeated with protons and deuterons to illustrate the charge and mass dependence of the stopping power formula [see Eq. (3.14) in Chapter 3]. Interesting experiments on the emission of secondary electrons from targets bombarded by fast ions can be performed. The processes of sputtering or ion erosion of surfaces can also be investigated.

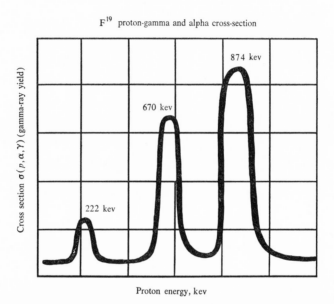

FIGURE 12.20

Proton capture resonances of F^{19}.

12.5 RADIO-FREQUENCY ACCELERATORS

No discussion of ion accelerators would be complete without mentioning the cyclotron and other accelerators using alternating electric fields to accelerate ions. The first really successful version of such a machine was the cyclotron developed by the late E. O. Lawrence in the early 1930's. The machine operates by accelerating charged particles repeatedly through a small potential. If this is done often enough, very high energies can be attained. This indeed was (and still is) the major advantage of the a-c machines over the electrostatic machines discussed in the previous sections. The d-c potentials which can be obtained in electrostatic accelerators are ultimately limited by breakdown problems in the insulators. Lawrence and his co-workers realized very quickly that no such upper limit exists for a-c machines.

The geometry of the cyclotron is shown in Fig. 12.21. The machine consists of a pill-shaped cylindrical vacuum chamber placed between

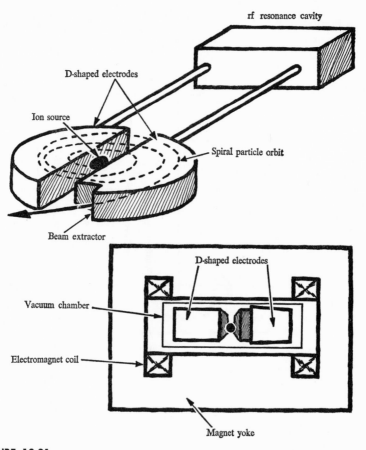

FIGURE 12.21

Schematic diagram of cyclotron "dees" and deflecting magnet.

the pole pieces of a large magnet. Inside the vacuum chamber there are two D-shaped hollow electrodes. A radio-frequency field is imposed across these electrodes and the particles are accelerated as they pass through the gap between the two electrodes. The particles are confined in the vacuum chamber by the magnetic field perpendicular to the particle orbits. The circulating beam also tends to be stabilized by the

272 *Ion accelerators*

fringe field of the magnet and by the shape of the radio-frequency field between the D-shaped electrodes.

An ion source is mounted at the center of the machine and a target is mounted on the edge of the chamber. The operation of the cyclotron depends on the orbit equation of an energetic charged particle in a magnetic field. This equation has already been used to determine the paths of ions passing through the analyzing magnet at the ground end of the Van de Graaff machine [see Eq. (12.5)]. Dividing each side of Eq. (12.5) by the particle velocity v gives

$$\frac{mv}{R} = eB \qquad (12.23)$$

The ratio v/R is related to the time necessary to make one orbit:

$$\omega = t^{-1} = \frac{v}{2\pi R} = \frac{eB}{2\pi m} \qquad (12.24)$$

The important point about Eq. (12.24) is that the orbital frequency of the charged particle is independent of the velocity of the particle if ω is adjusted to fulfill the condition of Eq. (12.24). A particle starting out from the ion source in such a way that it is accelerated across the gap the first time will therefore arrive at the gap after the first half revolution in time to be accelerated again. This happens again and again until the particle reaches the target, that is, the particles tend to remain in phase with the radio-frequency field. The higher the velocity of the particle, the larger the radius of the orbit in accordance with Eqs. (12.5) or (12.6). The final energy of the particle is given by Eq. (12.6). For modest values of the radius ($R \approx 0.2$ m) and the magnetic field ($B \approx 1$ weber/m²) rather high energies can be obtained:

$$E \approx 2.0 \text{ mev} \qquad (12.25)$$

It is for this reason that the cyclotron has been so very useful. The machine can deliver very high particle energies even though it is quite small in size. In such a machine, radio-frequency potentials with a 5 kev peak-to-peak potential difference are employed, so that the number of orbits is approximately

$$N = \frac{E}{\Delta E} \approx 400 \qquad (12.26)$$

By successive accelerations in each orbit, high-energy particle beams can be produced without the use of high voltages.

The upper limit of the energy which can be reached by the fixed-frequency cyclotron described here is determined by the validity of Eq. (12.24). As the velocity of the particle increases, the classical kinematic laws of motion cease to work and relativistic ones must be employed. In practice, the maximum proton beam energies that can be produced by the constant-field, constant-frequency machine illustrated in Fig. 12.21 are about 20 mev. Deuterons and alpha-particle beams of roughly 40 and 80 mev can be produced by the same machine, provided that high enough magnetic fields are available. To reach higher energies, it is necessary to decrease the frequency of the radio-frequency field as the particles are accelerated to compensate for the increase in mass of the particle [see Eq. (12.24)]. A number of machines of this type have been constructed. The major design feature is that the radio-frequency oscillator is frequency modulated so that it applies a lower frequency when the particles reach larger radii orbits in the field. It can be seen that a frequency-modulated cyclotron cannot give a constant current beam, since the radio-frequency field must always be recycled through the appropriate frequency range. The recycling time corresponds to the time it takes a group of particles to travel from the ion source to the edge of the magnetic field. This has the consequence that the beam is "bunched" and that it has a much lower intensity than beams which can be delivered by nonrelativistic machines. Recently another method has been developed to compensate for the relativistic mass change by using a nonuniform magnetic field. In this case, the field is adjusted in such a way that the orbital frequency is constant in spite of the relativistic mass change. These machines are called isochronous cyclotrons. Particle beams with energies of several hundred million electron volts have been produced using these techniques to compensate for the relativistic mass increase.

12.6 THE OMEGATRON

The operational principle of radio-frequency accelerators can be demonstrated with the omegatron, which is a proton mock-up model of the cyclotron. The omegatron is shown schematically in Fig. 12.22.[7] The omegatron as shown should be operated in a small vacuum vessel (at 10^{-5} torr) which should be placed between the poles of a magnet.

Electrons emitted from the tungsten filament are accelerated to the brass shield by the 100-volt potential. The electrons pass through the small hole in the shield and are collected on the other side. In traversing that distance, some electrons will strike residual gas molecules, thereby ionizing them. Some of these molecules will be either H_2O or C_nH_{2n}, so that some protons will be liberated. In the central region, the protons will see the radio-frequency field applied to the accelerating electrodes (which can be sections of a brass cylinder 2 in. in diameter and approximately $\frac{1}{2}$-in. long). If the radio frequency is adjusted to the resonant condition of Eq. (12.24), the protons will be accelerated in phase and will spiral outward, eventually being collected on the collector. Once the protons strike the collector, they will flow through the microammeter to ground, thereby indicating a current.

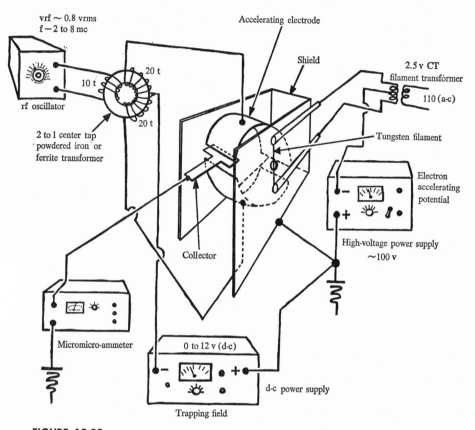

FIGURE 12.22

The omegatron, a proton mock-up model of the cyclotron.

The technique is to set the magnetic field constant and, from Eq. (12.24), to estimate the resonant frequency. This estimated value should be approached slowly while the collector current is observed. The microammeter will indicate its maximum current when the resonant condition is reached.

The resonant condition can be displayed on an oscilloscope in the same manner used in the nuclear magnetic resonance experiment of

Chapter 9. The magnetic field should be modulated at 60 cycles/sec, and this modulating signal can be used to drive the horizontal sweep of the scope. The vertical scope display should be the output of the microammeter resulting in a trace similar to that shown in Fig. 12.23.

This measurement of the cyclotron frequency of the proton along with the measurement of the Larmor frequency of the proton allows a precise determination of the e/m of the proton as is described in Chapter 9.

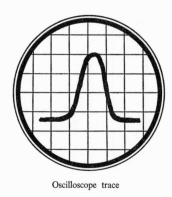

Oscilloscope trace

FIGURE 12.23

Oscilloscope trace of the omegatron resonance condition.

The cyclotron resonance experiment can also be performed using helium. The entire system should be filled with helium and then pumped down to 10^{-4} or 10^{-5} torr. This will increase the residual amount of helium and thereby increase the "source strength." In this case resonant frequency will be smaller by a factor of $\frac{1}{4}$ for the same magnetic field.

REFERENCES

1. Cockcroft, J. D., and E. T. S. Walton: *Proc. Roy. Soc. (London)* **A129**, 477, 1930.

2. Van de Graaff, R. J.: *Phys. Rev.*, **38**, 1919(A), 1931; Van de Graaff, R. J., K. T. Compton, and L. C. Van Atta: *Phys. Rev.*, **43**, 149, 1933; Van Atta, L. C., D. L. Northrup, R. J. Van de Graaff, and C. M. Van Atta: *Rev. Sci. Instr.*, **12**, 534, 1941.

3. Lawrence, E. O., and N. E. Edelfsen: *Science*, **72**, 376, 1930; Lawrence, E. O., and M. S. Livingston: *Phys. Rev.*, **37**,

1707, 1931; **38,** 834, 1931.

4. Lattes, C. M. G., G. P. S. Occhialini, and C. F. Powell: *Nature*, **160,** 453, 486, 1947.

5. Gardner, E., and C. M. G. Lattes: *Phys. Rev.*, **74,** 1236, 1948.

6. Tuve, M. A., L. R. Hafstad, and O. Dahl: *Phys. Rev.*, **48,** 315, 1935.

7. Marcley, R.: *Am. J. Phys.*, **29,** 90, 1961.

GENERAL BIBLIOGRAPHY

1. Livingston, M. S., and J. P. Blewett: "Particle Accelerators," McGraw-Hill Book Company, New York, 1962.

Appendices

I. OSCILLOSCOPES
II. CLASSICAL AND QUANTUM STATISTICS
III. PHYSICAL CONSTANTS

I. OSCILLOSCOPES

The oscilloscope is one of the instruments most frequently found in the laboratory. It is used as both an investigative, trouble-shooting tool (as in Chapter 4 where the oscilloscope is used to look at the output pulses of the photomultiplier tube) and as an analytical, measuring device (as in Chapter 7 where the oscilloscope is used to measure the time delay between the omnitron pulse and the first neutrons). For these reasons it is essential that the student become familiar with the operation and use of the oscilloscope.

Cathode-ray tube. The heart of the oscilloscope is the cathode-ray tube (CRT), which allows for the visual display of both an independent variable and its corresponding dependent variable. A schematic drawing of a CRT is shown in Fig. I.1. Electrons emitted from a filament

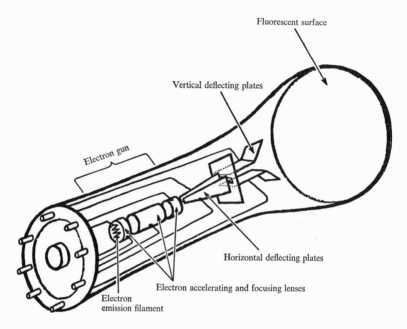

FIGURE I.1

Schematic illustration of a cathode-ray tube (CRT) used in an oscilloscope.

are accelerated and focused on the fluorescent screen by the portion of the CRT called the electron gun. Electron energies may vary from 5 to 25 kev in various oscilloscopes, but are fixed and not variable in a particular oscilloscope. The accelerated electrons strike the fluorescent screen with sufficient energy to cause the screen to fluoresce, creating a spot of light. The key to the great usefulness of the oscilloscope is that it causes the CRT electron beam to be traced out on the fluorescent screen. The behavior of the dependent variable as a function of the independent variable is thus displayed visually.

This deflection of the electron beam inside the CRT is accomplished by two sets of deflecting plates. The voltage analog of the variables being observed is placed across the deflecting plates, causing a deflection of the beam which is proportional to the variables.

Horizontal and vertical displays. The horizontal and vertical displays of an oscilloscope can be used to represent any variable desired, provided there is some way of converting the variable into a voltage analog. These voltage analogs are fed into the oscilloscope and displayed on the CRT via horizontal and vertical amplifiers.

Voltage signals being observed are frequently very small (millivolts) but the CRT deflecting plates may require a few hundred volts. Thus, there are internal amplifiers which will condition the input signals

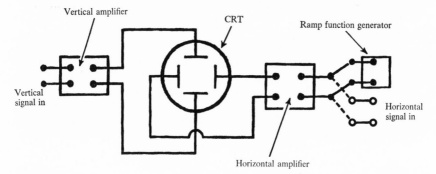

FIGURE I.2

Horizontal and vertical amplifiers which are integral with the oscilloscope.

for application to the CRT deflecting plates. This amplifier-CRT system is illustrated schematically in Fig. I.2. The amplifiers have large input impedances (10 megohms or more) so that, in general, they will not create an additional load on external circuits.

Examples of voltage analogs are:

1. *Time.* Time is such a common independent variable that all oscilloscopes have an internal time-base generator. A time base for the horizontal sweep is created by applying a ramp voltage (see Fig. I.3) to the horizontal deflecting plates. The time-scale or sweep-rate calibration (measured in sec/cm) is determined by the rate of rise of the ramp function. This is illustrated qualitatively in Fig. I.3. Note also that in Fig. I.2 the ramp-function generator is internal to the oscilloscope.

A typical use of time as the independent variable appears in Chapter 4, where the vertical display is the voltage pulses from the photomultiplier tube and the horizontal display is time.

2. *Current.* In Chapter 9, the oscilloscope is used to measure the current-voltage characteristics of a thermionic diode. The voltage analog of the current is obtained simply by putting a low-resistance shunt in the anode circuit. Although a voltage is measured, the current is given by Ohm's law so that the vertical deflection can be calibrated in units of current.

For other variable quantities, similar analog techniques are applicable.

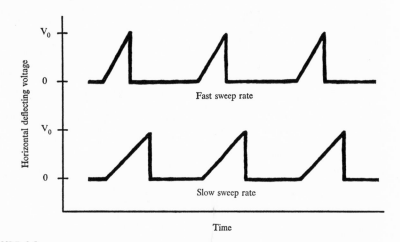

FIGURE I.3

Ramp-function voltages used for various horizontal sweep rates.

Oscilloscope controls. Controls found on oscilloscopes are by no means uniform, but vary both by model and manufacturer. Controls common to most oscilloscopes are:

1. *Display controls*
   a. *Focus control.* This control adjusts the focusing potential on the electron gun to form a sharp, well-defined image on the CRT face.
   b. *Intensity control.* This control adjusts the electron-emission rate of the filament so that the CRT trace intensity can be varied. On slow-sweep rates, care should be taken to ensure that the electron beam is not so intense as to burn the fluorescent face of the CRT.
   c. *Scale illumination.* Most scopes have a set of grid lines scribed in a plastic plate, which is placed on the front of the CRT. The intensity of these lines can be adjusted with the scale-illumination control.
2. *Position controls.* The horizontal and vertical positions of the beam can be adjusted independently by the horizontal and vertical position

controls. These allow for the most favorable positioning of the CRT trace.

3. *Signal inputs.* For reasons of versatility, most oscilloscopes have the input signals fed into preamplifiers (preamps), which in turn drive the main horizontal and vertical amplifiers. These preamps are removable (thus the name "plug-in units") and are specialized for such things as voltage sensitivity, multiple input and display, and so forth.

Most oscilloscopes are used with the horizontal axis representing time so that only the vertical input uses a plug-in, while the horizontal sweep is driven by the internal-ramp generator. Actually the horizontal display can be driven with an external signal, but the response is limited. More versatile oscilloscopes, of course, have both horizontal and vertical plug-in capabilities. As mentioned, plug-in units (vertical) have various performance capabilities, such as high-frequency response (up to 50 Mc), high voltage sensitivity (down to 1 millivolt/cm), or dual-trace display. Without elaborating, only the controls common to all types will be described.

All plug-in units have a selector which determines the vertical scale (in volts/cm) on the CRT face. The voltage of a signal is thus given by multiplying the size of the signal (in cm as measured on the CRT face) by the vertical scale factor (in volts/cm).

Other common controls are the a-c,d-c and polarity switches. With the a-c,d-c switch on a-c, the trace of the CRT is that caused by an a-c signal alone (that is, if a signal has a d-c component, the d-c signals are filtered out by a blocking capacitor at the plug-in input). In the d-c position, the CRT trace is simply the actual signal (both a-c and d-c components).

The polarity switch allows for an inversion of the CRT trace when it is changed from the positive to negative positions (or vice versa).

Other more specialized plug-in units are available and the reader should refer to the manufacturer's instruction manual before using them.

4. *Time base.* By far the most common use of the horizontal axis is as a time base. Its scale-factor selector generally allows sweep rates ranging from a few sec/cm down to a tenth of a microsecond/cm. The time of a voltage signal is measured by simply multiplying the length of the CRT trace (measured in cm) by the scale factor in sec/cm, milliseconds/cm, or microseconds/cm.

The most difficult aspect of operating an oscilloscope is to get a stable signal display. Quite frequently, the voltage signals being observed are random rather than periodic (such as the pulses from a scintillation detector). When a random pulse enters the oscilloscope, the horizontal sweep must be "triggered." This triggering is provided by the following oscilloscope controls.

The first control to consider is that which selects the triggering source. These sources usually include the signal itself which is indicated by INTERNAL (or INT.) on the oscilloscope, some external triggering signal which is fed into the EXTERNAL (or EXT.) trigger input, or the a-c line frequency which is indicated by LINE.

Another common control is one that selects the frequency response of the trigger network. These may include DC which responds to all a-c and d-c signals, AC which responds to all a-c signals, or AC LOW FREQUENCY REJECT (AC LF REJECT) which rejects lower frequency a-c signals.

After the triggering source and frequency response have been selected, two final controls must be adjusted. One is the TRIGGER LEVEL which acts as a signal-level discriminator. That is, it determines the level of the voltage pulse necessary to trigger the horizontal sweep. This adjustment is frequently useful when one is looking at a signal that contains considerable low-level background or noise. The noise can be prevented from triggering the scope by adjusting the TRIGGER LEVEL. The other common control is the TRIGGER STABILITY control, which provides adjustment of the sweep for triggered or free-running operation.

The control and operation of oscilloscopes as described here will provide only a general understanding of the operation of an oscilloscope. The best understanding can, of course, be obtained from the use of one in the laboratory.

II. CLASSICAL AND QUANTUM STATISTICS

Description of the properties of an ensemble of particles, such as the atoms of a gas or the conduction electrons of a metal, requires consideration of average properties rather than the identification of the motion of each individual particle. Thus, the treatment must be based on statistical considerations, and appropriate distribution functions for several variables must be derived. This statistical description can then be related to the usual macroscopic thermodynamic properties of the system (temperature, pressure, entropy, and so forth). The study of such macroscopic predictions is called *statistical mechanics* or *statistical thermodynamics*.

In this appendix, the energy-distribution functions for the three classes of particles shall be derived. The distinction between the types of particles is that they are particles obeying, respectively, classical and quantum mechanics. Classical particles are characterized by the property that their position and momentum can be specified exactly. However, the quantum particles are described by wave functions so that there is some vagueness about their position and momentum. This vagueness is expressed by the uncertainty relation:

$$\Delta x \, \Delta p \approx h \tag{II.1}$$

The distinction between the classical and quantum particle is simply that the location of the classical particle in position and momentum phase space can be known exactly, while for quantum particles Eq. (II.1) limits the precision with which measurements can be made. The result of this difference is that *classical* particles are considered to be identical but distinguishable, whereas *quantum* particles are identical but indistinguishable.

Consider the case of the molecules of a gas at STP. The molecular density is 10^{19} mol/cm³ so that the volume available to each molecule is 10^{-19} cm³. The molecular radius is approximately 10^{-8} cm so the molecular volume is approximately $(10^{-8})^3 = 10^{-24}$ cm³. Thus, the molecule is much smaller than the volume available to it, so that in principle it is possible to identify every molecule of the gas.

The situation is quite different for the conduction electrons of a metal. The density of electrons is approximately 10^{22} per cm³ so that the volume available to each electron is 10^{-22} cm³. The uncertainty of the position of the electron is given by Eq. (II.1) so that

$$\Delta x \approx \frac{h}{p} \tag{II.2}$$

For a 1 ev electron the momentum is

$$p = (2mE)^{1/2} = 1.6 \times 10^{-19} \text{ erg-sec cm}^{-1} \tag{II.3}$$

so that Eq. (II.2) gives

$$\Delta x \cong 4 \times 10^{-8} \text{ cm} \tag{II.4}$$

This gives as the volume of the conduction electron

$$v \cong (4 \times 10^{-8})^3 \cong 6 \times 10^{-23} \text{ cm}^3 \tag{II.5}$$

Comparing this with the volume of 10^{-22} cm³, which is that available to the electron, it is apparent that the electron wave functions overlap. This has the result that, although the electrons are identical, they cannot be distinguished from each other because of the overlap.

This gives us then the two general categories of particles to be considered—*classical* which are identical but distinguishable, and *quantum* which are identical but indistinguishable.

It should be noted here that when the quantum particle density is sufficiently low that their "vagueness" is small compared with the volume available to them, they also obey classical statistics. This will be explained later. It is simply a result of the correspondence principle encountered when going from quantum to classical mechanics.

It should also be noted that there are two distinct types of quantum particles—*half-integer* spin particles which obey the exclusion principle and *integer* spin particles which do not.

Distribution functions. To obtain an appropriate description of the energy distribution of the particles, we will regard the total possible energy range as being divided into a succession of small increments E_k to $E_k + \Delta E_k$, each increment being identified by an index k. We shall then describe the distribution by stating the number of energy states g_k which fall in each energy increment ΔE_k. Since the energy levels of the quantum particles are discrete, there will be a finite number of states in the increment ΔE_k. However, in most cases the energy spectrum will be continuous enough so that g_k can be regarded as being given by an expression of the form

$$g_k = f(E_k)\,\Delta E_k \qquad\qquad (II.6)$$

where $f(E_k)$ is a continuous function of energy.

To specify the condition of a system of particles as a whole, we will be interested in finding the number of particles n_k which lie in the available energy states g_k corresponding to the energy increment ΔE_k. To do this, we will have to consider the total number of ways the N total particles can be distributed among the g_k and ΔE_k and then establish some basis for obtaining the most probable distribution.

We will first consider the classical particles (identical but distinguishable) which will give us the familiar Maxwell-Boltzmann distribution function. Assume we have a system of N particles which are divided into groups n_k which occupy the available states g_k corresponding to ΔE_k. Clearly,

$$N = \sum_k n_k \qquad\qquad (II.7)$$

It is possible to divide the N particles into quotas containing n_1, $n_2, \ldots, n_k$ members in

$$\frac{N(N-1)\,\cdots\,(N-n_1+1)}{n_1!}\,x$$

$$\frac{(N-n_1)(N-n_1-1)\,\cdots\,(N-n_1-n_2+1)}{n_2!}\,x\,\cdots$$

$$= \frac{N!}{n_1!n_2!\,\ldots\,n_k!} \qquad\qquad (II.8)$$

different ways. The numerator of the first product is simply the statement that there are N ways of choosing the first particle on n_1, times $(N - 1)$ ways of choosing the second particle, . . . , times $(N - n_1 + 1)$ ways of choosing the last. However, we are not interested in the permutations of the particles among themselves so we must divide by $n_1!$. Similar arguments apply for the rest of the factors of Eq. (II.8).

Further, the n_k particles in ΔE_k can be assigned to the g_k levels in $g_k{}^{n_k}$ different ways. Hence, the total number of ways of finding a specified distribution n_k of classical particles is

$$\omega_{MB} = \prod_k \frac{N!}{n_k!} g_k{}^{n_k} \tag{II.9}$$

The first class of quantum particles we will consider will be the integer spin type (i.e., photons, phonons, etc.). These particles are not affected by the exclusion principle and are said to obey Bose-Einstein statistics.

To start, let us consider the n_k particles which are assigned to the energy increment ΔE_k with its corresponding g_k accessible energy levels. This can be considered to consist of n_k particles together with $g_k - 1$ partitions (which gives g_k levels in ΔE_k). This means that in ΔE_k there are $(n_k + g_k - 1)$ objects which can be permuted so that there are $(n_k + g_k - 1)!$ distinct ways of distributing n_k particles among the g_k levels. However, we are not interested in the permutations of the particles or partitions among themselves so we must also divide by $n_k!(g_k - 1)!$. This gives

$$\frac{(n_k + g_k - 1)!}{n_k!(g_k - 1)!} \tag{II.10}$$

as the number of different ways of selecting occupied states for the group k under consideration. This gives

$$\omega_{BE} = \prod_k \frac{(n_k + g_k - 1)!}{n_k!(g_k - 1)!} \tag{II.11}$$

as the total number of ways of finding a specified distribution, n_k, of Bose-Einstein particles.

The other quantum particle is the half-integer spin type. These particles are said to obey Fermi-Dirac statistics and differ from Bose-Einstein particles in that they obey the exclusion principle. As a consequence, it is evident that n_k can never exceed g_k. If the n_k particles were distinguishable, they could be assigned in

$$g_k(g_k - 1)(g_k - 2) \cdots (g_k - n_k + 1) = \frac{g_k!}{(g_k - n_k)!} \tag{II.12}$$

Classical and quantum statistics **287**

different ways without putting more than one particle into a given state of g_k. To make allowance for the indistinguishability of the particles, Eq. (II.12) must be divided by $n_k!$ so that in the Fermi-Dirac case

$$\omega_{\text{FD}} = \prod_k \frac{g_k!}{n_k!(g_k - n_k)!} \tag{II.13}$$

is the total number of ways of obtaining a given distribution n_k.

To find the most probable distribution of the N particles of our system, we want to maximize the expressions for ω_{MB}, ω_{BE} and ω_{FD}. This is done because the most probable distribution will result in the largest number of ways of distributing the N particles among the n_k states.

Taking logarithms of ω_{MB}, ω_{BE} and ω_{FD} (if ω is a maximum, $\ln \omega$ is also a maximum) and assuming that N, n_k, g_k and $g_k - n_k$ are large compared to unity gives

Maxwell-Boltzmann

$$\ln \omega_{\text{MB}} = N \ln N + \sum_k (n_k \ln g_k - n_k \ln n_k)$$

Bose-Einstein

$$\ln \omega_{\text{BE}} = \sum_k [(n_k + g_k) \ln (n_k + g_k) - n_k \ln n_k - g_k \ln g_k]$$

Fermi-Dirac

$$\ln \omega_{\text{FD}} = \sum_k [(n_k - g_k) \ln (g_k - n_k) - n_k \ln n_k + g_k \ln g_k] \tag{II.14}$$

These formulas have also been obtained by using Sterling's approximation, which is

$$\ln N! \cong N \ln N - N \tag{II.15}$$

when N is sufficiently large.

To solve the relations of Eq. (II.14) for the n_k which give the maximum of $\ln \omega$, we will use the technique of Lagrangian multipliers. The constraint on the system of particles is that both the number of particles, $N = \Sigma n_k$, and the energy of the particles, $E = \Sigma E_k n_k$, are constant.

Since $\ln \omega$ is a maximum, then $\delta(\ln \omega) = 0$ for all small changes δn_k. That is

$$\delta(\ln \omega) = 0 = \begin{cases} \sum_k [\ln n_k - \ln g_k + 1] \, \delta n_k \\ \sum_k [\ln n_k - \ln (n_k + g_k)] \, \delta n_k \\ \sum_k [\ln n_k - \ln (g_k - n_k)] \, \delta n_k \end{cases} \tag{II.16}$$

Similarly, conservation of particles and energy gives

$$\delta N = \Sigma \, \delta n_k = 0$$
$$\delta E = \Sigma E_k \, \delta n_k = 0 \tag{II.17}$$

Equations (II.16) and (II.17) can be combined by introducing the undetermined multipliers α and β which gives

$$\delta(\ln \omega) - \alpha \, \delta N - \beta \, \delta E = 0 \tag{II.18}$$

or specifically

Maxwell-Boltzmann $\quad \displaystyle\sum_k \left[\ln \frac{n_k}{g_k} + \alpha + \beta E_k \right] \delta n_k = 0$

Bose-Einstein $\quad \displaystyle\sum_k \left[\ln \frac{n_k}{n_k + g_k} + \alpha + \beta E_k \right] \delta n_k = 0 \qquad$ (II.19)

Fermi-Dirac $\quad \displaystyle\sum_k \left[\ln \frac{n_k}{g_k - n_k} + \alpha + \beta E_k \right] \delta n_k = 0$

Since the variations δn_k can be treated as arbitrary, these equations can only be satisfied when the coefficients of the δn_k are identically zero.

The distribution functions $f(E)$ are given by solving Eq. (II.19) for n_k/g_k (i.e., the probability that a given state is filled) so that the resultant distribution functions are given by

Maxwell-Boltzmann

$$f(E) = \frac{1}{e^{\alpha + \beta E}}$$

Bose-Einstein

$$f(E) = \frac{1}{e^{\alpha + \beta E} - 1} \tag{II.20}$$

Fermi-Dirac

$$f(E) = \frac{1}{e^{\alpha + \beta E} + 1}$$

Evaluation of multipliers. The Lagrangian multipliers α and β can be determined from the conditions of

$$N = \Sigma n_k$$
$$E = \Sigma E_k n_k \tag{II.21}$$

To evaluate α consider the integral forms of Eq. (II.21)

$$N = \int \frac{1}{e^{\alpha + \beta E} \pm 1(0)} \, dE \tag{II.22}$$

Classical and quantum statistics **289**

For the Maxwell-Boltzmann distribution, Eq. (II.22) gives

$$e^\alpha = \frac{1}{N} \int e^{-\beta E}\, dE \qquad (II.23)$$

However, in general there is no simple explicit solution for α in either the Bose-Einstein or Fermi-Dirac cases.

The multiplier β by contrast is not characteristic of the type of particles being considered. This can be demonstrated by the following argument. Consider a mixture of Maxwell-Boltzmann and Fermi-Dirac particles. The conservation conditions become

$$\sum_l n_l = N_{MB} \qquad (II.24a)$$

$$\sum_m n_m = N_{FD} \qquad (II.24b)$$

$$\sum_l E_l n_l + \sum_m E_m n_m = E \qquad (II.24c)$$

A solution to this problem will require three undetermined multipliers, α_1 and α_2 for Eqs. (II.24a) and (II.24b) and β for Eq. (II.24c). This will clearly lead to distributions that are similar in form to those obtained previously. Each distribution will have a different α but precisely the same β.

By evaluating the thermodynamic properties of the various particles, it can be shown that

$$\beta = 1/kT \qquad (II.25)$$

Using this equation, Eqs. (II.20) become

Maxwell-Boltzmann

$$f(E) = \frac{1}{N} \frac{e^{-E/kT}}{\int e^{-E/kT}\, dE}$$

Bose-Einstein

$$f(E) = \frac{1}{e^{\alpha + E/kT} - 1} \qquad (II.26)$$

Fermi-Dirac

$$f(E) = \frac{1}{e^{\alpha + E/kT} + 1}$$

The quantum particle distribution functions can be extended slightly further. In the case of photons and phonons (Bose-Einstein particles), these particles can be absorbed and emitted by the walls of the enclosing cavity so that $\delta N = 0$ is not valid. This has the result of causing α to equal zero (i.e., $\alpha = 0$).

For Fermi-Dirac particles, α is set equal to $-E_f/kT$ where E_f is called the Fermi energy and can only be evaluated from the particle conservation condition of Eq. (II.22).

Thus, the final distribution functions are

Maxwell-Boltzmann

$$f(E) = \frac{1}{N} \frac{e^{-E/kT}}{\int e^{-E/kT} \, dE}$$

Bose-Einstein

$$f(E) = \frac{1}{e^{E/kT} - 1} \tag{II.27}$$

Fermi-Dirac

$$f(E) = \frac{1}{e^{(E-E_f)/kT} + 1}$$

It can be seen that in the limit that $E/kT \gg 1$, the Bose-Einstein and Fermi-Dirac distributions approach the classical Maxwell-Boltzmann distribution. This results because the availability of states becomes much larger than the number of particles to fill them and the uncertainty relations become unimportant. The quantum particles then look like classical particles and thus obey Maxwell-Boltzmann statistics.

III. PHYSICAL CONSTANTS

The following table lists some physical constants that may be useful in a physical sciences laboratory. It should be understood that the values used are not exact. In all cases, the quantities had to be measured in a laboratory experiment so that the uncertainty in the value of one of the constants is a reflection of the precision of the measurement. This should not be interpreted to mean that the measurements are imprecise. Note that the velocity of light is known to 1 part in 10^7.

The values listed in this table are those considered by Cohen, Crowe, and DuMond ("Fundamental Constants of Physics," Interscience Publishers, Inc., New York, 1957) to be the most accurately reported values.

It is frequently necessary to make calculations using the physical constants where other quantities are only known to 1 part in 10, or 100, or 1000. In these cases, it is pointless to use the most precise value of the physical constant. Adjacent to the precise values is also listed a suitable approximate value which can be used for making quick calculations, especially in a laboratory when it is important to know the order of magnitude of a quantity.

Velocity of light
  $c = 299793.0 \pm 0.3$ Km sec^{-1} 3×10^6 Km sec^{-1}

Mass of electron (physical mass scale)
  $M_e = (5.48588 \pm 0.00006) \times 10^{-4}$ 5.5×10^{-4}
  $m_e = (9.1083 \pm 0.0003) \times 10^{-28}$ gm 9×10^{-28} gm

Mass of neutron (physical mass scale)
  $M_n = 1.008661 \pm 0.000003$ 1
  $m_n = (1.67470 \pm 0.00004) \times 10^{-24}$ gm 1.7×10^{-24} gm

Mass of proton (physical mass scale)
  $M_p = 1.007593 \pm 0.000003$ 1
  $m_p = (1.67239 \pm 0.00004) \times 10^{-24}$ gm 1.7×10^{-24} gm

Avogadro's number (physical mass scale)
  $N_A = (6.02294 \pm 0.00016)$
     $\times 10^{24}$ (gm mole)$^{-1}$ 6×10^{24} (gm mole)$^{-1}$

Gas constant
  $R_0 = (8.31432 \pm 0.00034)$
     $\times 10^7$ erg mole^{-1} deg^{-1} 8.3×10^7 erg mole^{-1} deg^{-1}

Standard volume of a perfect gas
  $V_0 = 22413.6 \pm 0.6$ cm^3 atm mole^{-1} 2.24 liters atm mole^{-1}

Electron charge
  $e = (4.80286 \pm 0.00009) \times 10^{-10}$ esu 4.8×10^{-10} esu
  $e' = e/c = (1.60206 \pm 0.00003)$
     $\times 10^{-19}$ coul 1.6×10^{-19} coul

Planck's constant
  $h = (6.62517 \pm 0.00023) \times 10^{-27}$ erg sec 6.6×10^{-27} erg sec
  $\hbar = h/2\pi = (1.05443 \pm 0.00004)$
     $\times 10^{-27}$ erg sec 1.1×10^{-27} erg sec

Boltzmann's constant
  $k = R_0/N_A = (1.38044 \pm 0.00007)$
     $\times 10^{-16}$ erg deg^{-1} 1.4×10^{-16} erg deg^{-1}
  $k = (8.6167 \pm 0.0004) \times 10^{-5}$ ev deg^{-1} 8.6×10^{-5} ev deg^{-1}

Stefan-Boltzmann constant
  $\sigma = (\pi^2/60)(k^4/\hbar^3 c^2) = (0.56687 \pm 0.00010)$
     $\times 10^{-4}$ erg cm^{-2} deg^{-4} sec^{-1} 0.6×10^{-4} erg cm^{-2} deg^{-4} sec^{-1}

Bohr magneton
  $\mu_0 = he/(4\pi mc) = (0.92731 \pm 0.00002)$
     $\times 10^{-20}$ erg gauss^{-1} 1×10^{-20} erg gauss^{-1}

Nuclear magneton
  $\mu_n = he/(4\pi m_p c) = (0.505038 \pm 0.000018)$
     $\times 10^{-23}$ erg gauss^{-1} 0.5×10^{-23} erg gauss^{-1}

Proton magnetic moment

μ = 2.79275 $\pm$ 0.00003 nuclear magnetons   2.8 nuclear magnetons

Mass-energy conversion factors

1 electron mass = 0.510976 $\pm$ 0.000007

       mev   0.5 mev

1 atomic mass unit = 931.141 $\pm$ 0.010 mev 930 mev

1 proton mass = 938.211 $\pm$ 0.010 mev   938 mev

1 neutron mass = 939.505 $\pm$ 0.010 mev   940 mev

Quantum-energy conversion factors

1 ev = (1.60206 $\pm$ 0.00003) $\times$ 10^{-12} erg 1.6 $\times$ 10^{-12} erg

Index